Reo Rio

'60's Illusions

A Novel

HARV LOUCKS

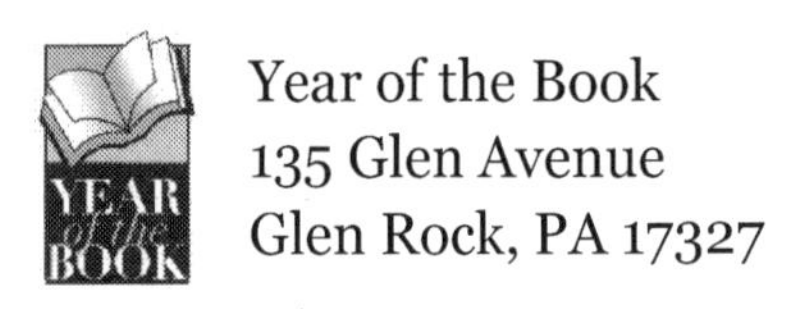

Year of the Book
135 Glen Avenue
Glen Rock, PA 17327

Print ISBN: 978-1-64649-014-1
Ebook ISBN: 978-1-64649-015-8

Dedication

To Paul Kittle, Kurt Wetzel,
and Permelia "dream babe" Atwood,
founder of the University of Rio Grande

Prologue

"We're closing, Mahl."

I opened my wallet to pay the tab and saw the faded clipping I'd read so many times. By now, it was burned in my brain. "Tragic car accident. One killed. One hospitalized. A certain M.H. Dickinger is being sought for information." Of course, there was more, but those were the basics that had burdened me for the last five years.

And with that reminder, a series of images came back. Things like the Blue Willow Lounge, Filthy Frank's Live Bait and Beer, the Silver Bridge collapse, and snake-handling preachers. I thought about the Mole Hole bastards, the night Abbie came to campus, and all the fine women I could have/should have had.

And of course there was Tavi. All of which took me back to late-'60s southeast Ohio, while the war continued in Nam.

The Kingsmen, "Louie, Louie," investigated by the FBI.
Dirty song if you want it to be.

First Day at Rio

Miss September, Angela Dorian, all-time best centerfold
464,000 American troops in Vietnam
13,643 dead since the war began

September 1967

We drove west through the tunnels of the PA turnpike, southwest through Wheeling, and south along the Ohio River, past the smokestacks at Kyger Creek, to Gallipolis and eventually to sleepy little Rio Grande, Ohio.

My dad took a left off Rt. 35 at the Baptist church and drove past several of the town's older residents, rocking on their front porches. We were part of a stream of cars, kicking up a cloud of dust into the late summer air. Some of the townies shook their heads at the license plates. The normally homogeneous town was in the process of doubling in size.

I was a third-year student, transferring from a junior college back east. And even though I was rather reserved, I was looking forward to this change of scenery, getting away from the family and the hometown.

Junior college had been basically a continuation of high school, so I was expecting this place to be a real, true-blue, bona fide college. My conception of *real* was something like Bucknell, back in Pennsylvania. My mom's cousin had gone there. It was a beautiful campus with an old, concrete football stadium, ivy-covered buildings, and stately fraternity houses. But as I made a quick scan of this campus, I didn't see any ivy climbing any venerable-looking structures. I had read in the college bulletin that there was no football team, so there wasn't a stadium of any kind to be seen. Maybe using Bucknell as *the ideal* was setting the bar kind of high.

Because of the distance and because I was pretty desperate to get into just about any college that would take me, this was the first time I had seen the campus. At junior college, I lived at home and didn't study. So with a 1.8 grade point average, I wasn't being recruited by MIT or

Harvard. Penn State said they'd take me on probationary status if I went to summer school, but I didn't feel like doing that. So I put my name into a national placement service, and about thirty colleges said they'd take me, 1.8 GPA and all. Most of them were small and in need of money, cashing in on the draft-evasion/baby boomer thing. They'd accept just about anyone with a checking account.

So I selected Rio Grande College—located not in Texas but in Rio Grande, Ohio. I picked it mainly because of a nice looking coed pictured in the college bulletin. Later I found out her name was Jeannie Hoskins. Leaning against a tree, she wore a madras top, a dark skirt, and penny loafers. Boring, but she had a really nice smile, big dark eyes, and dark, shoulder length hair. Anyway, Jeannie did it for me.

The other prerequisite for me was that the school didn't have a swimming pool. In Pennsylvania's state colleges, you had to demonstrate an ability to swim in order to graduate. Although I had gone to the YMCA and taken lessons, I never got the knack of surviving in water. No matter how hard I thrashed, I sank like a rock, probably because of a damn arthritic condition, which wasn't diagnosed until a few years after I left college. So this place basically met my criteria for getting a diploma and avoiding Vietnam, at least for a year or two.

On August 14, 1967, thousands of guys my age received letters saying something to the effect of, "Congratulations, you have been proven to be fit to serve your country against the communist aggression of North Vietnam." Instead, I received the following:

Dear Mr. Mahlon Haines Dickinger,

You have been accepted by Rio Grande College on probationary status. The maximum number of hours a student can take is seventeen. Since you are accepted on probationary status your adviser can at his discretion limit your schedule to twelve hours plus one or two hours of co-curricular credit.

Within 15 days after your acceptance by Rio Grande College, we must have an advance tuition deposit of $35, an advance room rent deposit of

$50, and a room safety deposit of $15. (Please make all checks payable to Rio Grande College.) If we do not receive these fees by this time, we will assume you are no longer interested in attending.

Your adviser will be Mr. William Truax.

If we can be of any further help to you, please do not hesitate to call upon us.

Sincerely yours,
Evan M. Roberts
Director of Admissions and Records

So with the receipt of the acceptance letter, I quickly sent a check for the various fees and tuition. The total cost for two semesters was $1606, a basic bargain.

And yes, Rio Grande was both the name of the town and the school. Apparently, the town once had a very common name, and the mail was always getting delivered to the wrong place. So around that time, a local resident got a letter from a relative who was fighting in the Mexican War, and the Rio Grande River was mentioned. The local yokel thought, "Why don't we rename our town Rio Grande?"

And that's what the hell they did. They obviously didn't know shit about the Spanish language, because from then on, they pronounced it as most of the area hillbillies would—"Rye-o-Grand."

My dad parked the '63 champagne-colored Ford Galaxie 500 in front of Holzer Hall, which would become my residence for the next six semesters. Mom stayed in the car while Dad and I carried my stuff into what I later found out was affectionately/derisively called The Mole Hole. Located below the first floor of the dorm, it was not the basement, but it housed the resident hall's laundry room and also a kind of rec room—although there was no TV, pool table, ping pong table, foosball table, or anything else that would provide recreation. Because of the lay of the land, the front of the floor was partially below ground.

As my dad and I walked down the hall, several students came and went, reacquainting themselves. Near the bathroom area, some guy with crazy, uncombed hair and a red face stuck his head into the hall and shouted, "Fuck." But it wasn't just a simple, run-of-the-mill "fuck." It was a throaty, extended, multi-syllabic "fuck." I thought, *Welcome to Rio Grande College.*

Room 12 had three beds with about a foot between each one. On the third bed next to the window sat a guy I presumed was one of my roommates. He stood up and cordially introduced himself as Clark Buck. He was a freshman, but he looked more mature than the typical eighteen year old. He was a decent looking guy, about 6'0", 210 pounds, but he still had the old greasy hair thing going. Not that it was objectionable, but by this time in 1967, most guys were going toward the dry look.

I had been apprehensive about who I'd be rooming with, after my sister's unpleasant dorm experiences. But I didn't have any say in the roommate thing. Clark explained there were temporarily three guys in a room until the new dorm was finished, which would take about three or four weeks. So with introductions aside, he helped to unload the rest of my stuff.

I walked back to the car and said goodbye to the parents. No hugs or kisses. That's just how we did things. Whenever I saw other people doing the "I love you/embrace thing," I thought it was phony and unnecessary. After all, we all knew we loved each other, and we seemed to get along just fine like that.

I gave my dad a handshake. But this handshake was a little different from the usual. It was firmer and extended. As I looked at him, it seemed like he wanted to say more than goodbye but nothing else came out.

I walked into the dorm, thinking all kinds of things. Maybe he wanted to say something like, *A lot is expected of you now.* He never had the chance to go to college. Well, in a way he did—on the GI Bill after the Big War—but because he was a husband and father by then with a job which gave him some stability, he decided to forego college.

Up to this point, I hadn't projected a very dynamic image. I hadn't been a big personality in my high school class (I was ranked 103 in a class of 210). And I wasn't tearing it up with the babes. Dad might have been implying something like, *Time to get the lead out of your skinny ass.*

As they drove away, I turned on my heel and entered Holzer Hall where a population of late-adolescent males were looking for hot girls and cold beer. And although I was entering my third year, I had an anemic social life and a ton of naivete. *[Motherfuckle!]*

Herbie Hancock, piano. Maiden Voyage *album (Blue Note), with the great Freddie Hubbard on trumpet.*

Settling In

114 GIs killed in four-day battle

I spent the next day going through the tedious registration process and getting acquainted with Clark and the campus. He knew a lot about the school since an older friend had graduated from Rio a few years earlier. This guy had connections with the admissions department and arranged to get a substantial academic scholarship for him.

With high SAT scores, Clark was also a talented lineman on the high school football team. A few small colleges had offered athletic scholarships. But I guess his friend had done a pretty good selling job about Rio, and Clark was kind of tired of football anyway. He was a freshman biology major who listened to The Doors and Cream, smoked unfiltered Camels, drank Stroh's beer, and dated his high school sweetheart. So in terms of a roommate, I pretty much lucked out.

The next morning, I woke up to find someone in the middle bed. I hadn't heard him come in during the night. When I started to get up, he stirred a little, opened one eye, then slowly extended his hand and said, "I'm Mac." The triumvirate of Room 12 was complete.

Everything flowed smoothly as I went through the first round of classes. Some actually seemed interesting, and the students came across as genial. When I came back to the room around two o'clock, I found seven or eight guys sprawled out all over the place. Most had lived on the floor the previous year, and they seemed genuinely happy to see each other. They congregated in Room 12, when word got around that Mac was back. But most of all, they were glad to see this Zittle guy. They wanted to know about his summer at the Jersey shore—like how many babes he bonked, how much he partied.

Eventually their attention turned to Clark and me. Clark told his scholarship story and where he was from and all that. I told them my name was Mahl Dickinger, and like most guys, they got all hyped up.

"Dickinger?!? You mean like you're DICKING HER, right?"

So I said something like, "Yeah, I wish."

Then one of the others said, "Wait a sec. Your first name sounds like *mail* as in *mail a letter*?"

"Yeah. It's short for Mahlon. I know, weird name."

I told them I was from York, PA, thinking no one had ever heard of the place. But one guy said, "That's where they had the race riots this summer, right?"

"Yeah, it was pretty tense," I answered.

Another guy said something about York Peppermint Patties. Someone else knew about the York US 30 Dragway, where Dave Strickler raced his "Old Reliable" 409 Chevy. Another one said he'd played in a basketball all-star game a few years ago with some guy from York. He even remembered the name, Bill Fry, who had been an all-state selection. And then this Zittle guy said, "That's where York Barbell's located. My dad took me down there to get started with a lifting program."

All this took me by surprise because I didn't think York, PA, was that well known. For some reason things like race riots, drag racing, barbells, and a name like "Dickinger" provided a kind of gravitas. My weird brain flashed back to reading Vonnegut's *Cat's Cradle,* which used the word "karass" to define a group of people linked in a cosmically significant manner, even when superficial linkages were not evident. I wasn't sure about that cosmic shit, but suddenly I felt like I was part of the group.

Turned out most of them were from back East. The guy who owned the middle bed was Bill "Mac" McCarthy from Smithburg, New Jersey. He'd played high school football and baseball. I assumed he spent a lot of time at the shore because he was deeply tanned. Like Clark, he still had the greasy hair thing going. He used some kind of gel called Dippity Do.

Mac's good friend was John "Jack" Callison. Both had attended Bordentown Military Institute, an old prep school in Jersey. Like Mac, Jack was into baseball. In fact, he was the best hitter on the school's team. During the previous year, Mac and Jack had shared a room with Jim Nuxall, who was from the Cleveland area. The three of them were known as Mac, Jack, and Hack Wack. The name "Hack Wack" was used derisively, because Nuxall was... a hack wack, a hand job, a half-ass, always used in a nice way, of course.

Then there was Craig "Gorilla" Pottorf from Elizabeth, NJ. He had hair growing on virtually every inch of his body. In the mornings, he not only shaved his face and chin, but also the back of his neck. It was like he was wearing a hair coat. When he'd return after a night of drinking, he'd crawl around on all fours in a circle on his bed, like a lion or bear, and then he'd lie down and fall into a deep snore.

The guy who'd known about York US 30 Dragway was Tommy Landis, better known as "Hillbilly" because of his thick country accent. He was connected to some dragstrip around Ironton, a few miles west of Rio. Tommy was a nice guy but cheated on almost all his tests.

Dirk Zittle was from Mount Carbon and roomed directly across the hall from Clark and me. He was the red-faced bastard who'd screamed the multi-syllabic "fuck" as Dad and I walked down the hall. Mount Carbon is located in the anthracite coal region, which conjures up images of miners with blackened faces, explosive coal gases, black lung disease, fire-in-the-hole dynamite, destruction of the natural environment and all kinds of other crappy shit.

Dirk's father was a successful pharmaceutical salesman, and I'm guessing he wasn't home much. But his mother was probably the most cultured resident of Mount Carbon. A New York-trained mezzo-soprano and friend of the internationally famous Lily Pons, she also was a good friend of Virgil Fox, the flamboyant classical organist—the Liberace of the pipe organ, known for dressing in capes and other assorted ornaments.

So Dirk embodied the toughness of the coal region but also his mom's refinement. His dad took him to work out at York Barbell, which was run by the renowned Bob Hoffman who had coached the United States Olympic weightlifting team. When I heard this, I guessed Dirk's old man was probably supplying Hoffman with some steroidal concoction to bulk up his weightlifters.

Anyway, although Dirk was only 5'9", he was stuck together rather well and projected a larger physical presence. He'd played football for a prep school in D.C., where a lot of Pentagon employees sent their sons. Maybe his parents sent him there to overcome some sort of behavior problem. Maybe they just wanted him to get a better education. Who knows? Anyway, after prep school, he attended Kutztown State but for some reason, he didn't last very long there.

Rio Grande had become a repository for all kinds of misfits and malcontents. Of course, there were plenty of normal kids who came from the East, but population density and the post-war baby boom pushed entrance requirements pretty high in eastern colleges. You could usually enroll more easily in the Midwest with lower entrance requirements and often lower tuition rates.

So for various reasons, guys were drawn to this Dirk guy. He was charismatic. That's an overused term, but it fit. His first year at Rio, he got into a dorm fight with Griff Brady, a big dude from Nitro, West Virginia, and who was about six inches taller and thirty pounds heavier. Dirk grabbed a desk lamp, slammed the base of it into Griff's head, and knocked him out cold. From then on, Griff and Dirk were the best of friends, and Zittle's reputation was solidified as someone who shouldn't be fucked with. Despite his upper-middle class background, he had an affinity for the average-joe types. Plus, he espoused all the *correct* political and social causes, got along with the few campus minority students, and wasn't afraid to express how he felt about the various issues of the day.

In some ways, appearances were everything. People saw me with Zittle, in the Mole Hole, in the cafeteria, and around campus. So some thought I must be like him. If Zittle talked with me, ate with me, and laughed with me, then I must have some of his qualities. Plus, since I was new and an upperclassman, then some thought I must have some street cred. But I looked like a bookworm with glasses, and because I was in the library a lot, other guys weren't too sure about me. I might embarrass them in a debate because I appeared to be smarter or better read. Plus I hung around that crazy Zittle bastard. I liked that bogus perception.

Wes Montgomery, guitar, Tequila *album.*
Known for innovative thumb technique.

English Major

Surrealistic Pillow *album*
Bonnie and Clyde *movie*

At the junior college, I took the neutral route and declared a liberal arts major. Basically that meant I didn't know what the hell I wanted to do when I grew up. I was into music, having taken piano lessons for ten years and showing a fair amount of proficiency. I also played alto sax and oboe, so I'd considered a major in music. Ideally, I would've liked to be a studio musician, but realistically I didn't have the motivation. The only other route for a music major was to become a teacher. But I figured that would probably suck out all my enjoyment of music.

Then I thought about majoring in history. I was always kind of interested in the Civil War and World War II. But I was told that history teachers were a dime a dozen, so I just declared liberal arts.

As part of that curriculum, of course, I took a few English classes. In high school, we begrudgingly diagrammed sentences and identified parts of speech. Literature classes usually got around to some Shakespearean play like *Macbeth* or *Hamlet*, which had plenty of good plot lines, but the language was too ridiculous for me. So English was not exactly my best subject.

Actually, I should amend that a little. My senior English class was pretty good. The teacher, Rodney Swartz, was a cool dresser, which had nothing to do with the quality of the class. But hey, that's the kind of superficial shit that high school kids think about. So anyway, Swartz always wore nice suits and ties, but the coolest part was that he wore Clarks of England desert boots.

As advertised in *Playboy*:

> "Montgomery's men needed a rugged, lightweight boot that could breathe in the blazing heat of the desert. It also had to be so comfortable that it could be worn on long marches without tiring the feet. So we built the Desert Boot. The original. Made of supple sand suede with plantation crepe

> soles. No hard edges anywhere to dig into your ankles or put pressure on your toes. A sole so cushioning, your foot feels like it's riding on air. Today, it's the ultimate in casual comfort. The Desert Boot. Made only by Clarks of England, about $25.00."

Anyway, Swartz wore those desert boots, so the cool guys went out and bought them at Lehmyers, the only store in town that sold them. At the time, they were kind of expensive (for me, anyway), so I bought a knock-off pair at the Franklin Discount.

One of Swartz's assignments was a comparative analysis of literature. We'd read Melville's *Billy Budd* and Twain's *Huckleberry Finn*, and I mentioned that I had read Salinger's *Catcher in the Rye* on my own. So Swartz encouraged me to use all three for the paper, with a coming-of-age theme. I had to give the guy credit because *Catcher* was considered verboten in school. Something about bad language and a social misfit (cool, right?). My older sister had a copy and I carried it around school wrapped in a brown paper bag. I wasn't much of a reader at the time, but I felt an affinity for old Holden Caulfield. I finished the book in just a few hours. Then I tried to read *Franny and Zoey* and a few of Salinger's other stuff about the Glass family, but they didn't hit me like *Catcher*.

Later, some English classes at the junior college caught my interest. One professor—a short Jewish lady named Leah Gottfried—emphasized the writer's motivation in her analyses of various literary works. She encouraged me to read *The Erotic Motives in Literature*. That grabbed my interest, since the author basically said that sex is the driving force behind all great literature. Obviously influenced by Freudian thought, the book not only got me thinking about how sex influences writers, but it also made me wonder about other environmental stimuli that pushed a person to write.

So when I transferred to Rio Grande, I decided to major in English, knowing full well I'd probably end up becoming a damn English teacher. But more importantly, I was under the assumption that cool girls who liked to sleep around tended to pop up in English classes.

Some people thought that only gays majored in English. My response was that many pre-law students were English majors because good writing skills were a prerequisite for law school. Not that I ever wanted to be a damn lawyer, but it sounded like a good excuse at the time.

My life's ambitions had gone from wanting to be a cowboy to a baseball player to a professional musician to probably the most unlikely thing for me—a damn English teacher. *[Motherfuckle!]*

Martha Reeves and the Vandellas, "My Baby Loves Me."
Pain in Martha's voice, strong recording.

Bevo, Newt, and Rio B-Ball

May 7, 1967, Coltrane played his last gig at Baltimore's Famous Ballroom

In the late '60s, college basketball had many great players. Some notable scorers were Calvin Murphy, Earl Monroe, Lew Alcinder (aka Kareem Abdul Jabbar), and Pete Maravich. However, none of them came close to a 1950's Rio Grande player.

As improbable as that might sound, it was absolutely true. None of the Rio Grande brochures ever mentioned this. It was as though the college was ashamed of it. But once I was on campus, it didn't take long to hear the legend of Bevo Francis and his coach Newt Oliver.

Oliver had been coaching a local high school team. He had this big, gangly kid named Clarence Francis, who had been compiling tons of points. At 6'9", he made a lot of shots close to the basket. But he also had a smooth outside jumper from fifteen feet. He got the nickname "Bevo" from a popular near-beer drink that his dad consumed in large quantities.

Newt was a man of big ideas. He talked his way into a coaching job at Rio and brought his scoring machine with him. Although Rio only had about ninety students, he boldly predicted his team would play in Madison Square Garden, and he was true to his word. He recruited several above-average high school players and told them the MVP award would go to the player with the most assists—meaning he expected Bevo to get a lot of passes and score tons of points.

And that's exactly what happened. In their first year, Bevo was throwing in forty, fifty, even sixty points per game. Hell, he scored 116 points one time. But that was against a junior college, so that record didn't count. Around campus, we joked that Bevo scored all those points against the Ohio School for the Blind. But then in 1954, he scored 113 points against Hillsdale, which was a four-year college, so the record stuck.

The team went on to give strong games against some of the best in the East: Villanova, Providence, Miami, North Carolina, and Wake

Forest. Bevo was named to the second team All-America squad. Unfortunately, the euphoria came to an abrupt end when the star player got suspended from the team for missing classes and low grades. When Bevo came to Rio, he brought with him a young wife and baby, which understandably contributed to his poor academic performance.

Some people said the school showed their integrity by suspending him from the team. But others thought they missed a great opportunity to attract more students to the economically-stifled institution. Bevo's situation with his family and classes could have been accommodated, but the school showed no imagination or regard for the athlete or the viability of the ninety-student college. Newt and Bevo got the team to Madison Square Garden. That was big-time shit. *[Motherfuckle!]*

David "Fathead" Newman, alto sax. "Hard Times."
The epitome of a perfectly developed jazz selection.

Religion Class

The Graduate: *Dustin Hoffman, Anne Bancroft, with Mike Nichols (director)*

One of the requirements for graduation was a religion class, even though the college was no longer affiliated with the Baptist church. Actually, it was a choice between religion or philosophy, the latter of which somehow seemed like more work. So I signed up for New Testament. After all, I had gone to church for a long time. How hard could that be?

When I first came to Rio, I thought I'd give the Methodist church a try since it was only a couple blocks from campus. Parental guilt made me do it. My family had gone to a Lutheran church every Sunday without fail. Although the religion thing was never really pushed on me, my mom often said, "If you miss just one Sunday, it will be a lot easier to not go the next Sunday."

My dad's religious wisdom was something like, "It's good to believe in God because you never know, it might be real." He believed his faith brought good luck to Mom and him in terms of health, happiness, family, and job. But I always wondered about all the other faithful who lost a job or died from cancer or got run over by a Mack truck.

Despite my devout parents, I tended to be a slacker when it came to church. I flunked my catechism exam and had to re-take it because I forgot to study. I played in the Sunday School orchestra. After the SS opening, we were expected to go to our designated class. But Jimmy Gardner and I would often cut class and drive up the street to Legore's for two or three 15-cent hamburgers.

The week after I got my driver's license, I volunteered to drive. We got the burgers, but as I was pulling out, I missed the exit and went over the curb, pulling the muffler off its bracket. We found a wire coat hanger in the trunk and pulled up the muffler. Everything looked good. But as we were pulling into the parking lot, everybody was streaming out of church. And there was the family, standing in the vacated parking space. That didn't go over too well with the old man, especially when we drove home, and the Ford sounded like a damn stock car.

For me, going to church was more of an obligation than a spiritual belief. However, I still had that fear-of-God thing and that going-to-hell thing in the back of my mind. So one Sunday, after a few weeks on campus, I put on a coat and tie and walked a few blocks to church. I thought that, at the very least, there might be some nice looking babes there.

It took a lot for me to get out of bed and go hear a sermon since no other bastard on the Mole Hole was busting his butt to get to a damn church. Walking by Moulton Hall, I started thinking, *Hell, they're all still sleeping*. But I kept walking and after a few minutes, I entered the church.

I wasn't sure what to expect, but I thought I could have been more welcomed. No one said "Hello," or "Welcome to our service," or "Are you new here," or "God bless you, young man." I figured all the locals had been coming there all of their lives, and anyone from the outside would probably be looked at with caution or as a threat to the status quo.

To my surprise, the preacher was none other than my New Testament prof, the Rev. Wesley Howell. I thought, *Hmm, maybe some brownie points for showing up*. So I sat through the service, which was pretty damn boring and uninspiring. And to be honest, I didn't really have my heart in it. So before I could get out of the pew, I told myself that this religion stuff would be put on the back burner out here in the wilds of southeastern Ohio.

As I left, I shook hands with the minister/prof, and that was the last time I went through that door. He didn't say a word to me. Maybe he didn't recognize me, but hell, I'd been in his class for a month or two by then. He could have said something like, "I don't remember seeing you here before," or "Nice to see you. Come back next Sunday," but he didn't say anything. He just had a pained smile on his face and nodded his head at me.

Howell seemed like he was always in some kind of pain. He was thin, his hair uncombed, his clothes wrinkled. He could easily have played the part of the guy who kills himself in that play *Our Town*.

At the beginning of every class, he would record attendance and then close his eyes, bow his head, and give a prayer. After a few weeks of this routine, I noticed some of the guys in the last row crawling out the door on their hands and knees during the prayer. Howell must have picked up on this eventually, but he never did anything about it. So I figured I'd give it a try, once or twice, maybe more. But I still had to pass the damn class, so I didn't do it too often.

I later found out that Howell had been in the Coast Guard during the War. That was a surprise to me. I had always heard Coast Guard training was rigorously demanding. Maybe that perpetual grimace was because he'd experienced a traumatic event, like defending the east coast from German U-boats or something.

So, like I said, I never went back to church while I was at Rio Grande. And when I went home in the summer, I started slacking off also. I'd go once in a while to please the parents, but there were too many aspects about the church that I had trouble accepting.

One was the idea that you had to take Jesus Christ into your heart to get to heaven. So what happened to the people who never heard about Jesus? Or the ones who came from troubled families or poor living conditions or the damn jungles of deepest Africa? Or what about the babies who died before they could be baptized? Or the Jews who don't believe in Jesus as their savior? Or the Muslims or Buddhists? And what about everyone who died before the birth of Christ?

Then there was the prodigal son story, where the good son did everything correctly and the bad son went out and partied real hard and came home and said he was sorry and was lovingly accepted by the old man. Where's the justice in that? So if you live a really lousy life and hurt all kinds of people, but just before you kick the bucket, you take Jesus into your heart of hearts, then you go to heaven, right? Yet if you live that same screwed up life, but die before you can ask for forgiveness, then you're damned to hell?

It started to look like God was just playing around with people's souls, like it's just one big game. What about all the good people who contracted terrible brain tumors or pancreatic cancer or bone cancer, or penis cancer? They were all really good people and went to church all the time. Other people prayed their brains out for those afflicted, but they still died painful deaths. Then some preacher smiles and says something like "God works in strange and mysterious ways," or "God has a reason for everything that happens," or "God will never give you anything that you can't handle," or "We all have our own cross to bear."

I also questioned the Bible, which is supposed to be the word of God. Originally it came from an oral tradition. Then it was written in

Greek and then Latin and then Old English and then Middle English and a ton of other languages. Later monks and all kinds of scholars transcribed manuscripts, and people like King James created his own version. Along the way, meanings of words changed and things were exaggerated and on and on.

Where did the Catholic Pope come from and where is he mentioned in the Bible? How did the Pope get established like that, with all that wealth? Where's his vow of poverty? And how many Popes were really corrupt but were still canonized?

What was the deal with no women allowed in the church hierarchy? What was the thing about the so-called Christian Crusades, where all those damn knights went to the Middle East and slaughtered thousands of people just to uphold the tenants of chivalry? What about all those other religions and how their followers believe their god is the real god and all others are damn infidels?

So-called good Christians believe that the government should be a theocracy. They believe Thomas Jefferson and George Washington were religious zealots, which they weren't. Then they get the idea that the church should not be separate from the state. When election season comes along, politicians all of a sudden become really religious, hoping to get the Christian vote.

I started to use the word "agnostic." I decided I wasn't intelligent enough to comprehend the concept of God. How do you explain the Holy Trinity? How do you explain those miraculous things that happened in the Bible, but you don't see any burning bushes today?

I began to think that religions evolved from the earliest homo sapiens who saw various natural phenomena that couldn't be explained. They decided there must be something in the sky that created the universe and controlled things. And you didn't want to piss off that thing up there because it could shoot down fire and brimstone, destroying everything in its path. So they started worshiping the sky-thing. The worship evolved over the years to the point where old Constantine came along and declared that the whole Roman Empire should be Christian, and things really spread at that point.

I recognized that many really intelligent people over the years had been sincerely religious and had written all kinds of scholarly papers about the existence of a god. They were all a lot smarter than I was, but I still couldn't get rid of the idea that the whole thing was cooked up by some post-caveman dude, and things just snowballed after that. *[Motherfuckle!]*

Curtis Mayfield and the Impressions, "I'm So Proud." Great slow dance song.

Ohio Drinking

Monterey Pop Festival: Jefferson Airplane, The Who, Grateful Dead, Jimi Hendrix Experience, Big Brother and the Holding Company, Eric Burdon and the Animals, Otis Redding, Ravi Shankar, the Mamas and the Papas

Being in a dorm room with two other guys might have been hectic, especially a room designed for only two occupants. I enjoyed being around Clark, who was pretty uncomplicated. He didn't have a pretentious bone in his body. Open-minded and intelligent, he always spoke with a purpose and had a healthy sense of humor.

I guess the best thing was that he studied his butt off. That enthusiasm rubbed off on me, who previously was about the most uninterested student in all of academia. Clark's only fault was that he smoked a lot of non-filtered Lucky Strikes, but my eyes and lungs got kind of used to that after a while.

On the other hand, Mac was also a decent roommate, mainly because he was hardly ever in the room. And when he was, he was usually sleeping. He'd say, "Just give me one more minute and then get me up, just one more minute." Then, after realizing he was already five minutes late, he'd fly out of the room, unshowered and barely dressed, to his first class.

Mac was in a pretty hot relationship with a girl back home. Every three or four weeks, he'd hitchhike back to Jersey on a Friday for a weekend of romantic bliss and then thumb back for class on Monday. That took a lot of effort and luck to hitchhike over 500 miles, one way, just for the sake of a girl and her convivial delights. Somehow he did this for four years (or maybe it was five) and still managed to get a diploma.

Most of the guys on the floor were pretty easy to get along with, even for a social retard like me. The two on the other side of the partition in the next room were Kim Pataky and Tom Lindgren. They were members of Pi Delta, which some people called Pig Delta for various reasons. But these guys were decent, at least when they weren't around their Greek brothers.

They were continually blasting stuff like Iron Butterfly, Jimi Hendrix, Deep Purple, and Country Joe and the Fish. Both were into gadgets and electronics, with all kinds of wires and speakers spread throughout the room. Somehow they rigged their alarm clock to a stereo, so instead of the clock ringing, it would trigger the turntable. Every night, they'd place the tonearm on the exact spot where the rooster crows at the beginning of "Good Morning, Good Morning" on the *Sgt. Pepper* album. It was a nice idea... to wake up to a crowing rooster, but it got a little old after a while.

Like many campuses at the time, Rio had a no-alcohol policy in the dorms. My first semester, I was cool with that idea, because at that point I wasn't a drinker—only one beer party under my belt. At Rio, plenty of guys drank in the dorm, even though they knew they could be expelled if caught. So with me being pretty much of an anal personality, it bothered me when I saw the drinking rule being ignored.

One Saturday evening when Clark had gone home to see his girlfriend, I heard the guys in the next room mixing drinks and yucking it up while I was trying to study. They weren't really causing a disturbance or anything. It just pissed me off.

So being a non-confrontational type of guy, instead of going next door and politely asking them to pipe down, I wrote a letter to the resident assistant of the Mole Hole and said I was filing a complaint. The next day, I slipped the letter under the RA's door.

Obviously, I hadn't thought this out very well. The RA would have to report it to Mrs. Rimmel, the dorm mother, and then he might be put on notice. Then he'd be pissed at me, and I'd have to pass him everyday in the shower room and on campus. And he'd tell the rest of the guys on the floor that I was being a rat, and I'd be ostracized, beat up, hogtied, and driven out to Tycoon Lake where my swimming skills would be put to the ultimate test.

Sure enough, the next day Ron Singer, the resident assistant, came down to Room 12 and asked about my complaint. I told him I wasn't happy about the drinking on the floor and how nothing was being done about it. Ron said he had been one of those guys in the next room, downing rum and Cokes and clinking the cubes in his mug.

He appreciated me bringing up the incident and said that it was wrong, and of course he would notify Mrs. Rimmel. But with a calm and controlled manner, he also said there was an unwritten rule that most guys followed. As long as no one was barfing up their guts in the middle of the hall and there was no broken glass, he said drinking would probably continue in the Mole Hole. And as long as that unspoken rule was followed, there wouldn't be any trouble. Everyone would be happy and things would remain hunky dory.

So as he was talking, my brain caved like it usually did in confrontational situations. I started thinking he was a nice guy, and I didn't want him to get in trouble. So I impulsively blurted out, "Don't worry about it, Ron. I'm sorry for even bringing this up. And you don't have to say anything to Mrs. Rimmel." So we shook hands, and he went back to his room with a damn smile on his face.

But soon after this potentially traumatic experience, I started going down the road to alcoholic perdition. As much as my good buddy Clark enjoyed studying, he also liked to blow off steam once in awhile. So somewhere around the first week of October, we hitched a ride into Gallipolis, which was the closest substantial town, thirteen miles away.

Clark had been given a pretty good tutorial on the college and the surrounding area by talking with Butch, the family friend who helped get Clark's scholarship. So when we got to Gallipolis, he said we should go to The Grande Cafe, which apparently had been a kind of watering hole for Rio students over the years. I assumed the name Grande somehow related to the college because of the spelling, but I never saw any other kind of linkage between the bar and the school. And I have no idea how the place got the moniker of Cafe, because in my eyes it was just some old hillbilly bar.

It was dark inside with fishnetting on the walls for atmosphere. The jukebox played only Country and Western. But Clark had been told about some off-color songs. One was "The Golf Game." It dealt in double entendres for golf terms like "hole," "shaft," "hairy patch," "balls," "gripping the shaft," "a good lie," "rimming the hole," and on and on and on. So he played the song, and all the old guys at the bar thought it was so damn funny, even though they had heard it many times before.

We sat in one of the booths and ordered some Stroh's, one of the Ohio beers I'd never heard of. But at that point in my life, I didn't know a whole lot about Pennsylvania beers either. My dad would buy a case of Rolling Rock cans, maybe once every two years. Or my parents might have a cocktail with their card club, but there wasn't much drinking in the Dickinger household.

However, there was one guy in the family who was far from a teetotaler. Uncle Elby was married to Aunt Marg, one of my dad's sisters. He was a really great guy who worked at the *York Dispatch* as the circulation manager. He pulled a few strings and got me the newspaper route that I had in high school. When he was a young man, he dressed up in a red riding coat and rode the lead horse as the racehorses entered the track at the York Fair.

But Uncle Elby was conveniently used by my mom as "the bad example" because he smoked about twenty packs a day which eventually led to lung cancer. He also was a functional alcoholic—meaning he was proficient on his job, but he couldn't stop drinking when he went to the club or any place where there was booze. Aunt Marg had to go out and look for him at night, and if she could find him, she had to drag him to the car to get him home.

From the time I knew anything about smoking and drinking, my mom always said, "Don't ever smoke a cigarette because you'll get hooked. You don't want to die a terrible death like Uncle Elby." Then she'd say, "Don't ever take a drink because alcoholism is in the family. You might end up like Uncle Elby," even though the poor guy wasn't blood-related.

So, back at The Grande Café, a couple bottles of Stroh's came to the table. I took a sip, and maybe because it was kind of hot in the bar or because it was nice to get away from campus, the beer tasted real good. The first one went down fast. So we got a bag of chips and ordered another. Clark started playing songs on the jukebox like Buck Owens' "Tiger by the Tail," George Jones' "The Race Is On," and other hillbilly shit. But with the beer, they all sounded pretty damn good.

After about four or five Stroh's, we decided we better get back to campus if we wanted to catch the evening meal in the cafeteria. So we walked to the edge of town, stuck out our thumbs, and sure enough, someone from campus happened to be driving by and picked us up. It'd been a good day, having broken my maidenhead in terms of drinking in Ohio.

The Dovells, from Philly, "Bristol Stomp." Great energy and feel to it.

Bernie

Woody Guthrie died, Oct. 3, 1967

One Saturday afternoon, about three weeks after arriving at Rio, I went to the Student Center to watch a football game. "Student Center" was a liberal use of the term, because this place provided barely a modicum of entertainment.

There was a snack bar, which actually had pretty good food, but on a limited burger type of menu. The ladies who worked there were great people. One time, I asked if they made fried bologna sandwiches—one of those comfort foods back home. The lady said, "We have cold cut sandwiches with bologna in them. But I'd be glad to fry one up for you." So she quickly disassembled a couple sandwiches, threw the bologna on the grill, and fried it up. "What do you put on the bologna? Mustard? Ketchup? Lettuce?" she asked.

I said, "How about some pickle relish?"

"No problem."

I got my fried bologna sandwich, done just right. The lady made it as though she was doing it for her son. Some students took these ladies for granted and gave them a bunch of crap at times, I guess because they were local yokels. But in my mind they were just as important as any of the other campus employees.

Besides the snack bar, the Student Center had a couple pinball machines, a jukebox, and some tables and chairs. That was about it. But then I found out there was another room with a black and white TV. At the time, it was one of only three TVs on the whole damn campus; the others were located in the lobbies of Davis and Moulton Halls, female dorms.

So I went into this anteroom to watch Michigan State vs. Notre Dame. It was the year after the infamous game where Notre Dame's venerable coach Ara Parseghian went for a tie instead of a win, hoping to save the school's #1 ranking. That was one of the reasons I disliked

Notre Dame. I can say that in an unbiased, clear-headed manner, and not because I was anti-Catholic or anything like that.

One of the first memories I have of watching football on TV was when I was maybe seven or eight years old. I didn't know anything about football, but just by watching the beginning of this game, I could tell it was pretty damn exciting. The student body had formed a tunnel for its team to run through as they entered the field while the band played a pep song.

So as I was watching, I asked my mom who was playing. She said the one team was Notre Dame and they were traditionally pretty good. And right there, I got hooked. I thought all that Notre Dame spirit was pretty neat, not realizing at the time, that most colleges had the same kind of spirit.

As I got older, I noticed that virtually every Catholic person I knew thought Notre Dame was the best of the best, simply because it was a Catholic school. It was like a divine-right thing, that God was on their side, and they could do no wrong. Consequently, because of that parochial, narrow-minded view by the faithful followers, I decided never to root for the Fighting Irish again, and loved to see them lose.

On this particular Saturday, I went into the TV room and saw some upperclassmen, but mostly dorky freshmen, none of whom I knew. I mean, hell, it was a campus of only 800, but I didn't know any of them from Adam.

So I took a seat. This one girl kept turning her head, looking back at me. She was kind of cute, with big brown eyes and short brown hair. She and her friends were yucking it up, and eventually she turned around and flat-out asked for my name.

"Mahlon," I said.

"Hi Mahlon, I'm Bernadette, but everyone calls me Bernie. And this is Jackie and Debbie and this is Roland and Jimmy..." and she went down the whole damn line and did the "this-is-so-and-so" thing.

Ordinarily, it would have annoyed me, but for some reason I let it slide. Hell, a girl was talking to me. So I sat there and tried to watch the game. Then every two or three minutes, she'd turn around and ask me something, like where I was from and what I was majoring in, and on and on. I tried to be polite and answered her questions.

When the game was over, most people got up to leave, so I followed her and her chums out of the Student Center. As I was turning toward the dorm, she said, "Well Mahlon, nice meeting you. Maybe we can talk some more sometime."

"Yeah, sure," I said.

I went back to the dorm thinking about this Bernie person who talked a lot. After a little while, it was time for supper, so I went over to the cafeteria, got my food, and took a seat at a table by myself. As I started to dig into some over-cooked meatloaf, in came Bernie with her pals, and they all joined me at the table.

Mostly freshmen, it appeared they'd bonded quickly, so they were real chummy and laughed at the dumbest things. I guess that was alright, but I wasn't too interested. The two guys, Roland and Jimmy, were pretty damn close to being queer, if you know what I mean. And again, that was fine with me, but I didn't really enjoy that kind of company.

Over the next few days, I started seeing Bernie, mostly in the cafeteria. In the evening after supper, I'd walk her back to her dorm and sit in the lobby and talk. It was her nature to introduce me to anyone she knew, so I met several other girls and their boyfriends this way.

Bernie was from Slippery Rock, Pennsylvania, and was majoring in Elementary Ed. She was a nice gal but after a couple weeks, I got rather tired of her. It was just a personality thing. She loved the *Peanuts* comic strip. She even had a Snoopy key chain and sketches of all the characters on her notebooks.

She was into schmaltzy music like Barbra Streisand, Rod McKuen, and Neil Diamond but showed no interest in learning about jazz or the blues. She would never think of saying "shit" or "fuck," and she wore one of those old lady watches—the kind with the really thin band and tiny face. She made obnoxious sounds when she ate, almost to the point where she took pride in the noise she made. You could hear her chomping above everything else in the cafeteria.

One evening after supper, we hiked up to the Baptist cemetery to see the tombstone of Clara Davis, the "weeping virgin." The mythical story is that she died tragically on her wedding day—run over by a horse or something. Actually, she lived to the age of seventy-two, but many still hang on to the myth—better story.

Anyway, supposedly, if you got there at the right time, you could see Clara's tears dripping from her face on the stone. Good old Bernie got all excited and thought she saw this phenomenon, but I saw nothing. She then said if you touched the stone, it would feel warm. And it did feel warm, but so did the other stones nearby, because the damn sun had just gone down.

So I had a rough time developing much of a feeling for Bernie. I guess the thing that bothered me most was that she was so sickeningly sweet. But it took me awhile to tell her I didn't want to see her anymore.

This will sound really terrible, but I wrote up a "Dear Bernie" letter and dropped it off at the front desk of her dorm. I know I should have told her, face to face, but admittedly, I didn't have the balls. So the next day, I found an envelope in my mailbox. She had produced her reply in the form of a *Peanuts* comic strip. It was well done and funny. So I guess she took it pretty well, and that left me off the hook. About a week or so later, I saw Bernie walking around campus with another guy, and that was just fine with me.

Horace Silver, piano, leader, "Song for My Father," "The Jody Grind," "Blue Silver." Known for great Blue Note albums. Strong sidemen, especially Joe Henderson on tenor sax.

Mole Hole, Room 12

Sgt. Pepper's Lonely Hearts Club Band

My dorm room for six semesters at Rio was on the ground level of Holzer Hall, named after Charles E. Holzer, a doctor from Gallipolis. Previous Mole Hole residents had contributed to the mystique of the place, to the point where people from other parts of the campus would enter the floor with cautious trepidation.

Just being part of this milieu, a Mole Holer tended to develop a kind of swagger and a feeling of exceptionalism. It was like people who come from a big city thinking they're hot shit just because of where they're from. To add to the special quality of the place, the laundry room for the whole dorm was on this floor, which took up the space of about three rooms. That meant there were fewer guys, so we tended to think we were a tighter group. I'm sure the rest of the dorm felt the same about their floors, but from our perspective, that was unadulterated bullshit.

As you walked into Room 12, my closet was to the immediate left. Above the closet was a small compartment for storing a suitcase and maybe a little more, like possibly a bottle of Ancient Age bourbon.

Between my closet and Clark's on the other side of the room was a study area, basically a veneered plank about eight feet long, which was on top of two sets of drawers. The wall behind the study area was a relatively thin piece of paneling, which allowed most sounds from the next room to be heard, including farts, ass scratchings, and snorings.

In the middle of this wall, Clark had hung a Nazi flag that his dad "liberated" during the big war. I was taken aback when I first saw that. He didn't have any neo-Nazi leanings. It was basically a trophy relating to his dad's war experience. As the year went on, this wall also collected numerous pictures, quotes, and snappy sayings (*Kumquats make you horny).*

Clark's bed was against the outside wall—mine against the inside wall. Both beds had a small chest of drawers next to it. On top of the drawers, Clark had placed an unfinished plank which held his brother's reel-to-reel tape recorder, a cheap turntable, and two speakers. He had brought a bunch of Carl's tapes and records, plus a few of his own, and I added my collection.

The outside wall on Clark's side of the room had a sliding window. The bottom of the window was about four feet above the floor, which happened to conform to the sloping ground outside. If you had to leave the dorm quickly, you could jump out the window.

Except for the study area, the other walls were constructed of white painted cinder block. On these walls, I hung several *Playboy* centerfolds, using white athletic tape (masking tape would dry up and fall off). Some notables were:

- Surrey Marshe, blonde, worked at the New York Club's gift shop
- Kim Farber, brunette, ticket taker at the Chicago Club
- Fran Gerard, auburn, 39-24-36, loan officer in a Los Angeles bank
- Gwen Wong, Asian, 5' 0", Los Angeles Lakers enthusiast
- Heather Ryan, 36.5-20-35, pre-law
- Angela Dorian, dancer and folk singer, lying in a hammock (fantastic) (best ever)

They added some class to the room and frequently elicited favorable comments from visitors. There were two beer signs that I filched from the Last Chance Carryout. One was a fake-copper Lowenbrau sign, and another was an inch-thick, wooden Pabst Blue Ribbon sign that said, "Next Time, Bring Your Wife."

I also had a large poster of a rooster digging his feet into the top of a guy's head. The caption read, "Excedrin Please." The centerfolds had come from the *Playboys* I lifted from Phil Hoff's garage back home, and I got the Excedrin poster for free in the mail. I liked to send away for free shit.

Something else I got for free in the mail was a poster from the Atlantic Richfield Oil Company. Actually there were two posters, both exactly the same, except one was in black and white and the other was in color. They each measured 26" x 36". They were a closeup photo of a girl's face. Her name was not given. The caption at the bottom said, "Making Things Happen with Petroleum Energy." The girl's face was captivating. Guys would come into the room and just stand there, looking at her.

It wasn't like a glamour shot, but it really grabbed you. She was looking right at you with wide eyes, almost in surprise, and her mouth was slightly open, like she had just taken a short breath. The photo was well-defined, except where her straight blonde hair approached the edges of the picture. There it became a little blurred, as a kind of aura framing her face. I never got tired of looking at her.

I don't think the Chinese Feng Shui was correct, but it worked for me—a Nazi flag, a pain pill advertisement, two beer signs, and lots of mammary glands.

Gary US Bonds, "Quarter to Three." Great energy in song. Headlined above the Beatles when they first toured Europe.

Farts

70,000 demonstrators try to levitate the Pentagon.
Che Guevara is captured and killed.

It was a Sunday evening, and a bunch of guys were in Room 12 for a BS session. Suddenly, Craig Pottorf busted in, stood in the middle of everyone, and started shooting farts as fast as he could.

Of course, this farting spasm was obnoxious and disgusting, but if a guy was going for the record for consecutive farts, he had to do it while the gun was loaded. And if this gaseous guy was relatively successful, he would earn a healthy amount of cred with the assembled group and other degenerates on campus. This whole scene could take place at any random time, because as stated above, while the gun is loaded—you know.

A day or so later, Kim Pataky and his roommate Tom Lindgren came into the room, just as someone cut a big-ass fart. As the "bouquet" slowly abated, someone broached the topic of lighting farts. This time-honored ritual was pretty simple, but it also took some skill. The lights were turned out, the farter dropped trou, and he held a lighter to his ass, while everyone waited for lift off.

From previous observations, I found this endeavor could be quite fruitful or also uneventful. At worst, it could be messy if someone tried too hard... if you know what I mean.

So this time, Lindgren was productive and ripped off two burners. As always, everyone went fucking crazy when that happened. Pataky—whose father was an emergency room doctor in East Orange, New Jersey—recalled a story his dad told about the dangers of lighting farts. Apparently, someone came into the ER with terrible burns in his anal canal. The poor guy had lit a fart, but his ass "inhaled," drawing the flame inside. Talk about a burning fart!

So being the intellectuals that we were, the conversation expanded on the act of expelling gas—aka *flatus, flatulence, stinker, toot, wind, cut one,* ad infinitum. This turned out to be one of the more profound discussions that ever occurred in Room 12.

The following precepts about farts resulted from our little talk.

Everyone does it. But so-called nice girls and ladies pretend they never fart. It was questioned by our group if it was a cultural stigma only in western society. For instance, in places like Russia or Saudi Arabia or Outer Mongolia, did people fart at will, in all social circumstances? Was there a society where blatant farting is considered in the same breath as say... breathing?

It was decided that one absolute truth was that everyone thinks *other people's farts smell worse than their own.*

Then there was Benjamin Franklin, foreign diplomat, statesman, inventor, librarian, postmaster, fornicator with foreign women, and quoter of pithy quotes like "Fish and visitors stink after three days." Or was it "Fish and pussies stink... period!"? Anyway, Old Ben once said, in a very profound way, *"FART PROUDLY."* I mean, if he said it... fire away, right?

The bathtub fart. There is no other sound like it. If you were blindfolded and you heard that sound, you would immediately know that someone just bombed one in the tub. And you'd laugh, because everyone knows that the person who farted enjoyed the experience. Who doesn't like to fart while sitting in a bathtub? And to go one step further, farting in a tub is a unique experience because you not only hear it, but you actually see it since there is an accompanying effect of one or two bubbles rising to the surface of the soapy water.

Another absolute about farts is that, as you age, *farts tend to take on a mind of their own.* That is, you find yourself farting without even knowing they're coming. At a friend's wedding, I was in the pew behind this little grandmother. When she knelt at the prayer rail, not one, but a series of small "put, put, puts" freely flowed from the proper old lady's butt.

Another absolute is *the five-second rule.* You're in a room by yourself. You feel one coming on. You say to yourself, "I'll just let this one rip. No one will hear it." But sure as hell, before five seconds elapse, some poor bastard walks in, immediately smells it, and gives you that look of "you pig!"

Another absolute is *the amplified fart.* In other words, you bounce the fart off a hard surface. Like you're in the last row of a boring class and you just can't take it anymore. You lean to your left and rap one off the hard wood of your desk seat. Of course, you do this at the risk of being kicked out of class. But if the professor is that boring, chances are he won't even know someone farted. Suggestion: the best place to shoot off an amplified fart is on a metal lawn chair. The distinct sound provides a great deal of satisfaction and often praise from those around you.

Perhaps this is an obvious given, but *farts are, by nature, funny.* This is proven by the fact that young kids naturally laugh when a fart sneaks out. However, the only problem about little kids farting is that there's always a 90% chance that they just crapped themselves.

The happy fart. You're in a crowded hallway. You let one rip, knowing that no one will hear it or maybe even smell it. And even if they do smell it, they'll never know it was you who dropped the bomb. So when you see someone in a crowd who has an unnaturally large smile on his face, you know what he probably just did.

The burning rubber fart. This is when your own fart smells bad, even to you. This is often the result of eating a pile of chili with lots of kidney beans in it. It literally smells like rubber burning and might even burn when expelled.

The religious fart. Some devoutly religious people believe that every event is part of God's divine plan. For instance, when a young person dies from a terrible death (run over by a Mack truck), God had a reason for that happening. In the same way, some religious people believe that God made farts smell bad for the sake of deaf people. They can't hear a fart but the smell tells them that some bastard just dropped one.

Applause-provoking farts (high skill level). This can occur, even in the most sophisticated restaurant. Someone premeditates a very creative fart, starting with a low-volume rumble and building up to a loud and really obnoxious bang, ending in a slow-release hissing and a short, but distinct pop. The entire restaurant, including waiters, old ladies, prissy librarians, and priests, spontaneously bursts into well-deserved applause.

The elevator fart. You're in this tight, enclosed space in the presence of two, maybe three people. Before you got into the elevator, you felt the presence of gas, and the more you thought about it, the more pressure you felt. But you have no choice. You have to get into the elevator. Of course, you don't know the other individuals, so you try to act real nonchalant as the gas kind of stutters out, in a slow, lisping manner. You look at the ceiling, hit a few of the elevator buttons, and hope that the smell doesn't permeate before the door opens.

Multiple show-off farts (high skill level). The farter expels single farts with each step he takes. He might be simply walking down the street and shoots off a fart for his every step. The ultimate show-off farter "performs" by walking up seven or eight steps, blasting a fart with each step. But this guy throws in a musical factor by going up the musical scale with each fart, starting with low bass notes and rising to the upper register.

Hide-a-fart (high skill level). The key here is to produce a distracting noise. Slam a car door or any door at the same time the fart pops out. In class, slam a book on the floor. At a vending machine, pretend the candy bar didn't fall, so slam the machine at the same time you fart. This takes much practice. The synchronizing of the fart and distracting noise is seldom, if ever, mastered.

Detecting a long-distance fart. In a restaurant, sitting five tables away, you see someone leaning unnaturally to one side. To further convince you that the person is farting, one tell-tale sign is that he is, at first, concentrating hard with a wrinkled brow. And then, after a second or two, he leans back and a smile of relief is proudly displayed.

Blaming it on someone else, hopefully a dog. If this happens in a room with another person and a dog, you immediately take the dog outside. That quickly defuses the problem. However, if no dog is present, then the source of the fart has to be diverted. You hear responses like, "What a hog!" as the farter points to an innocent person. This is a common practice of women who deny that they have ever cut one in their entire life.

Sometimes, the most disgusting things in life must be confronted head on: administrative tyranny, poverty, child abuse, bulbous hemorrhoids, and yes, even skidmark-causing farts.

Mose Allison, blues piano, "Wild Man on the Loose."
Most soulful, Southern, piano-playing white man.

Frank Denny's

541,000 troops in Nam, 1968.
19,600 U.S. deaths since the war began.

There was a small grocery store/lunch counter on the edge of campus, owned and operated by Frank Denny. He was a decent guy, although I'm sure he got pissed once in awhile with the college kids.

One time I went in there to buy a loaf of bread and some molasses. Back home, molasses bread was comfort food. You'd take a piece of bread (toasted or not) and spread butter or margarine on it, pretty thick. Then you'd pour molasses on the bread and chow down.

The trick was to eat it before the molasses ran off the bread, dripping onto your fingers, chin, lap, and table. You tilt the bread as the molasses slowly oozes so it evenly spreads on the bread.

You didn't use a knife to spread it, because that would just make things more sticky and unwieldy. It probably sounds disgusting to the uninitiated, but it's fantastic. I could probably eat a whole loaf of bread like that.

Anyway, I went into Denny's to buy this stuff, since it was the only grocery store within thirteen miles of campus. I asked Frank if he had molasses. He said he did, and, out of curiosity, he wondered what I wanted it for. I told him I was going to make molasses bread. He looked at me kind of funny, but he gave me the molasses, bread and butter. I paid him and took the stuff back to the dorm room, looking forward to this epicurean delight, salivating all the way.

I got back to the room and no one was around so I didn't have to explain what the hell I was doing. I spread the butter and poured on the molasses, letting it spread over the bread by tilting it one way, then the other, and then took a big bite. And, of course, it didn't taste like the stuff I had at home.

Turns out you have to use King Syrup, the brand with the lion's head on the red label. My mom's parents used so much of this stuff that they bought it in a pail—a damn bucket, like a paint bucket with a handle. They always had a small dish of it in the middle of the kitchen table. Anyway, Denny had sold me a jar of Brer Rabbit dark molasses, which I found out was used mostly for baking cookies, cakes, and stuff like that. It was way too bitter for molasses bread. The disappointment was unsettling. I had to sit back for a bit and recover my senses.

One Saturday morning, I didn't feel like having breakfast in the cafeteria so I walked over to Denny's to see what they had. My recovery from the molasses fiasco had been achieved. I found out they made really fantastic cinnamon buns. When they were served, they came right out of the oven and were topped with a thick white icing. Damn!

On this particular day, the place was full of loud students, bragging about their partying the previous night. Mostly fraternity dudes, they didn't really bother me because I was working on a cinnamon bun.

Then someone played "Green Onions" on the jukebox, and that just seemed like one of the best damn instrumentals I ever heard. It was nothing sophisticated or really creative like Coltrane or Miles would do. But it was so damn funky and fluid and relaxing. Whenever I heard Booker T and the MGs after that, my mind went back to that Saturday morning with the cinnamon buns.

Stevie Wonder, harmonica, "Fingertips, Part 2." Twelve years old. Marvin Gaye on drums.

Social Development

1968 Summer Olympics: Black athletes Tommie Smith and John Carlos on winners' platform in protest

My parents were great people—salt of the earth. But they tended to rely on outside forces to educate me. For instance, I was sent to the YMCA to learn to swim even though both of them learned in the local Codorus Creek. When it came to social graces, I was sent to this thing downtown called Junior Assembly. My sister would have loved it, but Mom never sent her. I guess she thought Sue didn't need it because she was more or less a social butterfly.

At the age of twelve, it wasn't like I was totally inept at dancing or being with girls. I had been going to the Friday night record hops at the Reliance Fire Hall. There was a disc jockey from a local radio station, such as WORK or WSBA, or WNOW. Good old Doc Dougherty or maybe another of the local celebrities like Ed Lincoln would be there, spinning the vinyl 45s.

You'd meet up with your buddies and gorge out on junk food the fire company sold. I liked the pretzel sticks that came in a flat box which opened so you could shoot mustard on them. And of course, you'd get mustard on your fingers and mouth that you weren't aware of. And you'd probably spill a little Pepsi on your shirt. But that really didn't bother you, or maybe you didn't even know you had spilled it.

You'd scope out the various babes who showed up. Of course, the girls had already been thinking about that dating stuff for a year, so they were sitting across the floor, all dressed up.

In 1959, there were a lot of good, slow-dance songs, like Little Anthony and the Imperials' "Tears on My Pillow," Ritchie Valens' "Donna," The Crests' "16 Candles," The Flamingos' "I Only Have Eyes for You," and Santo and Johnny's "Sleepwalk." The music pushed you into asking a girl to dance. You'd do your best to fast dance, which wasn't always the easiest thing to do. And it never looked as cool as the kids on American Bandstand. But at that age, you didn't really care about how you looked.

I'd dance with Nancy Kochenour or my favorite at the time, Cynthia Knooky. I'd hold her right hand in my left, and it felt soft and moist. My right hand would be around her waist. I wouldn't hold her real close, but as the evening went on, I might pull her a little closer, noticing her Palmolive soap girl-smell. She might lay her head on my shoulder, and I'd start to feel pretty damn good about myself. At that stage, I wasn't the basket case I'd later become, in terms of girls.

But this Junior Assembly thing was different. It turned out most of the other kids were from rich families. Many were children of doctors, lawyers, and executives who were members of the York Country Club, which, by the way, excluded blacks and Jews, no matter how much money they had.

When you got inside the door at the Women's Club, everyone would stand in single file, girls first, then the boys. We'd all shake the hand of the man who conducted the session. I think his name was Millard Ellsesser or something like that. He had a real uppity voice and attitude. And I thought to myself, *What kind of grown man would make kids do this stuff? Doesn't he have anything better to do? Or is he getting paid really well for this?*

All the girls had to wear white gloves. I guess that was the proper thing in those days. But get this. The boys had to wear white gloves also. And we all despised this. Some guys would try to get out of wearing the gloves by saying they forgot them or their mom forgot to wash them. But then you'd be fined a dollar, and Old Millard would give you a spare pair that they had for this situation. So this glove thing really set the tone for what would come next.

Everyone would enter the ballroom which was used for things like afternoon teas and adult shindigs... classy shit like that. At the one end of the room was a stage with a grand piano, and that's what produced the music for the evening. Some old guy, Mr. Collins, tickled the keys.

Chairs lined the two edges of the room, girls on one side, boys on the other. Old Millard would show us how to do various dances like the fox trot, waltz, cha cha, mambo... hell, he even showed us how to do the jitterbug. But that's where things got weird. The jitterbug is a feeling thing, not some contrived, instructed thing. But this guy told us how to point this toe and when to go from toe to heel, and on and on and on. To me, that wasn't dancing.

Anyway, he'd tell the guys how to ask a girl for a dance, and he'd tell the girls how to respond. None of it helped me later in getting dates or getting laid. Reflecting on this, I think my buddy Stoney Stonsifer had the best advice for this social stuff. One time he asked a girl to dance and she declined. Without batting an eye, he smoothly retorted, "Well then, I guess a blow job is out of the question."

Hugh Masekela, singer, trumpet, flugelhorn; "Baby, Baby, Baby."
Best song from Hugh Masekela's Latest, *his first album.*

Going to Columbus

Magical Mystery Tour

Clark had an older brother who was in the veterinary school at Ohio State. Every once in awhile, we'd hitchhike to Columbus, ninety miles to the north, mostly just to get away from campus, to see the big city, and to check out what Clark's brother was up to. Three or four times, we were picked up by the same guy, a Methodist minister who made the same drive every week from southeastern Ohio. All we had to do was put up with his religious congeniality for an hour or so, but hell, it was a free ride, and the best thing was that he'd drop us off wherever we wanted to go.

We always stayed at a rooming house on Hawthorne Avenue, close to the OSU hospital. This old couple rented rooms for two bucks a night. They were nice people and enjoyed the company of students, most of which seemed kind of strange. Anyway, we didn't hang around the place very long, so they weren't a problem.

Once we would get situated, we would head off to find Carl's place. He had been in the Air Force, so he was a few years older than Clark. The military experience had taken him out of his family's West Virginia hillbilly background and made him more worldly. He had acquired an interest in jazz, as evidenced by the many tapes he had copied on his state-of-the-art reel-to-reel tape recorder, which he'd loaned to Clark for our room at Rio.

One cut I remember was an extended live version of Herbie Mann's "Coming Home, Baby." Another neat album was *The Pair Extraordinaire*, which was performed by two black guys, one who sang and the other who played a stand-up bass. Carl also had several obscure European recordings of American jazz musicians in exile, most of which were never distributed in the U.S.

Another neat thing about Carl was that he had an acoustic string bass leaning in a corner of the living room. When asked to play the thing, he would reluctantly demonstrate with surprising dexterity, using all the correct block fingerings.

Perhaps the best example of his change in world-view was the fact that he had a black girlfriend who was also a veterinary student. He said she wasn't his girlfriend, but apparently she was very interested in him, was very intelligent, and liked to screw a lot. To me, that sounded like a girlfriend.

One lasting vestige of Carl's country background was found in the stuffed birds that were hung on the living room walls. As you entered the room, your eyes immediately moved toward the various mallards, pheasants, and quail that were hanging like recently killed Daffy Ducks in a cartoon.

We did a lot of walking in Columbus, or hopped on a bus, but mostly we hoped Carl would let us use whatever vehicle he was currently driving to scope out the big-ass OSU campus. One of the places we would frequent was a bar called Don's, which catered to both locals and college students. Various fraternity and Ohio State Buckeye signs were hanging up, and, unlike some bars in college towns, there never seemed to be any friction between the townspeople and the students. It was a good place to watch a football or basketball game.

In the front window of Don's was a green neon sign, "Frosty Mugs," which was how we always got our beer. It tasted so damn good with the ice sliding down the side. And at Don's we were usually served regular beer without being carded. In Ohio at the time, eighteen, nineteen, and twenty year olds could only purchase 3.2 beer. No hard liquor or full bodied beer. You had to drink twice as much to get the job done, and you also had to pee a lot more.

I always thought 3.2 beer was a good idea, because the bars where that was all they served, gave kids of that age a place to hang out, and they could drink legally.

In states like Pennsylvania, where the drinking age was twenty-one, underage kids had more unfortunate options to get inebriated. One was to steal beer from people's garages and run the risk of getting your ass shot off by a twelve-gauge. Another was to find some degenerate alchy who would buy the good stuff for you, in exchange for a few extra bucks for the service. Another more dangerous option was to drive long distances across the state border to an adjoining state with a lower drinking age. This practice often resulted in horrendous car crashes involving the deaths and/or mangling of six or seven adolescents.

So why not just have good old 3.2 served a block or two from your house, and everyone would be healthy, happy, and legal?

Sam Cooke, "Chain Gang," "A Change Is Gonna Come," "You Send Me"

Looking for Good Smut

"The most essential gift for a good writer is a built-in, shockproof, shit detector." –Ernest Hemingway

On one of our Columbus excursions, we decided to honor the right of free expression. In other words, good old porn. I'd been "reading" *Playboy* for a few years, but I had a hankering for something more adventurous.

Columbus was a relatively large town. We figured there should be all kinds of smut up there, as opposed to the tight-assed, conservative Gallia County where Rio was located. Well, Columbus turned out to be nothing of the kind. We went to book stores, newsstands, any place we thought might sell the stuff. Despite being in the so-called sexually liberated 1960s, we found zilch.

So we decided to take a different approach to the world of cultural depravity. We went to The Little Art Theater on North High Street, which had been recommended by some degenerate back at Rio. The name of the place was misleading. This establishment had nothing to do with the world of art. It was an out-and-out porno flick place. It was a whacker's dream, at least for a little while.

The people who ran the place tried to make it look legit. The ticket taker actually wore a uniform, and they even sold popcorn and candy. But once you entered the dark of the place, you knew what it really was. The first image I remember seeing on the screen was of a busty woman at a roller rink, totally nude except for her laced up skates, rolling around the rink with organ music playing in the background. I thought, *"Damn! Now we're talking."*

But I have to admit, soon it got kind of old. Seemed that good, hard-core porn hadn't really reached this place. After all, profanity laws still existed in many areas. Hell, just a year or two before this, the genius Lenny Bruce was still being arrested for saying "fuck" on stage or for talking about Eleanor Roosevelt's large tits.

Despite the boorishness of the films at the Little Art, there was still a healthy attendance of the raincoat crowd—old dudes with newspapers on their laps who liked to "abuse themselves." So we didn't hang around there very long.

When in Columbus, we always tried to avail ourselves of whatever cultural events were occurring. We saw a few shows at the Veterans Memorial Hall: Buddy Rich, Hugh Masekela, Tony Bennett, and Woody Herman. Granted, except for Masekela, they weren't the most current performers. But one time we saw The Doors, and as usual, Jim Morrison did something weird on stage, causing the cops to close the show.

Sometimes we found ourselves at The World Theater on North High Street. Yes, that's right. The main drag in Columbus was called High Street, which every adolescent at the time thought was so fucking funny. The World Theater hosted something called Underground Cinema-12. You'd pay 25-cents for a membership card, which would allow you in for screenings of so-called underground movies. I'm thinking the membership thing was just a legality so the place wouldn't be shut down, because some of the films were rather risqué and pretty damn weird.

The Saturday night shows didn't start until midnight. Sometimes they'd have a light show with a band, which appealed to the acid lovers. I remember some dude doing a sound check at the microphone, and instead of saying "testing, 1, 2, 3," in a very professional voice he said, "TESTES, 1, 2, 3!" which everyone thought was hilarious.

I'm guessing that many were under the influence of one thing or another, but at the time, I was kind of oblivious to the drug thing. It didn't really affect me. The crowd was a healthy cross-section of the campus community, with a lot of professor-types, free-thinkers, and snot-nosed freshmen.

The main attraction was the underground or avant-garde films. They were usually of poor quality and not the most interesting. One film showed some guy sleeping on his back. That was it... just sleeping. It went on for about ten minutes. You could see his chest rising and falling, but that was it. He never woke up, never said anything, no background music, no nothing. I'm sure there was some damn metaphorical implication about life or war or maybe just fuckin' sleep. Who the hell knows?

Another film showed a performance artist playing a cello in a rather violent manner. I'm guessing she was rebelling against the establishment, both musically and politically. But the real kicker was that she had wrapped her completely nude body in see-through Saran Wrap. And when I saw this, I immediately thought, *Hmm, boobs!* But it wasn't much of a turn-on, and she really sucked at playing the cello.

When I was eleven or twelve years old, a couple of my buddies and I had nothing to do on a Sunday afternoon, so we took a walk along one of the country roads near our neighborhood. Along the way, we saw the usual discarded items: beer cans, paper bags, dirty socks, etc. But we also stumbled upon a girly magazine, soiled and wrinkled, but the pictures were still intact.

> Camera Arts Monthly, *for camera enthusiasts, from casual shutter bugs to discerning professionals. Each month you can read articles on figure and glamour photography, color, composition, lighting, exposure, lenses, and retouching. Also, you will see an elegant display of feminine beauty in all its moods and magic.*

And sure enough, as the ad mentioned, there were some really great pictures of naked women in all kinds of suggestive poses. So for my buddies and me, this was like finding the holy grail. We all took a good look and then hid it somewhere in a field behind our houses so it would be out of the rain yet quickly available to anyone who wished to study the various camera and lighting techniques of a true-blue photographer.

A few years later, I became the yard boy for Mrs. Hoff, our next door neighbor. Her husband Gordon had died, and although her adult son Phil still lived at home, he didn't have time for yard work. So I mowed their lawn.

One day as I returned the mower to their garage, I noticed a neatly stacked pile of *Playboys*. They were bound in string, probably waiting to be picked up by the monthly Boy Scout scrap drive. I couldn't believe my eyes. They obviously belonged to Phil, who was the idol of all the boys in the neighborhood. He drove a big-ass white Chrysler convertible and dressed like a damn movie star. He dated the well-endowed Jannie Hykes, who lived behind the Hoffs.

But he never married, and a few years later, to everyone's surprise, Phil came out of the damn closet. Well, he didn't really proclaim it publicly. But like a lot of gay men, I guess he had to go through that phase where he projected the appearance of a true, red-blooded heterosexual American male. I suppose that's how the *Playboys* ended up in his garage. But it was really none of my damn business, one way or the other.

So after mowing the Hoffs' lawn a few times and seeing those perfectly good *Playboys* sitting there going to waste, I decided to put them to good use and sneaked them into the cubbyhole in my bedroom. At the end of that summer, I became the most popular bastard at the West York Bulldog Band Camp when I unrolled my sleeping bag and revealed the confiscated magazines. There were guys coming into my cabin throughout the whole week to borrow those classy publications... to read the articles, of course.

For my sixteenth birthday, my sister, away at college, sent a present in the mail. I opened it in front of the folks at the kitchen table. At the time, Sue had a really gorgeous roommate, and in the box was a clip of her blonde hair and a red lipstick kiss on a white note card. Plus, there was an unfiltered (*I'd Walk a Mile for a)* Camel.

But the best thing, and a real shocker, was what I unfolded in front of good old Mom and Dad: a *Playboy* centerfold, picturing a fantastically endowed blonde (Jan Roberts, Miss August '63). She was wearing some kind of see-through thing as she sat on a stool in *her kitchen.* My eyes just about popped out, but then I double-clutched because I figured if I made too much of a big deal about this, the damn thing might be confiscated. So I just kind of played it cool, but I was actually saying in my mind, *Holy fuckin' shit! This is fantastic!* I know the old man got a kick out of it, but Mom said something like, "That's disgusting!"

Around this time, Hugh Hefner started televising his "Playboy After Dark" TV show, which came on late at night on Saturdays. Everything about the show was so damn cool, except of course for Hef himself. He couldn't keep the damn smirk off his face because he knew he was the luckiest fuckin' bastard in the world. The set for the show was in his Chicago mansion, with all the overstuffed furniture, modern art, great music (Cy Coleman's "Playboy's Theme"), entertaining guests, and best of all, the fantastic women, either in bunny costumes or low-cut dresses. How could any red-blooded American male watch that and not want to be a guest at the Mansion?

A few years earlier, my Aunt Marion caught her son Johnny "abusing himself" one day. So because she believed in that reverse psychology thing, she allowed him to subscribe to *Playboy* when he was only in the eighth grade ($8.00 for a one-year subscription). It was delivered on a monthly basis, and the little bastard would unashamedly march out to the mail box to retrieve a nice clean copy of Hefner's whack-off magazine.

When I heard about that, it pissed me off big-time, especially since I was reduced to the level of stealing *Playboys* from my gay neighbor. However, when I was a junior in high school, I acquired my grandpa's four-door, 1950 black, Chevy Deluxe. Once a month, I'd drive into town to Bob's News Stand where no one knew me, and I'd pick up the latest copy of Hefner's magazine for 75 cents. I'd place it under the car seat and take it into the house when the parents weren't around, so I could later read all the articles... and once in awhile maybe take a gander at some of the pictorials.

Stanley Turrentine, tenor sax, Rough N Tumble, *Blue Note album. Industrial-strength soul; all-time best arrangement of "Walk on By."*

Stylin'

"Little Annie Fanny," Playboy *comic strip, by Harvey Kurtzman and Will Elder*

I never thought of myself as a fashion plate. But I liked to wear things that were a little out of the ordinary. One place to find stuff like that was Sunny's Surplus in my hometown which sold military clothes and equipment.

You could buy anything from socks to helmets to empty grenades to canteens to collapsible shovels. Kids loved this place. Back in the 1950s, everyone played "war," fighting the Japs or Nazis. It was part of our generation. Our parents were greatly affected by the Big War and talked about it a lot. We watched TV shows like *Victory at Sea* and *The Big Picture*, which made an imprint on our brains, showing us how terrible war was but also how we whooped butt on the Germans and Japanese.

So Sunny's Surplus was where I got my winter jacket when I went off to college. It was a U.S. Navy N-1 Deck Jacket (WW II issue). It had a jungle-cloth outer shell (olive drab), but its best feature was the man-made alpaca fur lining and collar. It wasn't flashy or trendy, but it kept me warm.

One time when I was sitting at the bar at the Blue Willow, the barmaid Angel, got a little frisky with a bottle of Cherry Kijafa and flipped the bottle into the air, like a baton twirler. She was pretty smooth with the whole thing, except that as the bottle was flying through the air, it left a trail of Kijafa down the front of my U.S. Navy N-1 Deck Jacket. I observed the well-defined red line, didn't say a word, and went back to drinking my 7 & 7. I never tried to wash it off and wore the mark as a red badge of courage (for drinking in a redneck, hillbilly bar).

Another part of my wardrobe was a fake Baracuta jacket. I didn't have a real one because they were pretty damn expensive. They were also called a Harrington. It was a khaki cotton jacket with a stand-up collar. The distinctive part was the traditional Fraser tartan lining.

Somehow, my dad found out about some outlet store that sold a knock-off, so I went out there and bought one. You couldn't tell it was fake until you saw the lining. But to make my jacket even more distinctive, I sewed an alligator patch on the left breast. I got the patch for free from the Alligator coat company, which advertised in *Playboy*.

My preference in sneakers was white, low cut Jack Purcells. When I say "white," I mean dirty white. Because if you walked around wearing clean, white sneakers, some people might think of you as a "dandy." Jack Purcell was a Canadian badminton champion who designed the sneakers specifically for his sport. Purcells were a good, substantial canvas shoe, with a blue smile on the toe. And the bottoms were distinctive in terms of sneakers, because they had no treads. The soles were totally flat, except for a blue and red cutout in the center.

For most practical purposes, the flat, non-treaded sole worked. You'd think you'd be sliding all over the place, but you didn't. So I wore those sneaks with all of the slacks in my wardrobe, including chinos, khakis, and my dark charcoal, $8.80 Devonrite dress trousers. And to make things a little more distinctive, I didn't tie the laces. I'd just tuck them into the sides of the sneaks. But they'd eventually start dragging on the ground, which meant that the plastic tip or aglet would wear off. And like I mentioned before, the more ragged they got, the better. And of course, it wasn't cool to wear socks.

Dressed like that, I was continually fighting off the babes... in my fucking dreams.

Mary Lou Williams, piano, arranger.
Influenced Dizzy, Miles, Monk, and others.

Homecoming and Jane Barakos

Andy Warhol, Campbell's Soup Cans

Rio's homecoming was usually held around the fourth week of October. It wasn't a big deal for me. For one thing, the homecoming game was basketball, because Rio didn't have a football team. For another, the game was played where all of Rio's home games were played—thirteen miles to the east in Gallipolis at the high school gym. This obviously detracted from the usual campus atmosphere. Another reason I wasn't real hyped up was that I didn't hear any guys in the Mole Hole talking about it. The fraternities had their own dance and reunions, but the non-Greeks had to fend for themselves.

By this time in the semester, I had become attracted to a girl in the band. Her name was Jane Barakos. With her last name, I guessed she had a Greek background, but that didn't really matter. She had big brown eyes and kind of an olive complexion. And she had a neat voice, kind of dark and smoky, with something like a street-wise Philadelphia accent. She reminded me a little of Anne Bancroft in *The Graduate*, but younger of course.

I hated to criticize, but this was a rather dinky band. Jane didn't seem like the type who would sit through rehearsals and put up with the lower level of musicianship. Maybe she just liked to play the flute and didn't really give a rip about the other crap. Which, if true, endeared her even more to me. She never put on airs, and to me, that was one of the most important qualities of a classy broad.

At the first band practice, I was sitting there with all these dorky types. I fit in just fine since I felt like pretty much of a dork myself. I had my alto sax and the oboe which Professor Krone, the band director, had scrounged up for me. I was working on my reeds, getting them ready to play, not really thinking about anything around me.

All of a sudden, I felt someone slide into the chair next to me, all out of breath. She quickly put the flute together and ripped off a couple glissandos. And with that, the director started leading us through warm-up scales. Immediately, I had trouble concentrating. She took me by surprise, and when I was taken off guard like that, I was worthless. After going over a few selections, the director told us to take five.

So she leaned over to me and said, "I'm Jane."

Two damn words, but holy crap, I was immediately in love. Her big brown eyes looked right at me and as she leaned in, she placed her hand on my knee.

Somehow I stammered out, "Mahlon Dickinger."

"So Mahlon, you're new on campus?"

"Yes."

But Old Man Krone was back at it. "Let's go back to section A and try that again."

We'd play that section and then he'd stop, and she'd whisper something else.

"So you're a freshman?"

"Sophomore/junior."

Krone: "Let's do section A again, but louder this time." And then he'd stop for a little explanation, and she'd whisper something else.

"Where're ya from?"

"Pennsy."

Krone: "This time, keep going to section C." And then he'd stop.

"What's your major?"

"English."

Krone: "Nope, I didn't like that. Back to section B, louder this time."

"What dorm are you in?"

"Holzer."

"Do you know Dirk Zittle?"

"He rooms across the hall from me."

"Really? You know Dirk? Wow."

And with every one of her questions, her eyes got a little bigger. I got the feeling she was glad to see a new face, like she was sincerely interested. She had the best damn smile, and her eyes were fantastic. She was wearing an old sweatshirt and jeans and a pair of old, clunky loafers, which all looked really terrific on her.

So that was my chance to get things started, but she'd taken me by surprise. Plus, I was so entranced, all I could get out were some simple-ass pedestrian answers, which didn't make much of an impression.

I seriously considered asking her for a date to homecoming. But a day or two later, I saw her hanging around with some bastard from Kappa Omega, and that put the kibosh to that idea. I guess that was one reason to belong to a fraternity... to get dates. But then you had to put up with all that other shit like pledging and brown-nosing and stuff.

On Saturday morning of Homecoming, I got up at a decent time to get ready for the game. The pep band was going to play, as we did at all home games, which was in itself embarrassing. Of course, Jane wouldn't be playing since she'd have a date.

I saw my buddy Zittle in the hall and told him I needed a ride. He said he was just leaving, and he'd be glad to take me along. So I grabbed my sax case, and we got in his old green Plymouth with the big fins. He drove over to Davis Hall to pick up his girlfriend Elaine and two of her sorority sisters.

This was another situation I wasn't expecting. Elaine sat up front next to Dirk. She was all gussied up and bubbly. I was relegated to the back seat with her two friends. And for being sorority girls, they actually seemed kind of nice. I think maybe they were on their good behavior because of Zittle, who never minced his words, especially around Greeks.

Dirk said, "This is Mahlon Dickinger. He's one of those cool guys from Pennsylvania."

They both gave their names, Linda Becker and Bev Epstein, who said, "Hey Mahlon, nice to meet you."

They seemed kind of interested in the new guy with the sax case between his legs who was apparently a friend of wild-man Zittle. And this, of course, would have been a good time to get to know them, but Dirk was running at the mouth like usual, and I couldn't get a word in edgewise. I was pretty sure he had downed a few shots before leaving. He drank a lot. So anyway, Dirk took the back way on 588 to Gallipolis, and we got there in record time.

At the high school, I jumped out of the car, thanked Dirk for the ride, and entered the gym. The pep band was situated at the end of the bleachers across from the two team benches. I got out my alto, moistened my reed, and was ready to go. Well, not really. I mean, I would have rather been in the stands beside Jane Barakos, but that wasn't going to happen. Then I looked up at the top row of the bleachers and saw old Bernie sitting beside her new boyfriend Elmer.

I thought, *Good for her, too bad for him.*

Although I was wearing a decent outfit, I still felt kind of dorkish sitting with this meager group—a tuba, three trumpets, a trombone, a French horn, a flute, three clarinets, my alto, a drum kit on the floor, and Old Man Krone playing tenor as he conducted. Despite that, the band didn't sound bad. And I'm guessing the crowd didn't really give a shit as long as it was loud and played the pep song at the right time.

This was the first time I had seen the team play. My expectations were not very high. Two of the players lived in the Mole Hole—Mike Lewis and Charlie Boggs—neither looked like b-ball players. So the Rio Redmen were led onto the floor by four cheerleaders and two Redmen mascots.

This will sound really bad, but the cheerleaders were not the greatest. Apparently, not many coeds wanted the job. In high school, it always seemed that being a cheerleader was a big deal. But here, about all they could scrounge together were four spots. And the girls who held those spots were not real "lookers," if you get my drift. Plus, they weren't very athletic. But despite that, they had a lot of spirit and gave it their all.

And then there were the mascots. This was Pi Delta's contribution to school spirit. They had two guys, Ron Stobursky and Jack Taylor, who dressed up in Indian costumes, with the rudimentary feathered headdresses, face paint, breech clouds, ankle bells, and moccasins. And if that wasn't enough, they were bare chested. For some reason, they painted black circles around their nipples. I confess my ignorance of Native American body painting, but I'm guessing Indians didn't do that.

At various times throughout the game, they would pound on a little drum and shake gourd rattles or maracas. Whenever the opposing team went into a huddle during a time out, these bastards would dance around them and shake the rattles as though they were casting a spell. It was damn embarrassing.

I guess I shouldn't criticize, but "Redmen" was a rather racist name to use for a college mascot. Many other colleges used similar terms. But in the eyes of true-blue Native Americans who knew of the extreme mistreatment over the years by the European bastards who slaughtered them and diseased them and tortured them with vicious dogs and other outlandish violence, the word "Redmen" was the equivalent of "nigger" or "kike" or "wop."

For a long time, I didn't understand why American Indians disliked terms like "savages" or "warriors" or "redskins." When I was a kid and watched cowboy movies, I always rooted for the Indians, thinking of them as noble people who worshiped nature. But after reading about the oppression of native peoples and seeing how they were relegated to non-human status, I came to understand their opposition. It was like saying, "Let's cheer for the Redmen/Niggers!" However, I assume there weren't many Native Americans in the area, so no one was upset about the racial slur, at least in 1967 southeastern Ohio.

So with the crowd cheering and the band playing, the team ran onto the floor. The two obvious stars were Bill Green and Miles Parker, two black guys from Dayton. Both could have started for much larger schools. Bill was about 6'6" and 220, but he played a lot bigger. He would go on to become one of the nation's leading rebounders for NAIA colleges. One of the most respected students on campus, he didn't say much but projected a commanding presence. One time in sociology class, he said that being called "nigger" was bad, but worse was being called "boy." No one called Bill either of those words, to his face or behind his back.

On the court, he was a real presence. And to the pleasure of the faculty and administration, he was one of those clean-cut black students—no big afro, no loud clothes, and no loud behavior. And best of all, he was married, so he was no threat to the white females of good old Rio Grande. I suppose to some he seemed like an Uncle Tom. But that wasn't the case at all. He was mature and chose to carry himself the way he did, not because he was trying to impress anyone.

Just as talented as Green, Miles Parker was a totally different player and person. At 6'2", 185 pounds, he was a shooter. He took long shots from the baseline and didn't seem to be real interested in rebounding. He wore canvas knee braces, the kind that laced up in the front. And he used extra-long laces, which whipped around when he double-faked his man, creating a distraction.

Some people called Miles a hustler. He knew how to handle himself in all situations. On campus, he played the game, always saying the right things, at times kissing up to certain people like professors. He liked the women, but he was smart enough to know that this campus would quickly kick his butt if he got involved with a white girl.

When there were no games scheduled on the weekend, you might see Miles, dressed in what some would call his "pimping" outfit—bright green, tight fitting suit; narrow-brimmed Stetson cocked a little sideways; and shiny black, pointed shoes—clothing he would never wear on campus. And he would be walking to the Greyhound bus stop, just off campus, for a ride back to Dayton and his other life.

Another real talent on the team was Ray Williams who was an ex-Marine and a few years older than the rest. At 6'2", 210, he was one of those odd white guys who could really jump. After returning from Vietnam where he was wounded, he was used by the Marines to notify next of kin when someone was killed. So this good looking Marine would show up in his neatly ironed dress-blues and give people the really bad news. After his discharge, Ray joined the Rio Redmen and brought a mature presence to the team. On and off the court, he was well-liked by everyone—a Mr. America type.

The rest of the team was more than adequate, including Mike and Charlie. Turns out Charlie was one of the top small high school players in Kentucky, and Mike had received honorable mention on Ohio's All-State high school team.

The team's coach was Eddie Boles. He'd been with the school for about six years. One of his first teams was pretty successful. It had been made up of all white players. So that wasn't a bad thing, but certain team members were part of what some would call the "good ol' boy" network.

At least that's what I heard from older guys in the Mole Hole. I mention it simply because that was a reflection of the time. In Boles' third year, there was a talented black guy who tried to make his way onto the team, but it didn't work out. He left the school and went on to have a successful career at a school in California. But when players like Green and Parker showed up, Coach Boles, to his credit, did a good job of working them into the program.

The team statistician was a student by the name of Fitzhugh "Fitzy" Bowers. He came from a redneck background, never hiding his feelings about blacks. But the ironic thing about Fitzy was that he was the guy who recorded all of Bill Green's rebounds and Miles Parker's points, which put those two guys into national prominence. If Fitzy liked you, he was a great guy to be around. But he was a real hot head. One time when he was up-river on a drinking spree, he got into a bar fight and was stabbed, causing him to miss a semester of school.

The opposing team for the Homecoming game was Wilberforce University, located close to Dayton. It was basically an all-black school, and this provided some extra motivation to Green and Parker, because they knew several of the players. The game was basically a run-and-shoot contest. Green played a great inside game, controlling both defensive and offensive boards. He scored from both the outside and under the basket. Parker put on a shooting exhibition, scoring an unbelievable 51 points, mostly outside jumpers from the right side.

So that was my first Reo Rio Homecoming. Good game, no date. Somebody told me there was a keg party arranged for the non-Greeks by the Circle K Club—aka the Circle Jerk Club as they were sometimes called. Guess I shouldn't have said that. They did a lot for the community, just like their father organization, the Kiwanis Club. Anyway, Clark and I grabbed our mugs and caught a ride with some guy from my Religion class. The place was out in the boonies off the Jackson Pike, and it set up well for this type of occasion.

There were about seventy-five non-Greeks there, including a healthy number of campus blacks, who added to the ambiance. We both got pretty wasted (free beer, right?), but there was a decent band, even though they kept repeating some songs, notably "Stormy" by the Classics IV, which I actually liked.

So with a little beer-courage, I asked a few girls to dance. One was Lorainne Lecrone, a kind of awkward but nice looking tall blonde. We were having a decent time on the dance floor, but as the night rolled on, someone reminded me that she'd had a few dates with none other than John "Griff" Brady, who luckily for me, wasn't at the dance. Griff was one of the tough guys in the Mole Hole, although I usually got along okay with him. Despite the booze, I found enough of my senses to tell myself I probably shouldn't dance with her anymore, just in case old Griff found out and took things the wrong way.

So then I danced with the much shorter Debbie Nailor. To my surprise, she turned out to be a pretty decent dancer. As my hands drifted toward her butt, she started playing with the hair on the back of my neck. So she was spinning a little of her magic on me. Unfortunately, toward the end of the shindig, my usually smooth dancing got downgraded because I was having more than a little trouble keeping my balance.

When the dance was over, someone said our ride had left about an hour before. We found someone who said they'd take us so we jumped into the back seat. But before I could close the door, good old Debbie Nailor plopped in on my lap. As we were flying up and down the hills on 588, my hand started moving up her leg, trying to find a little patch of paradise, but all I could find was the end of nylon stockings and snaps from a damn girdle or garter belt. She didn't seem upset, but her hand kept politely pushing mine away.

Back on campus, I pointed her in the direction of her dorm and hot-footed it back to the Mole Hole. Another failed attempt at romantic bliss by Mahl Dickinger. *[Motherfuckle!]*

Jerry Butler, "For Your Precious Love." Great slow dance song.

Silver Bridge, December 15, 1967

Kathy Switzer illegally runs in Boston Marathon and is eventually pushed out of the race because of her gender, despite several male runners trying to keep her in the competition.

I'd been at Rio just a few months, but I wasn't well-versed with the local landmarks and geography. So when someone busted into Room 12 and said the Silver Bridge had collapsed, I had no idea what they were talking about. I soon found out they were referring to the bridge that spanned the Ohio River, connecting Gallipolis and Point Pleasant, West Virginia.

The collapse happened in the late afternoon when the bridge was full of cars and trucks waiting for a damn traffic light to change. Apparently, some kind of design flaw contributed to corrosion over the years, and things just gave way, crashing the whole damn thing a hundred feet into the 44-degree Ohio River.

Forty-six people died. Talk about being in the wrong place at the wrong time. Some woman was in line to cross the bridge when she saw the supports swaying and moving, so she instinctively slammed her car into reverse, crashing into the car behind her. Saved her life and probably the people behind her.

Ned Bulk, a student volunteer with the local fire department, went to the scene to help recover the bodies. He said when they pulled the cars out of the river, the dead bodies were all swollen, pressed against the car windows, trying to get out. Gruesome shit.

The only good thing that came out of this disaster was that it inspired more bridge inspections and maintenance on a national level, even though an inspection wouldn't have found the internally corroded cables. Another bridge upriver at St. Mary's—of similar construction—was closed, and ferry service had to be used. Lyndon Johnson got his Congressional buddy, West Virginian Robert C. Byrd, to build a replacement, known as the Silver Memorial Bridge.

Weird stories started to emerge about mysterious lights, demons, and a bat-winged Mothman seen around Point Pleasant shortly before the bridge fell. There was also something about an eighteenth-century Shawnee Chief Cornstalk who cursed the area just before he'd been killed by a bunch of locals. *Spooky, eh?*

Anyway, from that point on, whenever a group of guys were driving over the various old bridges in Ohio and West Virginia, we'd jump out of the car and stomp our foot on the damn thing first, just to give us some false assurance that the bridge wouldn't fall down. *[Motherfuckle!]*

Shirley Scott, hard bop and soul-jazz organist.
Recorded prolifically, Philly native.

Golden Gloves at Rio

Tet Offensive began, January 1968

Although many students complained about the lack of entertainment on campus, I was always surprised at what popped up at this out-of-the-way place. One Saturday in the Fall of 1968, the school hosted a boxing exhibition inside Community Hall. Actually, it was both an exhibition and a first-round, regional competition for the Golden Gloves.

When I was a kid, my dad and I used to watch the Friday Night Fights, aka the Gillette Cavalcade of Sports. The show was sponsored by the Gillette Safety Razor Company, and they had this snappy theme music with the catch phrase "Look sharp! Be sharp!" The ring announcer was Johnny Addie, who would always do a bunch of introductions—fight judges, the referee, and a few other boxers in attendance.

The term *Golden Gloves* came up a lot on the broadcast, because many of the boxers had gone through the rigors of that competition. I remember watching 1950's greats like Sugar Ray Robinson, Archie Moore, Rocky Graziano, Willie Pep, Ezzard Charles, Jersey Joe Walcott, Carmen Basilio, and Bobo Olson.

Even though a lot of fights were fixed by the mob, and the various boxing commissions were pretty damn crooked, boxing was still popular. Most medical people agreed the sport wasn't real good for a guy's health, with all the brain concussions and cuts above the eye and detached retinas and broken noses and bleeding kidneys and cauliflower ears and punch-drunk brains and early dementia.

The promoters of this exhibition had set up an authentic boxing ring inside Community Hall. The preliminary bouts were open to any local amateurs who wanted to get into the ring. I always found it hard to believe why some guys actually enjoyed taking a hard right to the nose.

The first bout had Frankie Capezio—one of Rio's finest from Newton, New Jersey—going up against some black kid from Gallipolis.

When Frankie stepped into the ring, we all whooped and hollered as he danced around with his arms above his head and a big-ass smile. He appeared to be in pretty good shape.

But as soon as the bell rang, the black kid stormed across the ring and pinned poor Frankie in his corner with his head down, trying to ward off the barrage of punches. After about ten or fifteen seconds of this pummeling, the black kid stepped back, exposing Frankie's bloodied face, which looked like a piece of raw meat. The referee mercifully stopped the fight. Seeing blood on a black and white TV isn't quite as shocking as vivid technicolor-hemoglobin in person. So we all got a pretty good taste of reality, but quickly got over that and looked forward to the next bout.

Another local guy, Butch Hocking, was an out-and-out street fighter. Supposedly never beaten in a fight, he was a local legend. Tall and slim but strong and mean, he brought along a bunch of his henchmen from Gallipolis. They were all riled up and looking forward to seeing Butch beat the shit out of some uppity college kid.

His opponent was Joe Guiffrida, from Jersey City, better known on campus as "Jersey Joe." He had the stereotypical accent. One time, when Zittle was lining up a trip to the Kentucky Derby, Joe said he wanted to come along, but Dirk told him the car was pretty full already. So Joe asked who was the last guy to sign up, and Dirk answered Scott Nusz. Joe literally said, "Twoe da bum out," just like the mobsters in the movies.

Anyway, he looked tough, but he was a decent guy. But when he got into the boxing ring wearing his swimming trunks, it was obvious he wasn't in the best shape—a little flabby, if you know what I mean. So I thought, *Holy shit, here comes another bloodletting.*

The referee called the two of them to the center for instructions. "No low blows. Go to a neutral corner for a knockdown, stop fighting when I say break." While the referee was saying all this, Big Butch glared at Joe and slapped his gloves together. Joe just looked down at the canvas and didn't make eye contact. Finally the ref said, "Shake hands and come out fighting."

The bell rang, and Butch rushed over to Joe, immediately throwing a bunch of wild haymakers. But Joe dodged them and kept his distance. The big guy continued to crowd Joe, and we all thought he wouldn't make it through the first round. But somehow, he did, and when the bell rang, he went back to his stool to rest up.

The second round was more of the first, only this time the townie was swinging harder and more wildly. He was getting pissed, because his punches weren't landing. His buddies started booing and shouting that Joe was afraid to fight.

By this time in Butch's street fights, he'd be kicking, eye gouging, and biting. He would've finished off the other guy in about two minutes. But things weren't working here for old Butch, because Joe was just dancing away from him. Then once in awhile, Joe would connect with a solid jab to the bastard's nose.

In the third and final round, Butch came out and tried an all-out assault. But he was almost totally spent. His arms were hanging, allowing Joe to jab the guy's face, opening a sizable cut above Butch's right eye. Then Joe thumped a series of well-placed combinations to the head and body. His punches were hurting the bastard.

By now, we were all on our feet, punching the air, screaming and yelling for Joe to knock the bastard's head off. Just before the final bell could sound, Joe caught Butch with an uppercut to the chin, causing the guy's knees to buckle and down he went. He was counted out by the referee, and the crowd went fuckin' wild.

Joe tried to raise his arms to acknowledge the crowd, but he was too damn tired. Turns out Joe had some training back in Jersey City and knew what he was doing. So for the rest of his time at Rio, he got lots of pats on the back and free beers whenever he went into a bar.

The last bout of the evening showed why boxing was often called "the sweet science." Two black welterweights from Columbus got into the ring and danced around with smooth, efficient movements, making that "*sss*" sound every time they threw a punch. Well-schooled in both defense and offense, they peppered left jabs but also protected themselves with their gloves and arms. After watching the previous flailings, this bout was true art... if attempting to beat someone's brains in can be called an art. Hemingway would have been impressed.

Van Morrison, "Caravan," "Brown-Eyed Girl."
Most soulful singer to ever come out of Northern Ireland.

Purdue Game, October 13, 1968

"Have you no sense of decency, sir? At long last, have you left no sense of decency?" –Joseph N. Welch, Army-McCarthy hearings

I didn't play football in high school. That was too much work, plus I never learned to enjoy the tingle of getting knocked on my ass. But I suppose the deciding factor was that I was 5' 11" and 130 pounds. Besides, I was in the marching band, so I got into the games for free and never suffered an injury. Well, there was that one time when I broke a fingernail on the latch of my saxophone case. Hurt like hell.

When I was younger, my buddies and I did the neighborhood football thing. I had a cool helmet—dark blue with a white stripe just like the high school team but no face guard. And I had a decent set of shoulder pads. One Christmas I got a really good Wilson football. Those were three of my favorite possessions. Although I enjoyed playing sandlot, I never went out for Boys Club, where most guys got their start for the school team. Despite my lack of participation, I still liked football and watched tons of games on TV, both college and professional.

Like most football fans, I didn't want to admit to the dangers of the sport, such as how it screwed up feet, knees, sternums, kidneys, fingers, and worst of all, brains. I always got just as excited as the next guy when a player got knocked out cold, with maybe a few involuntary leg spasms.

Every medical person knew that concussions could cause terrible brain damage, loss of memory, severe headaches, and dementia later in life. But the mentality of football was that if you could tell how many fingers were held up in front of your face, you could go back into the game for the chance of more brain damage.

Besides the physical harm, there was another negative aspect of the game. High school and college players tended to get preferential treatment in the classroom because they were big stars. If they didn't get decent grades, they'd become ineligible to play. Of course, this wasn't restricted just to football. But some players were pushed through even though they could barely read.

And, oh yeah, there was something else. Football players always got really hyped up for games. But if they lost, they sometimes took out their frustrations on people around them. Those often-criminal offenses were overlooked by police, coaches, and friends so they could continue to play in the next all-important game.

Also, sometimes football players got really big heads and took advantage of adoring female fans, often to the point of forcing themselves on girls. The player seldom got in trouble. All this had been going on since the beginning of scholastic football. But I chose to ignore those realities since I really enjoyed watching the sport.

On one of our trips to Columbus, Clark and I lucked out. We got to see a big-time Ohio State game. It was a sunny Fall Saturday, and after hitchhiking to the city, we were walking around campus, just taking in the sights. After seeing the same faces every day at Rio, it was refreshing to be in this more expansive atmosphere. And the odds of seeing really nice looking girls were greatly enhanced by the 60,000-plus students as opposed to Rio's 800.

We noticed most people seemed to be walking in the same direction, toward Ohio Stadium, aka the Big Horseshoe, aka The Shoe. So we decided to follow along. We'd planned on finding a bar to watch the game but thought we would first get a glimpse of the stadium.

Being from Pennsylvania, I obviously had a bias for Penn State. But Beaver Stadium was located off-campus, out close to the cow barns of the animal husbandry college. Conversely, The Shoe was smack dab in the middle of campus.

Clark and I walked up to one of the gates at the open end of the stadium, just to look through the wrought iron fencing. As we stood there, hands on the bars, looking at the whole scene, two guys came up behind us and asked if we wanted to get in to see the game.

I said, "It's sold out. We'll never get in without a ticket."

They told us they were program sellers, and that after they got inside, they'd pass their badges to us through the fence, and after we got inside we could then slip them two bucks. That sounded a little too easy, but what the hell? We flashed the badges to the ticket taker, went through the gate, paid the two guys, and we were inside fuckin' Ohio Stadium.

Because we didn't have real tickets with seat numbers, we somehow crammed ourselves into the middle of a bunch of people in the bleachers at the open end of the horseshoe. It turned out we were in the middle of a load of Purdue fans who came the whole way from West Lafayette, Indiana.

All of a sudden, we were part of over 84,000 screaming people. Hell, that was more than the population of my hometown. And there was the OSU marching band in their black uniforms, white crossed belts, and spats. And the cheerleaders and the football team in their crimson and grey home jerseys. And the nation's number one ranked team, the Purdue Boilermakers in their gold helmets.

Of course, Ohio's legendary coach Woody Hayes was there in his short-sleeved white shirt, black tie, and black baseball cap—the cap the equipment guy always cut up a little so Woody could rip it apart when he threw one of his patented tantrums with the officials. The same Woody Hayes who was a WWII Navy hero, who idolized George Patton, and who was a personal friend of Richard "the dick" Nixon. The same Woody Hayes who mingled with protesting students on campus and urged them to express themselves but also told them to be civil about it. The same Woody Hayes who later lost his coaching job and reputation when he punched a player on an opposing team.

Being a sports junky, I had read about this game. The Buckeye team, ranked number four in the nation, was filled with some talented sophomores—quarterback Rex Kern, running back John Brockington, and fullback Jim Otis. They were young and inexperienced. Purdue had big time talent in quarterback Mike Phipps and consensus All-American Leroy Keyes, who happened to be one of the last big-time college players to play both ways—offensive running back/flanker/defensive back. So this promised to be a real challenge for Ohio, especially after Purdue had soundly beaten them the previous year and Woody Hayes' reputation was on the line.

Things were pretty even throughout the first half. I kept hearing the name *Tatum* on the loud speaker. "Tatum stops the run." "Tatum breaks up the pass." "Tatum assists in the tackle." He was all over the field and especially all over Leroy Keyes, holding him to just a few yards of rushing and receiving.

I had never heard of Jack Tatum, but he made a name for himself in this game. Of course, he later went on to play for Oakland in the pros. And in the Immaculate Reception game with Pittsburgh, he was the guy who clobbered Frenchy Fuqua, causing the ball to squirt into the air for Franco Harris to grab it and run for the winning score. And he was the guy who hit Darryl Stingley in an exhibition game and left him paralyzed... and never apologized. He was also the guy whose nickname in the pros was The Assassin. But no matter how terrible this all might sound, most of his hits in college and the pros were ruled to be legal, hits that people loved to see, no matter what damage they might have inflicted.

Halftime came, and I saw something I had never seen before: the truly remarkable Script Ohio. This is, of course, when the OSU band marches in single file, led by the drum major, and writes "Ohio" in cursive on the field as they play some old French march (*Le Regiment de Sambre et Meuse*). The whole stadium stands and claps in unison to the beat.

The climax comes when the drum major breaks away from the rest of the band and leads one of the tuba players to the space above the "i." The tuba guy follows, exaggerating his high steps as he comes to the designated spot. The crowd starts to swell in volume. He clicks his feet to attention, doffs his cap, and dots the "i" by dipping the bell of the sousaphone to the ground. And the crowd goes crazy.

I got all choked up. Maybe because it was such an honor for the tuba guy to be selected. Maybe because tuba players are often the butt of jokes and only play those boring bass notes. Maybe because I was an old band guy, and band people are seldom recognized like athletes... and here was a stadium of 84,000 people stomping their feet and screaming for this dude to dot the "i." Maybe it dredged up memories of how I never realized my full musical potential.

So the second half started, and Tatum continued to clobber Keyes, who was noticeably slowed and whose uniform was literally ripped and bloodied. After awhile, the Purdue coach took out the poor guy, and despite the fact that quarterback Rex Kern had to be replaced because of an injury, OSU won the game and the place went crazy. I have to admit that I became a damn Ohio State fan at that point. So we left Ohio Stadium with big shit-eating grins.

Someone once said that everyday we should do three things—learn something new, have a good belly laugh, and have a good cry, either in sympathy for someone or maybe just to exude some emotion from your heart. I could usually stifle a cry, but the emotion was always there, deep down. So that day in Columbus did the job. I laughed, almost cried, and learned something. Life was good.

"Locomotion," by Carol King. Sung by Little Eva, King's babysitter.

Milkshake

January 1968, 94,000 U.S. troops wounded since the war's beginning.

I always thought of myself as a somewhat compassionate guy. When I was a kid going to Sunday School, the church had something called "extended session," which occurred between Sunday School and children's chapel, when Mrs. Groft would put a few of us in the back of her Rambler station wagon and take us to visit shut-ins.

We were called The Cheerful Cherub Club. But at the time, I found this to be a real task, because some of the old folks were unkempt, drooling, and smelly. I understood they were in poor health and couldn't take care of themselves, but it was kind of tough for a ten year old to see. However, because of that awkward and somewhat repulsive experience, I gained empathy for others who were different or in dire straits. I say this as a preface to what follows.

Around campus, this guy was known as Milkshake. He walked on the inside of his feet, knees bent, arms flailing, always out of breath. You could hear him coming, especially in the library when he climbed the steps to the second floor. People would say, "Here comes Milkshake," and usually move to a different part of the building because he made so much noise.

He breathed heavily, drooled, and always tried to talk to those around him. But his utterances were more like muted moans than regular speech. To say the least, he was severely handicapped.

His nickname came from his daily appearance in the cafeteria. There was no way he could carry a tray with a bowl of soup and a glass of milk. At first he tried, but the cafeteria ladies got tired of cleaning the messes off the carpeted floor. So someone would go through the line to get his food.

Usually, he had a table to himself. Because of his spastic and unpredictable movements, his meals always turned into an explosion of flying food. He placed paper napkins over the front of his body and the surrounding area. The highlight was when he attempted to drink his milk. By the time the glass got to his mouth, most of the liquid was on his tray or had been turned into a jiggling froth which sloshed all over his face. Thus the name Milkshake.

It was cruel to label the guy, but no one openly bothered him with insults or derision. The thing that many people didn't like about him was that he had an attitude, like he was always pissed about something. Like when he couldn't get through a door or when he tripped on the sidewalk or when his books would pop out of his arms and his papers would blow across campus.

He would blame people around him for causing these things, or for not helping before they happened, even though he often said he didn't want any help. So people tried to avoid the guy. Most seemed to think that all handicapped people should be docile, placid, and always smiling, but this guy proved they were just as human as everyone else. In his condition, I suppose he was more than worthy of having a pissy attitude.

But this was 1968, and people weren't always real sensitive. Most of us grew up watching comedians like Milton Berle and Jerry Lewis, who unashamedly made audiences laugh by walking and talking like spastic, retarded people.

But Milkshake wasn't retarded. He had gotten a scholarship from some state or federal grant that the college was happy to accept. Rio needed all the money they could get. Plus they were seeking accreditation, and having a student like Milkshake would look good for student diversity. So, good or bad, this guy was a true-blue college student even though just a few years earlier, he would probably have spent his life in some damn institution.

In a wacky kind of way, Milkshake was lucky. He didn't have to worry about flunking out, getting drafted or being sent to Nam. Once in awhile, a certain slightly overweight but nice-looking female student would sit with him in the cafeteria. Well, not really with him, but close to him. Rumor had it that she was fucking the guy. She was one of those girls who apparently got her jollies by screwing the freaky types, kind of like a pity fuck. We all imagined the gyrations he would put her through in pursuit of the ultimate coitus.

Of course in my mind, if ever there was someone who deserved a pity fuck, it was me. But instead, here's this milk-stained, spastic guy with a bad attitude, getting laid on a semi-regular basis. So when I saw Milkshake on campus, I'd shake my head and say to myself, "Lucky fuckin' bastard!" *[Motherfuckle!]*

Dan Hicks and His Hot Licks, "I Scare Myself," "Canned Music," "Where's the Music"

The Draft

"The whole world is watching." –Democratic Convention, August 28, 1968

Despite my lack of female contact, I was a lucky bastard in some ways. Unlike Milkshake, I wouldn't have to go through life with all his deformities. And despite my mediocre high school grades, I got into college which gave me a student deferment from the draft. Plus, I had enough money to afford tuition. Many guys who didn't have the money or grades ended up in a lousy rice paddy in Southeast Asia.

I always wanted to go to college, even if there hadn't been a Selective Service. So I never considered myself to be a draft dodger. Yet other guys attended just to get a deferment. The Selective Service later devised a test (the College Qualification Test) to prove if you were really bona fide college material.

The exam was about three hours long, but after the first hour I got the shits of it and walked out. Luckily, I answered enough questions to get a passing grade and keep my deferment. However, I knew another guy who didn't take the test, and the poor bastard got drafted.

When I came to Ohio, I had to transfer my name to the local draft board in Gallipolis. They were notorious for going after anyone who had what they thought was a questionable deferment, especially college students from back East who spoke with that strange accent.

Somehow they decided I should be re-classified to 1-A, which meant I would have no deferment—something about my 1.8 GPA and not being a full-time student. True, I was on academic probation, and taking only twelve credits, but that was the normal policy for probationary students. When I was notified of the 1-A thing, I beat a path over to my faculty adviser, Dr. Truax, and convinced him I was capable of handling fifteen credits. Thankfully, he signed me up for a psych class, and the draft board begrudgingly gave me the 2-S classification.

One problem was solved, but then I found out Rio didn't accept all of my credits from the junior college. And then there was the problem of my low grades. Basically I lost over a semester of credits.

But in a way, that worked to my advantage because to get my undergraduate degree, I had to attend an extra year. And I still kept my 2-S deferment. Thus another example of how unequal the selective service system was handled. If I had been a good student and graduated in four years, I probably would have been drafted.

Just before the Big War, my dad had been drafted into the Army Air Corps. He served with distinction for five years, reaching the rank of Warrant Officer, Junior Grade, defending the strategic city of San Antonio, Texas. His most risky assignment was a flight to Goose Bay, Labrador, and the Azores off the coast of Portugal, flying over and returning in just a few days.

Mom lived with him most of this time in Texas, where my older sister was born. So even though he didn't want to be in the military, he lucked out big-time, avoiding the atrocities of the Krauts and Japs. Apart from the really hot and humid Texas weather—and the continual threat of being shipped overseas—he basically enjoyed the experience.

I always thought, if my country called, I'd be willing to go. I just didn't want to go to Vietnam or Cambodia or Korea... or just about any other threatening place where I might have my skinny ass shot off.

My strategy, if I thought I was going to be drafted, was to audition for a spot in a military band. A high school friend made a Navy band, and except for a lot of drills and marching, he played at various bases or on ships with a case of beer under his chair. Not real patriotic, but to me, that would have been a great way to serve my country, playing my E-flat alto saxophone and drinking beer.

James Brown... 'Nuff said.

Clark's Flora and Fauna Collections

Huey P. Newton, Black Panther, convicted of voluntary manslaughter

As I mentioned before, Clark Buck was unique. He could handle himself in most social situations, but he was a lot happier counting fruit flies in the lab or doing field research. I suppose that was one of the influences that Biology prof. Doc Byrd had on him.

One Saturday, I told Clark I was going to hitch into town to drop off some laundry, and he asked if I'd do him a favor. He gave me some money and told me to buy a cheap pair of high-top sneakers. He wanted to go stomping around some swampy area, looking for exotic plants or newts or salamanders or whatever, hoping to find a new species or just to make a general survey of a particular block of land.

He wasn't doing this for any class assignment. This was just something he enjoyed. Back home in Southington, he helped people build ponds and small lakes on their properties and had developed a local reputation as a pond expert.

In Gallipolis, I dropped off my laundry at A-1 Cleaners and then went to the 5&10 store. I bought the ugliest, cheapest pair of black, high-top sneakers I could find. I came back to campus, gave the shoes to Clark, and it was as though I had gifted him a pair of $100 wingtips.

He put them on (no socks) along with a crappy pair of slacks rolled up at the cuffs, topped by a ripped sweatshirt. Off he went, with butterfly net, trowel and specimen bag. When the weather was suitable, he would go off on these sorties and bring all kinds of stinky stuff back to the room, including his sneakers and slacks which were caked in some kind of disgusting black ooze. He'd closely examine the specimens, and then, if he found anything of interest, he'd take them to the biology lab for Doc Byrd to check out.

The craziest thing he brought back was a big old white owl–live of course. According to Clark, this was a great find because these raptors were rarely seen in this neck of the woods. It had a wounded wing, so that gave Clark a chance to capture the ordinarily evasive bird. He and his brothers had netted hawks before, so he knew what he was doing when he picked up this big-ass bird and put it in a special box rigged for transport.

For a couple days, we had this big old white owl in Room 12. Everyone in the Mole Hole made visits to watch it chew up laboratory mice and spit out the remnants in the form of little balls. It was a beautiful bird, with its rotating head and big eyes. But then Clark took it over to the bio lab and eventually set it free.

Then there was the time he brought two big-ass snapping turtles back to the room. These bastards were aggressive at first, but then settled down. One day, Rio's two basketball stars, Miles Parker and Bill Green, were passing through the Mole Hole and looked in our open door to say hello. When they saw the turtles, they came in.

These guys were from Dayton and had never seen turtles up close and personal. So they squatted down on their haunches and just looked at them. Clark jammed a stick in the mouth of one of the turtles, and it promptly snapped the damn thing in two. Miles and Bill were impressed and continued to watch. Then all of a sudden, Miles asked matter-of-factly, "How day fuck?"

Trying to stifle a laugh, Clark proceeded to explain the copulation process. And with that, the two stood up and left, impressed and educated on the love life of snapping turtles.

Grant Green, guitar, massively underrated artist.
I Want to Hold Your Hand, *great Blue Note album.*

Drunken Poetry

May 10, 1968: U.S. and North Vietnam begin peace talks, debating the shape of the negotiating table.

Somewhere along the line, I took a Modern Poetry course taught by Ruth Gavin, a wonderful person and teacher. At times, I criticized her (not to her face) for avoiding the racier side of literature. She was a published poet and editor of a poetry review, but I often thought her work could have been enhanced if she had been more worldly.

Obviously that is a terrible thing to say about someone. She led an independent lifestyle, never a slave to fashion, and participated in various writing conferences like the Bread Loaf Writers' School and the Iowa Writers' Workshop. But it just seemed that if she'd incorporated some of Doc Byrd's debauchery into her life, she might have had more juicy material for her writings and teachings.

The poetry course included respected poets of the twentieth century: Lawrence Ferlinghetti, Robinson Jeffers, Philip Larkin, Richard Brautigan, Robert Creeley, and Gary Snyder. The closing assignment was a choice of two items to be completed in three weeks. One was a research paper on a contemporary poet, including critical analyses of poems and biographical influences. The other was to compose eight original poems, reflecting deep thought and structure of style (no sentimental shit).

By this time in my career as an English major, I was *over-research-papered*. I not only wrote papers for my classes, but I also wrote papers for beer money. The lazy bastards in the Mole Hole would pay good money for a paper.

Money was tight in those days. If I was lucky, I might get a ten-dollar check from home, once a month. So if I wanted to keep wetting my whistle, I had to scrounge up money somewhere. Hell, I even sold a few of my neckties. So when I heard Professor Gavin's choices for the assignment, I quickly fell for writing the original poetry. To hell with another damn paper.

The only problem was that I had never written anything in verse. Well, that's not totally true. Back in high school, I'd scribble cute little rhymes for Donna Copenhaver, who lived on my newspaper route, and she'd respond with similar mundanities. But these were on the order of haiku or maybe a stupid limerick. In terms of quality for this assignment, I was basically screwed.

Being an habitual procrastinator, I let the whole thing slide until the night before it was due. Looking at a blank piece of paper is always daunting, but when you've never written verse before, the blank page can be debilitating. I knew many great writers were alcoholics: Hemingway, Fitzgerald, Faulkner, Dylan Thomas, James Joyce, John Berryman, Dorothy Parker, ad infinitum. Not realizing that most of them didn't drink when they wrote, I grabbed the bottle of Ancient Age bourbon from the compartment above my closet and started toking on it with pen in hand. Surprisingly, the words appeared. After an hour or so, I had eight "poems" on paper.

As I read over them at 2:30 in the morning, I thought they were just as good, if not better, than some of Robert Creeley's or William Carlos Williams' things. Come on now, who couldn't write something like "The Red Wheelbarrow" or "This Is Just to Say" about a guy who ate the plums? So I submitted the "poems" the next day to Prof. Gavin. She always seemed to favor me as a student, but I'm thinking she must have fallen off her damn chair when she read the garbage I submitted. Here are the four *best* ones.

Feeling Good on People
Everyone's together
and it's
cool.
The semantics
are gone,
but it's
There.
We are
I,
and it's
there.
Tomorrow is
Now.
We are
here.

Missing Out
Get a job,
save your
money,
raise a
family,
buy a car,
house, insurance.
Work hard,
wait,
wait,
wait.
What can I do?
What can be said?
It's going
Too Fast!!

Good Old Holden
Comin' through the
Rye.
Man, does it
Hurt !!
Trying to
accept
what isn't
there.
It's like
seeing Jimi Hendrix,
but askin'
for more,
or like hearing
Isaac Stern
with no encore.
Are people
really living?
What is there
to give?
Good old Holden
and his superfluous
phonies.
But what is
even worse??
I'm phony.

Identifying
There's this thing
about making
it.
But everybody's
going their
way.
But there's
this thing
about identifying.
And there's
people
all around
you,
and they're
significant
others.
So, it's
not really
self discovery;
rather it's
not having
insecurity.

[Motherfuckle!]

Richard Davis, prolific bassist in jazz, classical, rock.

College Golf

Roberto DeVicenzo loses the Masters because of a scorecard error.

Mike Lewis was one of those guys who was competitive in all sports. When he found out I had an interest in golf, he said we should play a round sometime. I said I'd bring my clubs after Spring break.

My dad played once or twice a year, and like Mike, he was naturally competitive. But sports weren't important to him. When I was a kid, he acquired a partial set of clubs from some old guy. When I showed a little interest, he took the driver and cut off the shaft below the grip to suit my stature.

The only problem was that this was a vintage wooden shaft, which twenty-five years later might have been worth ten times what it originally cost. Anyway, my dad's friend Jack, who was a good golfer, came over to visit one time. And when he saw me swinging the driver in the backyard, he said I had a natural swing. That planted the golf bug in my brain.

When I was sixteen, I bought a cheap set of clubs at JM Fields, whose sporting department was far from on par with a real pro shop. I played a few rounds but never came close to a decent score. The problem with golf, of course, is that you will probably hit one or two decent shots during an otherwise bad round, and then tell yourself you can hit the ball as well as the pros.

Somewhere around the end of April, Mike, Ray Stokes, and I went to a nine-hole course up in the hills close to Jackson. It was an actual country club, although rather modest but in a good way, and it was open to the public. I think the name was something like Fairgreens or maybe Fargreens. To my surprise, it was in great shape and had a decent layout. Because it only had nine holes, you'd play it twice, but the second time around, you'd hit from different tee boxes.

As usual, Mike showed his natural talent. And Ray impressed me with long drives and a good short game around the greens. I was surprised because I didn't think he'd know which end of the club to hold. He was a hillbilly type, but he easily beat my crappy score.

Although I didn't hit many good shots, I had a good time with these two guys who played at a quick pace and handled themselves well in terms of etiquette and respecting other golfers on the course.

So this Fairgreens course turned out to be a real gem, especially at the nineteenth hole. Established several years before, the little clubhouse had one of those old bars like a Scottish pub, with lots of dark paneling and most importantly, a classy young barmaid.

After our round, Mike, Ray, and I sauntered up and ordered a beer. Patty, the barmaid, asked if we wanted a bottle or a fishbowl. A fishbowl? She picked up on our doofusness and quickly grabbed a frosty, fifty-one-ounce goblet out of the fridge. When we saw that and found out it only cost 50-cents a throw, we quickly said, "Fill 'er up!"

And that's what the hell she did, drawing fifty-one ounces of Stroh's into each of our glasses. Because the thick glass was so damn big, you had to hold it with both hands. But the Stroh's went down real well, and somehow we each got a second fishbowl down the gullet before we left for campus.

While eating in the cafeteria, we kept gabbing about how great the golf course was and how great the barmaid was and how great the fishbowls were, and on and on. There happened to be a bunch of Kappa Omega assholes next to us, and they picked up on what we were saying about Fairgreens. They asked where the place was located and a bunch of other questions. Without thinking, we told them all about it, and sure enough they all said they wanted to play there.

At the time, Mike, Ray, and I didn't think much about it. The following Saturday, the three of us went up there again and had another great time (golf, fishbowls, and Patty). There was hardly anyone else on the course, so we sailed around the two nines in about three hours, which gave us enough time to put down a couple fifty-one-ouncers and still get back for supper.

However, the third time we went up there was a different story. The Kappa Omega bastards had scrounged together some clubs and showed up just before we got there. Those idiots totally screwed up our round because they had no idea how to behave on a golf course... or if they did know, they didn't give a crap.

First, they couldn't play for shit, which was okay, but they were always looking for lost balls and shanking shots into other fairways without yelling "Fore!" They didn't replace their divots or repair the ball marks on the greens. So basically, they acted like the same assholes

they were back on campus. In fact, they made such a spectacle of themselves that the manager of the course told them to get the hell out of there and never come back. He was so pissed, he banned all Rio students from playing there, including us, the bastard. So thanks to Kappa Omega, we lost the chance to play the little "Augusta of the Hills."
[Motherfuckle!]

The Band, straight-ahead rock and roll. Dylan's band, "The Weight"

Sara Bracey

Rowen and Martin's Laugh-In

The music building was a converted two-room schoolhouse on the north side of campus. It was a nondescript structure, but it served the purpose of handling various musical groups, such as the chorus, wind ensemble, and also the music theory courses. I found out the building was open until 10:00 every evening, so I would go over there and practice.

Usually there was no one else there. I would play the piano in a practice room and make futile attempts at improvising. When I screwed up, no one was there to hear. It was a good way to escape the banalities of campus.

I did a lot of finger exercises on the piano. Sounds crazy, but I actually enjoyed that. It was therapeutic. I also enjoyed writing arrangements for the pep band, adapting sheet music and recordings to fit the instrumentation of the ensemble. I wrote a complex arrangement of "Up, Up and Away," based on Hugh Masekela's rendition.

I probably should have made it more straight-ahead instead of keeping it true to the recording, but that's the way I wanted it. So I wrote out all the parts and showed it to Old Man Krone. He seemed impressed but implied it might not be suitable for the pep band.

The bastard seemed like a control freak. Like I was upstaging him. Like he was saying, "Who are you to do this? I'm in charge here. I have things under control." Maybe I was wrong, but that's just how I saw it.

At the next band practice, I distributed the arrangement. Everyone made a valiant attempt, but it came out awkwardly. So Krone told me to play my part, since I wrote it as the lead line along with the trumpets. They picked up on the syncopation and rhythm the next time we went through it. Later with the help of Mike Bortner on lead trumpet, it all fell into place.

At the next basketball game, after playing "The Magnificent Seven" about ten times, we did "Up, Up and Away," and my alto kind of took over. We received a favorable response from the crowd, which usually didn't happen. So I felt pretty good about the whole thing, and it had a healthy effect on the band, since we played something with a little extra pizzazz.

One evening I was in the practice room, banging on the keyboard, fantasizing I was in Carnegie Hall, eyes closed, trying some awkward ad lib shit, when someone knocked on the door. It scared the crap out of me because I thought I was the only bastard in the building. Plus, I was getting ready for the standing ovation from the Carnegie crowd. I popped off the piano bench, opened the door, and standing there with an aura around her was a woman/girl/female-type person. She asked, "Are you playing jazz?"

I immediately became a mumbling idiot, plus I tried to brace myself for the usual response of "I hate jazz, can't stand it, makes no sense, just a bunch of noise." So I muttered, "I was just kind of playing around."

She said, "Well, whatever it was, I liked it. I didn't think anyone around here played jazz."

"So you like jazz? Most people wrinkle up their nose when they hear that stuff."

"Oh, I haven't really heard much jazz. I just thought it was refreshing. I'm sorry if I distracted you."

As this encounter continued, my mind kept grabbing at who she was, what she was doing here, where'd she come from. She was nice looking, although a little thin.

So I said, "What are you doing in here? I never saw you before."

"Well, I was supposed to have a vocal lesson with Professor Krone, but he never showed up. I guess he forgot or something."

"Oh yeah, Professor Krone... he's a busy guy, I guess. So what... you were sitting out here, waiting for him, and you heard everything I was playing?"

"Actually, I'm glad he didn't show up, because I enjoyed listening."

"Well, thanks. I'm not very good. By the way, I'm Mahlon."

She stuck out her hand and said, "Hi, Mahlon. I'm Sara. So, Mahlon... that's a different kind of name. How do you spell it?"

"M-A-H-L-O-N," I said, as I shook her soft hand.

"How'd you get that name?"

"Long story," I said, not wanting to go through the whole thing about Mahlon Haines the Shoe Wizard and how he handed out silver dollars, and blah, blah, blah.

"I'm sorry. I shouldn't have asked. Maybe I should go outside to wait for my sister to pick me up."

"You don't live on campus? Where do you live?"

"Down the road a ways... close to Thurman."

"So your sister drops you off for classes and then picks you up?"

"Well, I get rides with other people sometimes. I think I heard a car outside. Guess I better get going. Nice meeting you, Mahlon."

"Yeah, nice. See ya."

And with a swish of a skirt, out the door she went, down the road to Thurman.

My brain was scrambled. She seemed different, maybe a little naive, innocent, almost pure, compared to the run-of-the-mill campus babes. She liked my playing. That was a boost. Over the next few weeks, she kept showing up. But by then, Old Man Krone remembered to be there for her lessons. She came and left, another lost opportunity. *[Motherfuckle!]*

Ray Charles, consummate musician. Brazilian fans offered their eyes to him.

Chinese Restaurant

Gen. Nguyen Ngoc Loan executes Viet Cong prisoner with pistol on Saigon street.

Growing up, I was a *sneak,* a *picker* when it came to eating. I'd down a whole glass of milk and spend the rest of the meal pushing food from one side of the plate to the other. About the only things I really liked were sugary breakfast cereals or waffles with butter and brown sugar. As I got older, my palate expanded, but even as a teenager I still had a limited diet. And like a racist or bigot, a *sneaky eater* has a very limited view of the world.

On one of our trips to Columbus, Clark picked out a Chinese restaurant for lunch. He was what some people would call... *an eater.* All conversation came to an end. A look of intense concentration would appear, accompanied by various guttural moans and hums. As the plate was cleaned, a smile of satisfaction would break out.

I assumed he'd consumed this Asian stuff before, so his enthusiasm pushed me into this exotic establishment. I found the interior to be impressively gaudy. There was a lot of red wallpaper and gilded trim. And the waiters were all dressed up in some kind of bow-tied outfits. Clark took a quick gander at the menu and immediately found some of his favorites.

On my side of the table, I might as well have been reading a damn phone book. All I saw was a bunch of names that made no sense: Lon Dow Yuk, Woh Sui Op, Bo Lo Op, Moo Koo Gai Pin, Lung Fong Gaikew, Subgum Chow Mein. I asked the waiter for a little assistance, but he got snippy. When he offered a few explanations, that made things even less appetizing. So I panicked and blurted out, "Cheeseburger, no onions."

Lesson learned: so much of life is missed by living in a closed world. By hanging around Clark, I learned to eat just about anything, including all the disgusting stuff I grew up with: hog maw, pon haus, snits and knepp, fastnachts, pot pie, fried mush, rivel soup, butcher baloney, smoked and sweet sausage, chow-chow, corn fritters, and other Pennsylvania Dutch delicacies including a favorite of mine—fried crackers.

Actually, this last item was more of a Depression dish than a PA Dutch thing. Whenever my mom's cupboard produced a box of stale crackers, she wouldn't throw them away. Instead, she'd soak them in a bowl of water. Then, she'd wring out the water and throw them onto a skillet with some butter. As they started to brown, she'd crack a few eggs over top and produce the poor person's delicacy known as fried crackers. They would be enhanced with salt and ketchup. Pure ambrosia.

So as my eyes opened and my palate expanded, I became aware that all cultures had their own idiosyncrasies of food. I'd return from semester break with PA Dutch butcher bologna. The Italians from Jersey brought sticks of pepperoni or *biroldo* or *ciauscolo*. I don't know what the Polish, Blacks, Jews, or Hillbillies brought from home, but I'm sure their culinary backgrounds would seem strange to outsiders. Without getting too metaphysical, it's pretty obvious that prejudices are not restricted to tastes in food.

Miles Davis, trumpet, Kind of Blue *album. Shaped jazz in the '50s and '60s.*

My Radicalization

After a battle for the village of Ben Tre, a U.S. officer said, "It became necessary to destroy the town in order to save it."

In high school, I was a virtual Casper Milquetoast—one of those kids in the back that teachers didn't like because I rarely contributed. On the other hand, I caused no problems. I'd defer to the real troublemakers who got detention or maybe even suspended. I'd just kind of egg them on, and they were happy for my encouragement.

My one after-school detention experience was actually kind of cool. We were supposed to do homework with our heads down in shame for whatever the hell we had done. But some bastard in front of me was "reading" a *Playboy*. He brazenly unfolded the centerfold, which of course took two hands and entailed lifting it above his head so all the damn handjobs behind him could see. This detention thing didn't seem too bad.

What threw me into detention-incarceration occurred in Spanish class when I took off my socks. My buddy Dave "Stony" Stonsifer and a couple others decided it was cool to wear penny loafers without socks, so that's what the hell we did. We took off our socks, put them in our gym bags, and sat there in the language lab cubicles with those crazy headphones on, repeating what we heard on the tapes: "*Hola, que tal,*" "*como esta usted,*" "*aye, carumba.*"

We thought Mr. Jacobs wasn't watching things. But this one day, he walked around the lab and saw our white ankles flashing below the cuffs of our khaki slacks. I guess our snickering caught his attention. So following the school's dress code, he promptly sent us down to the damn principal's office. Of course, he could have just told us to put on the socks, but this was 1963, and rules were rules. So down to the office we went.

We sat on the bench in front of the office secretaries who gave us a bunch of hard looks. I could feel their scorn as they were probably thinking something like, *Your sister would never be sent to the office, let alone take off her socks!*

Principal Goodling, who usually acted like a hard ass, took us into his office and asked why we were kicked out of class. Stony was used to being in trouble, since he was one of the first bastards in school to violate the long hair policy, before anyone ever heard of the Beatles. It was called the Ivy League style. You combed your hair in the front, down over your forehead, not real far. But at the time, it was kind of shocking to parents... and especially to barbers, who were pissed because kids weren't getting their hair cut as often.

It was an extension of the haircuts the older cool guys were sporting called the "Peter Gunn," which was the style of that TV show's star Craig Stevens. This was in contrast to the damn flat tops we all had as little kids, that our parents thought were so cute. You got your hair cut real tight on the sides and back, and then the flat top was damn close to being scalped. The front was held up straight with some greasy goop called Butch Wax.

Anyway, Stony let his hair get long in the front (nothing over the ear or anything like that), and some teachers were sending him to the office. He affected an attitude, which was pretty much unheard of in those days. So he came into the principal's office with this kind of baggage. But fortunately for him and the rest of us, Old Man Goodling must have been busy, or maybe he was just amused. He gave us one night detention and sent us back to Spanish class with our socks on.

It's hard to believe, but back in those days, we could have been suspended for three days and had our parents notified, which was always worse than the school punishment. In any event, from that point on, whenever I had a chance, I went sockless—one of my first examples of rebellion against the damn system.

In my senior year of high school, I took a course called Earth and Space Science. I don't remember much about it, but I know that Carolyn Diffenderfer sat directly behind me. I had a tendency to slouch, and one day she leaned forward and started playing with my hair which was creeping over my shirt collar. This, of course, caused me to get kind of excited in my nether region. I thought, *Holy shit, I guess that obligates me to ask her for a date!* Somehow, I got up the nerve, and she accepted.

When Carolyn was in grade school, her family lived across the street. At that stage of things, I didn't really care about girls, except that she and her sisters were royal pains in the butt. So I ignored them, except when all the kids played hide-and-seek or other damn games like that. However, I liked her dad Jack, who always talked to me, probably because he was the only male in a house with five females.

By the time old Carolyn got to twelfth grade, she was one of the hottest girls in school. A natural blonde with a nice figure, she wore dark-framed glasses that somehow made her even more attractive. So I asked her out for a date. I kind of figured she was just playing around with me, knowing that I didn't date much and was rather inept with girls. But anyway, she said she'd go, so I decided to take her to a movie.

It was a Saturday night, and I got all dressed up: khaki slacks, light blue oxford-cloth shirt, a rep tie that my mom's cousin had given me, my wool sport jacket, and a healthy splash or two of English Leather cologne—pretty powerful stuff, supposedly a sure-fire way to get girls in the mood.

One summer, I had a bottle on a little table in my bedroom. My family went to the seashore for a week, and when we came home, the whole house smelled like English Leather. My room was on the second floor, which wasn't air conditioned. It got so damn hot up there, with all the windows closed, that the cologne bottle literally exploded. It took the finish off the top of the table.

As advertised in *Playboy*: *Nothing reflects a masculine outlook as much as English Leather All-Purpose Cologne. Brisk as a salute; in distinctive redwood gift boxes, $2.50, $4.00, $6.50.*

Anyway, back to this Carolyn thing. That's how guys dressed for dates in 1964, and I felt pretty good about how I looked but also awkward with a buttoned collar and tie. My dad reluctantly let me drive the champagne-colored Ford Custom 500. I got to the Diffenderfer house on Bannister Street, and Carolyn invited me in. I was thinking her parents would be happy to see me after all those years.

But to my surprise, they weren't home. In fact none of her older sisters were either. It was just old Carolyn and me. So for some reason, she took me to see her bedroom. This was turning into every guy's greatest dream. *Holy shit!* But then I started to think... *Yeah right. You put some moves on her, and the damn parents come home right in the middle of things.*

I just said something like, "Nice room," and we got in the Ford and went to the movie. Another example of a lost opportunity for connubial bliss.

She was real nice about things, making small talk or whatever. But somewhere in the middle of all the chit chat, she said something about being on a date with Steve Bell and how nice he was, and how when a waitress spilled something on him, he was so cool about the whole thing.

My mind started spinning. She had been dating older guys, so it was going to be hard to measure up. Steve Bell took her out to a damn restaurant, and I was taking her to just a movie. I knew this guy. He was pretty smooth. So I went into a damn panic mode. All kinds of crap was flying through my brain which inhibited me from coming up with anything creative to say.

When we got to the Capital Theater, I thought about taking her up to the balcony, but the place was packed. Some damn usher with a flashlight directed us to two seats just a couple rows from the front of the theater. So we had to sit there with our necks tilted back to see the gigantic screen. And being in the front of the slanted theater, all the spilled soda and malted milk balls from the elevated seats behind drained down to our feet.

To top it off, the movie was *Sex and the Single Girl*, starring one of my all-time favorites, Natalie Wood. What a title for a date movie! Like she probably thought I picked this because of "sex" in the title and like I'm going to put some really suave moves on her or something. Well, that just added to the pressure to perform, an area where I was greatly lacking, especially with babes like the really hot Carolyn Louise Diffenderfer.

As we watched the movie, I thought about putting my arm on the back of her seat, but the wool sport coat and long-sleeve shirt were too damn cumbersome to maneuver my elbow over her head. Then I kept trying to guess if I should use the arm rest or let her use it. After a few minutes, it seemed that the temperature jumped to 95 degrees, causing the damn English Leather to cook in my armpits.

When the movie was over, we beat it back to the Ford. I should have taken her to some place like the Ramona, across the street from the theater, to get something to eat. But it looked like tons of people were going in there, and I didn't feel like fighting all that congestion. Besides, I felt sorry for old Carolyn, because she had been so good through the whole ordeal, and I didn't want to bore her anymore. So I drove her back to Bannister Street, walked her up to the door, and said goodnight. At that point, a kiss was out of the question, plus it looked like the parents were home. She had been a real trooper. But I really wished she hadn't said anything about Steve fuckin' Bell.

Anyway, like I said, Carolyn Diffenderfer was about the only thing I remembered about the Earth and Space class, except for one really neat experience. The class took a field trip to Washington, D.C.—twenty-five kids and one teacher, on the rudimentary yellow school bus.

Our destination was the Pathological Museum. I'm not sure how that related to Earth and Space Science, but it didn't really matter. In those days, a field trip was something special. Plus, Carolyn *hot babe* Diffenderfer was on the bus. And despite the movie fiasco, she continued to humor me; however, I always detected a slight snicker whenever she said hello.

One of the nerdy guys on the trip, Barry Stover, said there were two exhibits he wanted to see. One was the grotesque leg of some poor African guy who had been bitten by some kind of dreaded parasitic worm which caused the disfiguring and ugly elephantiasis. And the other exhibit was the gigantic pickled penis of the famous bank robber John Dillinger.

I don't know how he knew all this shit. He said after Dillinger was killed by the FBI, a photo of his dead body appeared in all the national newspapers. Except for his head and feet, his corpse was covered by a white sheet. And the thing that caught the world's attention was that Dillinger appeared to have a gigantic erection as indicated by a tent-like projection of the sheet at his body's midsection.

How he could have a hard-on in death didn't make a lot of sense to me. Barry suggested rigor mortis or something like that. He also said Dillinger was a lousy lover. Whenever he got sexually aroused, he often fell into unconsciousness because all the blood from his brain rushed to his gigantic schlong. So all the guys (and probably some of the girls) on the trip were now keenly looking forward to this damn museum.

As we neared the big city, we noticed a lot of other buses on the highway. But at the time, we didn't think much of it. The Pathological Museum was close to the Smithsonian, so our West York Area School District bus parked on the Mall. We hiked into the museum to see the damn grotesque shit that awaited us. Despite the fact that we didn't see Dillinger's big dick, the museum stuff was actually somewhat interesting and vaguely educational.

However, whatever we learned inside the museum that day didn't hold a candle to what we saw when we came out. We had stepped into the first significant anti-Vietnam War protest in the nation's capital.

Crowd estimates ranged from 15,000 to 25,000, marching from the Washington Monument to the Capitol Building.

There were contingents from the Ivy League and other prestigious universities, each carrying large banners emblazoned with names like Harvard, Princeton, Brown, and Amherst. The college students were orderly and clean cut, some with beards and long hair. Apparently, there were two sponsors for the march: the Women's Strike for Peace and the Students for a Democratic Society (SDS), which later radicalized into a strong force of protest against the War and other causes.

Taking in the whole scene, we stood there, mouths agape, in front of the school bus. To our surprise, some protesters came up to us and asked if we were from York, Pennsylvania. Shockingly, we said we were.

They said we should be really proud of our city because we had a fantastic newspaper, the *York Gazette and Daily*. This rocked us back on our heels, almost laughing in their faces. The *Gazette and Daily*, in our eyes, was a dinky morning paper that had a decent sports page, crop news, hog prices, and weather predictions. But then the protesters gave us actual photocopies of editorials from the paper, things that we had never taken the time to read. One photocopy was entitled:

VIETNAM WAR—TRAGIC BLUNDER
STOP! NEGOTIATE!

It had an excerpt from the *Gazette and Daily* from February 16, 1965. Included on the same page were excerpts from *The New York Times*, *The Philadelphia Evening Bulletin*, and quotes from Walter Lippmann and Pope Paul VI. The editorials from the *Gazette* were written by J.W. Gitt, the paper's longtime publisher and editor. Gitt was an unabashed socialist, an ardent labor union sympathizer, and an outspoken critic of police brutality, especially when it came to the use of police dogs to handle local racial conflicts.

Reflecting on this, it's hard to believe that the *Gazette* and Gitt continued to publish for so long in deeply conservative York County. Many locals called Gitt a communist, but people still bought the paper, maybe because it had a morning edition and was cheaper than the evening Y*ork Dispatch*. Gitt was continually investigated by the FBI for communist affiliations, but the feds could never directly link him to anything like that.

But when those college students gave us copies of the *Gazette's* editorials, it made me look at things in a different light. I thought, *Holy shit, if intelligent people from those damn Ivy League schools are reading stuff from my hometown paper, maybe I should open my eyes to not only things around me, but also to things beyond York, PA.*

From that point on, I started to question traditional practices of government and politics, thanks to a damn field trip to see strange, pickled body parts.

Nina Simone, powerhouse singer and piano player, High Priestess of Soul *album. Non-compromising artist and civil rights advocate.*

The Beatles

The Kerner Report: "The nation is moving toward two societies, one black, one white—separate and unequal."

The music I listened to in the early '60s was mostly the stuff played on American Bandstand. That included singers like Fats Domino, Chubby Checker, Little Richard, Jerry Lee Lewis and Chuck Berry. However, the area where I lived produced a healthy array of local R&B groups: The Del Chords, The Mandells, The Soul Clinic, The Invictas, The Tranells, The Crystalaires, and Little Duck and the Drakes. When I'd collect money on my newspaper route on Saturday mornings, I'd hear the soulful R&B sounds of the Doc Dougherty radio show coming out of the houses where my buddies lived.

On the national music scene, the Beach Boys popped up with their surfing stuff, and I thought that was pretty cool. They had a swagger but also a laid back cool that was appealing. All this music was a healthy change from the Pat Boone-Frankie Avalon-Fabian-Brenda Lee stuff of the previous decade.

The first time I heard about the Beatles was on a brief clip on The Jack Paar show. On a stage in some town in England, they were all dressed in suits, wearing some kind of pointed boots, which I wouldn't have been caught dead in.

Of course, they had the hair, which really wasn't that outrageous. It was longer than what was happening in the states at the time, and it had none of that greasy stuff. But really, it was just a longer version of the Ivy League look. And like I had previously mentioned, my buddy Dave "Stony" Stonsifer was wearing his hair close to that length before The Beatles became famous.

So initially, most people thought the Beatles would be just a flash in the pan like others who unsuccessfully tried to follow up on the success of Elvis. But when their songs started popping up on the radio, it was hard to ignore the fact that there was something unique about their sound. It had little to do with the lyrics, but there was a definite sound or beat that was unique and captivating. Sure, it was a ripoff of several American bands, but they pulled it off.

When I was in eleventh grade, a local DJ picked up on this phenomenon and played their songs over and over again. After awhile, people started taking notice. And then, of course, the Beatles came to the Ed Sullivan show. I couldn't understand why the girls screamed so much, but like everyone else, I found myself watching their performances. I started going a little longer between haircuts. I'd stand in front of a mirror, listening to "I Want to Hold Your Hand" and shaking my head so my hair would flop on my head like Paul McCartney. Sounds gay, I know, but that's what the hell I did.

Their first appearance on Ed Sullivan was quite an event. The next day, everyone was talking about it at school. And the cool guys, who listened to local R&B groups back home didn't want to admit it, but they were eventually impressed. The next Beatles appearance on the Sullivan show was in Miami, Florida.

On most Sunday evenings, my family went to my grandma's house, and on this particular Sunday, my Aunt May and her kids were there also. We were all intently watching the black and white TV in anticipation of the Beatles' appearance.

However, the mainliner of this show was Mitzi Gaynor of Hollywood fame. She danced and sang a few songs, and in my mind, stole the show, but not because of her singing or dancing. Apparently, the air conditioning system was malfunctioning, and she was profusely perspiring in a semi low-cut outfit. As she sang, she kind of fondled herself as the perspiration virtually splashed out of her pores.

My cousins, Steve, Bill, Tom, and I sat there with our mouths open as we watched those gleaming boobs bouncing in front of the camera. And Grandma, Mom, and Aunt May all condemned the whole thing and scornfully said something like, "That's just not right." Dad condescendingly agreed, as he tried not to smile. Mitzi Gaynor's performance was more suggestive than anything old Elvis had ever done with his gyrating pelvis when he was on Sullivan's show back in the '50s.

The Beatles eventually made their appearance, doing their usual thing. And of course, they continued to grow and produce over the next few years. *Rubber Soul, Sgt. Pepper, Magical Mystery Tour,* and *The White Album* were inventive. But one thing I liked most about the group was that they had a healthy understanding of good old rock and roll.

Richie Havens, Mixed Bag, *great first album. First performer at Woodstock.*

A White Minority

"A rich man is nothing but a poor man with money." –W.C. Fields

Walking across campus after a 3:00 P.M. Irish Lit class, I saw the basketball team getting on the bus to go play Central State. This was a big game because both teams were in contention for the conference championship. I wasn't real fanatical about following the team, but I saw Larry "Ballsie" Ball and Howie Utley already on the bus, so on the spur of the moment, I joined them. It just seemed like the right thing to do.

The group included the fifteen members of the team, a couple managers, two coaches, six cheerleaders, Pattie Wood, and the driver Mr. Sexton. We hit Rt. 35 west for an hour and a half ride to Central State, located in Wilberforce, Ohio, which also happened to be the home of Wilberforce University. We would soon be in the middle of two predominantly black campuses.

Fitzy Bowers, the team's manager and statistician, was one of the most hard-nosed, redneck racists on the Rio campus. Actually, he got along alright with the black guys on the team, but the poor guy was a deep-down-George Wallace nigger hater. He couldn't help himself. That's just the way he was raised. He was always okay around me, probably because he knew I was a buddy of Dirk Zittle's, and for some dumb reason, he and a lot of others thought I was some smart-ass, like Dirk. Anyway, except for Fitzy's big-time racism shit, he could be a fairly decent guy.

Pattie Wood had been going to Rio games since Bevo was playing. She was a chubby little 4' 10" ball in a red and white outfit. About thirty-five years old and never married, she seemed to have rather unhealthy feelings for strong-forward Ray Williams. A long-time secretary in the admissions office, she was the unofficial college mascot.

Pattie was a time-link between the old Rio and the new, just like the old creaky bus we were riding in. This antique clunker was a holdover from the Bevo days back in the '50s. It had been patched, welded, and overhauled so many times that the only person who was qualified to drive it was this old black man in the driver's seat. He had a kind of ESP for every squeak, backfire, and gasp of this 1948 Flexible Clipper.

So after a long, uneventful ride, Mr. Sexton got us to the Central State campus, safe and sound. Upon arrival, we found there was a construction site next to the field house, which meant the bus had to be parked about two blocks away. To get to the gym, we had to walk between two large dormitories.

At first, that didn't seem like much of a task. But the team members were carrying their duffle bags, and the managers were carrying bags of towels, tape and other stuff, and the cheerleaders, dressed in their outfits, were carrying their pompoms. We soon noticed windows opening in the dorms, and people were hanging out, yelling all kind of things at us.

We thought they were just haranguing us because we were a visiting team, but then we started hearing "honky-go-home" catcalls. At that point, my fellow Caucasians and I got a taste of what it was like to be a racial minority. I wasn't really angry at the black students for doing this. After all, we were easy targets, and these kids probably didn't get many opportunities to vent like that. Miles, Bill, and Herky, the three blacks on our team, were laughing their butts off at us.

To be honest, it was a little unsettling to go through that kind of abuse, but we were soon sitting on the field house bleachers behind our team, surrounded by about 4000 screaming African Americans. After the usual warm-ups, things got started. It was one of those games where the score went back and forth, with both teams playing their asses off. Since Miles and Bill had been big-time high school standouts in nearby Dayton, a lot of the people in the stands knew them. They were unmercifully taunted throughout the game. But despite being a visiting team and all the harassment, our guys played up to the competition.

Halftime came, and Central State was up by five points. Ordinarily, halftime gives everyone a chance to get up and stretch and maybe go to the bathroom or get something to drink. But our little group didn't move a muscle. I looked over at Fitzy, and you could see the steam coming out of his racist ears.

During the game, every time our cheerleaders tried to do a cheer, they were overwhelmed by a thunderous round of boos. However, when the Central State girls ran out on the floor, the entire crowd loudly cheered in precise unison. Some of their cheers were specifically slanted toward us. One was something like, "Go home! Go home! You're jive melon farmers and ya ain't no good. Go home! Go home!" Their fans were all having one fuckin' great time.

When the teams returned to the floor, they picked up right where they left off, trading baskets at a furious pace. And when the game came down to the last few seconds, we were behind by one point. Somehow Mike Lewis got the ball and called time out. Coach Boles huddled up the team, but the place was so damn loud, the players could hardly hear what he was saying.

Central State was expecting Miles Parker to go for the winning basket since he was the best shooter. But instead, Miles passed the ball to Herky who shot a ten footer and missed, but he was fouled in the act. The place went crazy with all kinds of yelling at the ref for making a bad call. So Herk went to the line and calmly made the first shot. He took his time on the second. When he finally fired it up, it was like one of those movie slo-mo shots where the damn ball just hung on the rim for what seemed like ten seconds and then fell through.

Central State tried a long, half-court shot but missed. So the Rio contingent naturally jumped up and started screaming. We all ran onto the floor and danced around with our fists in the air and slapped the guys on the back. Ballsie, Howie, and I started hugging the cheerleaders, having one hell of a good time. I even gave little Pattie Wood a hug.

Then, all of a sudden, it dawned on us that we had to get out of this place which was now filled with 4,000 really pissed off fans. The team had to take their showers before we could leave, so the cheerleaders and Ballsie, Howie, and I sat there in the bleachers.

We quickly realized that the scene we had experienced on the way into the field house was nothing compared to what we were facing right now, with all these pissed off Central State people pressing in on us from all directions. At that point, I actually wished we had lost the damn game. For the next twenty minutes, we heard the repeated chant of "Go home! Go home! You're jive melon farmers and you ain't no good! Go home! Go home!"

We found out later from Herk that *melon farmer* actually meant *motherfucker*. Luckily, someone on the college's security staff saw what was taking place and called for police reinforcements. So after the team had showered, dressed, and returned to the court, we were all escorted back to the bus. Of course, we had to walk between those two big-ass dorms again, and this time the cat-calling from the windows was twice as bad.

Finally, we got to the bus, and thanks to Mr. Sexton, he had the old Flexible Clipper all warmed up and ready to go. A cop car put on its siren and escorted the bus out of Wilberforce and back onto Rt. 35 east.

On the ride home, Fitzy was big-time pissed. He said if the tables were turned and Central State had beaten us like that at Rio, our campus wouldn't have treated them like they treated us. He might have been right about that, but it didn't really bother me that much.

Sure, I had felt pretty damn intimidated and worried about our safety. But this was 1968, and the black kids were keenly aware of the Freedom Rides, the Pettus Bridge confrontation, the Birmingham church bombing, and their own experiences in 1960's Ohio. And all those events just kind of bubbled up, consciously or unconsciously. And despite the fact that they displayed really poor sportsmanship, I gained a pretty good understanding of what it felt like to be a minority in 1968 Ohio.

The Majors, "A Wonderful Dream." Mindless pop stuff, but good stuff.

Rio's First Protest Demonstration

The Supreme Court rules 7-1 that burning a draft card is not an act of free speech protected by the First Amendment.

There were two ways to get back to Rio Grande from Gallipolis. The conventional way was to take Rt. 160 north to Rt. 35, which was a decent, direct route. That's the way most people went. But for some reason, most of the guys I rode with took the back way on Rt. 588. I guess they thought it was faster, although it was basically the same mileage. But the back way had more ups and downs and curves, which made for an adventurous drive. And bad weather and night driving made things more dangerous.

So when Mike Lewis, Larry Ball, Donnie Gross, and I would go up-river, we'd pile into Lewis' metallic-blue 409, four barrel '64 Chevy Super Sport to check out some of the local hot spots. Lewis and Ball were good to have along because they both had the colloquial twang and could maybe defuse any conflicts between the regulars at the bar and any out-of-state student who talked funny and dressed a little too slick for the locals' tastes. Ballsie, who was about 5' 6", had all kinds of stories about picking up hillbilly women and dancing with them. The thought of little Ballsie dancing with some fat forty-year-old babe always cracked me up.

Before I go on with this, I have to add something. At one time or another, there were usually four or five black guys who were part of the Mole Hole. Everyone always seemed to get along. Of course, you'd have to ask the black guys how they felt about that. But in my eyes, they were assimilated into the general flow of things. They'd take part in bull sessions and took general ribbing from everyone like all of us.

But when Mike Lewis loaded his car to go up-river, we never asked any of the brothers to come along, and I'm sure none of them wanted to. And the simple reason was that no sane black person would step foot into the Blue Willow or the Green Gables or even The Grande unless they were carrying some heavy heat and planned to shoot up the place. It was just accepted that blacks were not part of that culture. Sad but true.

Anyway, when we went on those up-river jaunts, the first stop would probably be the Green Gables, which was a few miles north of Gallipolis on Rt. 7. The Gables served drafts in thick glass mugs. For some reason, whenever I had a few drinks in me, I had a tendency to abscond with mugs like that, and I had accumulated a few. Sometimes this place had bands on the weekends, but they also had semi-regular fights and stabbings in the parking lot. However, during the week, there usually wasn't much happening, so if there were no willing divorcees or women-on-the make, we'd take a hasty exit.

The next stop would be the Blue Willow Lounge, which was located close to where the Silver Bridge collapsed. This place usually had more to offer in terms of entertainment. When you walked in, the bar with about six stools was to the left. Directly across from the door were the restrooms, which were usually in pretty bad shape. Frequently, the urinal and commode weren't working, and the bare light bulb was often burned out or broken. You'd have to prop the door open with one foot to let in some light and then try to piss in the pisser without hitting your shoe. Of course, if you were really talented, you tried to avoid the bathroom altogether, but that was pretty tough on the old bladder, especially after putting down four or five Stroh's.

To the right of the front door were a bunch of tables and chairs, a small dance floor, and a one-step stage for the band, which was usually Charlie Lilly and the Earthquakes, aka The Poorside. For being a local country-western band, these guys were fairly competent. They were good at doing Buck Owens stuff, a little Creedence Clearwater, and some Elvis like "Suspicious Minds" and "In the Ghetto," which had a really ironic sound in this hillbilly environment.

Beyond the dance floor was a section with a pool table. That was where most of my time was spent, since the women who came in here seldom mingled with the college boys. However, the waitresses, Gypsy and Angel, were usually open to a little flirting and maybe an ass slap or two toward the end of the night.

So after playing some pool and listening to the country stylings of the Earthquakes and drinking a bunch of Stroh's and feebly trying to hit on some local hillbilly girls, we would pile into Lewis' car and head south for Gallipolis.

We always stopped at The Grande, but by that time it was after 2:15 A.M. We usually got in the door, but they'd always kick us out, not only because it was after Last Call but also because we were pretty damn obnoxious at that time of night. There was a barmaid who was always nice to us, but she would get us the hell out of there before we got into trouble.

By this time, we would usually be pretty damn hungry. There was a Bob Evans burger joint in Gallipolis that was open twenty-four hours. If we had any money, we'd scarf down a few burgers and fries and totally gross out the poor women who worked there.

Then it was back to Rio. And because this Bob Evans was located close to Rt. 588, that was the logical road to take. But it was around 2:30 in the morning and there was no non-drinking, designated driver in Lewis' Super Sport. So we'd go careening through the curves and ups and downs of 588, and if luck would have it, we'd arrive back at Rio, safe, drunk, and relatively sound.

Unfortunately, that wasn't always the case with everyone who left campus in pursuit of those crazy libations. In fact, the year before I got to Rio, a terrible car accident occurred, resulting in the deaths of three students and severe injuries to two others. So this and several other car accidents over the years contributed to the college's first sit-in protest.

This was a big deal at Rio. Traditionally, any negative expression against college policy would be met with great disdain from the administration. And for students to advocate the need for a bar on campus was totally out of the question. After all, this was originally a religious school, plus the township was dry, so legal drinking on campus was not an option.

However, it was difficult to ignore the fact that lots of students left the campus to procure alcohol by either driving the thirteen miles to Gallipolis or two miles into the boonies to Filthy Frank's Beer and Live Bait concession out at Tycoon Lake, neither of which were healthy options for boozed up college kids.

So with the help of some pointed articles in *The Signals*, the school paper, and some fruitless attempts to broach the subject at student senate meetings, word spread that an *impromptu* protest would be held to draw attention to various issues.

A sit-in would take place on the main campus thoroughfare between Allen Hall and Davis Library. I found a piece of white cardboard which came with some of the jazz records I had received in the mail, and with a red magic marker, I printed the word "POWER" in big fat letters. I bent a coat hanger and affixed it to the sign, and Clark, Zittle, and I went up to join the demonstration. On the way, we were accompanied by at least half the people on campus.

Everyone sat in the street between the two buildings and stopped campus traffic for about two hours. And although this might not seem like a big thing compared to protests at Berkeley or Columbia, it definitely set the tone for later confrontations with the administration. Yale Gary, president of the student senate, had rigged up a portable P.A. system, and although he sometimes came across as rather pompous, he did a pretty good job of outlining the reason for the protest. And you had to give the guy some credit, because representatives from the college administration were present, including old A.R. Svenson, the college president. So Yale diplomatically presented a few items of concern relating to student input on policy.

Then Joe "Mad Dog" Scarfo took the mic. This is the guy who got his hand caught in a soda machine, trying to pull out a can without paying for it. They had to break the latch on the machine to get him loose, and he went to the damn hospital to save one of his fingers. This is the guy who, as a freshman, lived on the third floor of Moulton Hall. And thinking he'd be cool, he shuffled out onto the window ledge of his room to take a whiz. While he was out there, his roommate closed the window, and Mad Dog had to stand there for over an hour, screaming for someone to let him back inside.

Anyway, Joe was a decent guy, despite the fact that he belonged to Pi Delta. So here he was, microphone in hand, in trench coat, with cigarette and coffee, adding to Yale's remarks. He mentioned something about the fatal car accident two years before caused by drunk students driving back from Jackson. So despite Joe's various eccentricities like high-altitude urination and accosting a soda machine, he fed right into the general discontent of the student body.

Soon, other random comments emanated from those squatting on the street. People were pissed because there wasn't much to do on campus. A few other people brought up the alcohol issue, stating that many campuses in Ohio had 3.2 bars for the students, or they were located close to off-campus bars, which provided ample (and legal) entertainment.

Country boy Larry Ball grabbed the microphone and mentioned that Rio students needed more power. They needed to have more input into policy and operations. This elicited a few *right ons* and *amens* and *tell 'em, Ballsie*. And as he was finishing, I pushed up my red-lettered POWER sign, and Zittle initiated a rhythmic chant of "Power, Power, Power, Power, Power..."

So at that point, fearing things might get out of hand, Dean of Students Herman took the microphone, and in his usual wrinkled-brow expression, started to make a few general but innocuous comments without really addressing any of the issues. Then Big Cheese Svenson piped up and said the various issues would be addressed, but it was time to disperse so the daily operation of the college could continue. And although he didn't really offer a threat, he strongly insinuated that actions would be taken if we didn't get our sorry asses out of the street. So everyone slowly got to their feet and straggled away, feeling pissed and short-changed. But the seeds of dissent had been sown.

The sit-in got some coverage in the Gallipolis newspaper, and two enterprising local yokels saw an opportunity to cash in on the students' love of beer. They purchased a building about three miles down the road on Rt. 35 in the next township. After a few months of renovations, the place was converted into a bar, the Redman Inn. And surprisingly they did a pretty good job. They served a decent pizza and 3.2 beer, which tended to keep the older locals out of the place. It turned into a pretty good hangout for students. The only problem was that it still required a car to get there. And, of course, it wasn't nearly as much fun as getting plastered at the Blue Willow and flying back to campus on 588.

Jimi Hendrix, industrial-strength guitar, "Purple Haze," "All Along the Watchtower." Had to go to England to get recognized.

Why Nam?

My Lai Massacre exposed; 347 old men, women, and children killed.

Saturday evenings in the Mole Hole were subdued. Several of the guys would go home to see their girls. Others never cut the apron strings—couldn't stay away more than five days. Then there were the hard-core drinkers who got plastered and wouldn't return until 3:00 A.M. And finally there were those who studied Saturday nights—mainly because they were socially retarded and terrible at getting something going with a girl.

Okay sure, there were plenty of guys who dated girls on campus. They found some way to hook up, like at the student center or the lobbies of Davis or Moulton Halls, or they took walks, or if they were lucky and had a car, they could go park somewhere or go to a movie in Gallipolis.

This one Saturday, Clark had gone home to see Dianna. I was trying to read *The Rime of the Ancient Mariner*. Once in awhile, I'd take a break and scan the latest *Playboy* centerfold, marveling at the clarity and definition of the photography. I stacked a few albums on the record changer: Richie Havens' *Mixed Bag*, Booker T and the MGs' *Green Onions*, Hugh Masekela's *Latest*, The MJQ's *Pyramid*, and The Ramsey Lewis Trio's *Live at the Bohemian Caverns*. Around 10:30, Howie Utley and Larry "Ballsie" Ball came into the room with a bottle of Old Crow and some drinking glasses.

Howie said, "Come on Mahl, what's this studying shit? How 'bout a little nightcap? Get your glass."

So I pushed the books aside, and the three of us started sipping the hooch... straight, no chaser. And the BS'ing began. Like me, these guys weren't deep thinkers, but they were honest and open to all points of view. We started in on the war.

Ballsie said, "It pisses me off how most of these anti-war types put down our guys for fighting over there, especially when they come home. They shouldn't disrespect them, because, for one thing, the draftees don't have much of a choice."

"They could go to Canada," said Howie.

"But they probably couldn't come home... ever," Ballsie added. "And then there's that conscientious objector thing, where they empty bed pans for two years... or worse, they'd become medics right in there with the GIs in the jungle. But if they refuse all of those things, they could go to jail for two years, making it really hard to get a job later on."

The music changed from Ramsey Lewis to the MJQ.

"Of course, there's the guys who enlist because they believe in the domino theory... like if Nam falls, then Australia's next, then Tahiti, then Hawaii, then Disney World—which is bullshit, of course. But I'm thinking those guys enlist because their old man was in WWII, or maybe it's a macho thing, or because they're patriots and love this country, good or bad. I guess that's all fine and dandy. All wars suck the big one, but this one is just plain stupid. It was cooked up by asshole politicians who didn't want to be weak on communism."

"So what was it?" I said. "Johnson got faulty info about the North Vietnamese attacking one of our ships in the Gulf of Tonkin, right? And he gave the OK to attack—just like that. The military jumped in with both feet because they love a good war, and all the contractors saw a great chance to stuff their pockets, and things were off and running. We already had advisers over there, going back to Eisenhower, but assholes like McNamara and Westmoreland pushed us to the point of no return."

Taking a sip of the Crow, Howie chimed in, "So all this shit's going on because one of our ships thought it was being attacked, but what they really saw was some freaky weather mirage. They're all assholes. It's like they needed an excuse, and they basically manufactured one."

So I said, "It wasn't until I saw pictures in *Life* magazine showing the shit that napalm does to the environment, but worse, to innocent people who happen to get in the way. Like it fuckin' sticks to the skin. I guess they use it for deforestation, to help expose the Viet Cong. Too bad if some innocent civilian gets smacked with it."

Ballsie said, "This is hard to believe, but so far I haven't really known anyone who's been to Nam. And if you aren't directly exposed to it, it's easy to ignore."

I took a tug on the Crow and said, "Last summer, I was working at the casket factory... my third summer. And even if you've worked there before, you still have to get a physical from the company doctor. So they put us in a van and drove us to the doc."

Howie picked up the Fall football issue of *Playboy*.

"I was in the van with this other guy, maybe two or three years older than me. He was pretty thin and just stared straight ahead... didn't say anything. That was awkward, so I asked him, 'Where'd you work before you came to York Caskets?' He seemed to be in a haze, like he didn't hear me. And then he mumbled, 'I was in the Army.' Trying to be congenial, I said, 'So where'd you serve?' Again, it was like he didn't hear me. He just stared straight ahead and then said, real matter-of-factly, 'Nam'."

Howie tossed aside the *Playboy*.

"It seemed pretty obvious he didn't wanna talk—like I was going too far, invading something he didn't want to open, especially to some schmoe like me."

Ballsie poured more Crow.

"He didn't ask what I did before, and I sure as hell wasn't going to say anything like, 'Oh, Nam? That's nice. I've been living at home, attending junior college with a 2-S deferment while you were over there trying to save your ass from booby traps in rice paddies.' Hell, the poor bastard had to go through all that shit over there, and now he's back home, sweating his ass off in a damn factory for $1.60 an hour."

"That sucks," Howie said. "They send these guys over there and don't do shit for them when they come back."

Ballsie went on, "I started to realize how bad things were when I read that 500 of our guys were killed... in one fucking week. And it quickly dawned on me, in terms of sheer numbers, the entire male population of Rio could have been wiped out. Like one day, you're walking around and everyone's here, and the next week they're all dead. And then the following week, at another small campus, 500 more are gone. And it just keeps going like that."

"Yeah," Howie said. "It really makes you think. And if you aren't killed or wounded, you're still gonna be pretty fucked up in the head. You have to worry about a little kid or a peasant woman blowing you up. Or you're forced into some rotten situation, shooting everything you see... old men, women, little kids, like that My Lai thing."

"Then think about how you can be drafted at eighteen," I said, "but you can't vote until twenty-one. Hell, in some places, you can't even buy a drink in a bar, and of course a lot of those guys over there never see twenty-one. Even if they come home, it's still terribly wrong to have been exposed to all that shit, because the whole damn war is wrong... and fabricated and mishandled and unnecessary."

I flipped over the stack of records, and we drifted to other things, like which girls on campus do or don't. After awhile, the drunks started coming in, breaking the quiet of the Mole Hole. Howie and Ballsie took off with what was left of the Crow.

I never protested the war. I never went on any anti-war marches. I always knew the whole war-thing was wrong, but I never did anything about it. I just kept going to class, and I kept getting drunk. I stayed in my own, miserable little world, hoping I would somehow get something going with Janie Barakos. *[Motherfuckle!]*

Ritchie Valens, "Oh Donna." Great slow dance song.
Died in plane crash, 1959.

Harvard Debate Team

The Supreme Court unanimously ruled that an Arkansas law prohibiting the teaching of evolution in public schools violates the First Amendment.

A lot of people who went to Rio frequently put down the place as being small, podunk, backward, inferior, on and on and on, unfairly comparing it to Ohio State or Miami of Ohio or Antioch or whatever. Many of those who did the most complaining had flunked out of, or were kicked out of, or couldn't get into those other more prestigious schools. And I have to admit, I often fell into that same pattern of complaint. On the other hand, I was sometimes impressively surprised at what took place at this institution of higher pedagogy.

Ron Hansen was a campus legend. He was a communications prof and the college's speech coach. Apparently, as an undergrad, he was a national debate champion. When he came to Rio as a professor, he spiffed up the department in terms of his classes and the college's participation in various debate and speech competitions.

He recruited a healthy diversity of students for the speech team, which was traditionally made up of nerdy types who sported lots of pencils, pens, and slide rules in the pocket protectors of their shirts. But Hansen attracted hot babes, athletes, and hell-raisers, which brought fresh blood to the formerly stilted and boring team. And sure enough, his people produced results and put Rio on the map.

So with this lofty reputation, Hansen created an annual debate tournament at Rio. But this event invited not only the surrounding small colleges like Marietta, Ashland, Denison, and Kenyon, but get a load of these other schools: West Virginia, Nebraska, Dartmouth, Harvard, and MIT. (I'm thinking the Ivy League teams might have brought their JV squads, but what the hell, they were still Ivy League, right?)

I was never really sure why these big schools would come the whole way to the scrubby hills of southeast Ohio, but I suppose that said a lot about the power of Ron Hansen. A two-day tournament was held in November with over twenty colleges competing in debate, oral interpretation, oratory, and extemporaneous expression.

Because there was only a modicum of available motel rooms in the area, some participants had to be squeezed into vacant dormitory beds of Rio students who went home on weekends. And sure enough, five Harvard men showed up in the Mole Hole for a two-night stay. And the Mole Holers displayed amazing congeniality by offering these guys a chance to participate in an entertaining evening of local merriment. As I remember, the invitation came from Doug Gross who said something like, "Hey, yous guys wanna go drinkin?"

In a tone which was just as pleasant as the invitation but with more than a tinge of condescension, the Harvard contingent responded by saying, "No, thank you. That sounds like a dandy time, but we have to prepare for tomorrow's first round of debates."

So they obviously missed a great opportunity to experience the musical, liquid, and sensory delights of the Blue Willow Lounge, the likes of which they would never see in their small, parochial world of Cambridge, Massachusetts.

Big Momma Thornton, "Hound Dog." Better than Elvis' version.

I'm a Racist

I Know Why the Caged Bird Sings, *by Maya Angelou*

When I was about five years old, the Hoffs, who lived next door, became the first and only family on Sycamore Road to have cement curbing installed in front of their house. For some reason, Gordie thought the front of his property needed curbing, probably to increase the property value.

One summer day, a work crew dug a ditch for the curb's foundation. Being an observant five year old, I noticed the laborers' darker complexions. When I asked my mom about this, she matter-of-factly said the workers were just like other men, but they simply had darker skin. She didn't say anything about staying away from them or they were bad people. Her response satisfied my curiosity.

Over the years, I always thought she handled my question in the best possible way, especially considering her cultural background. She grew up in a little Pennsylvania village called Glatfelter's Station. It was out in the boonies, with about ten houses, a general store, and a small railroad station. There were plenty of poor people in the area but no blacks within a ten-mile radius. The only minority was a recluse known as The Greek.

Most of the locals never had a face-to-face meeting with a black person. Since the village was a quick stop on the Pennsylvania Railroad, they had seen, but not talked with, the black porters on the passenger trains. My grandfather loved the *Amos and Andy* radio show, which promulgated negative racial myths. And my mom's Aunt Edna, in her most dignified voice often said, "There's Negroes and there's niggers, just like there's white people and white trash."

That was the sentiment of most good church-going folks in the area. It tended to encourage the use of "nigger" when making judgments of blacks. And it was justified by saying there were low-life whites also. But "white trash" was seldom used.

My dad was from the nearby town of York. As a youth, he witnessed Ku Klux Klan parades on Market Street. Although there weren't many blacks in the city in the early twentieth century, they were expected to know their place and behave accordingly. Some towns in the surrounding area forbade blacks to be within the town limits after dark.

I remember my dad talking to neighbor Gordie Hoff about how great Jesse Owens was at the Hitler Olympics. He showed that the Germans weren't a superior race. But they didn't mention that after the Olympics, national hero Owens returned to the U.S. with his medals and had to put up with the same discrimination that existed before he went to Germany. Walking down the street, he was still a nigger.

In the 1950s, many local residents joined private swimming clubs. Any white person could show up, pay the daily admission price, and be admitted. No need to fill out an application. Just jump in the pool and swim in the cool, non-integrated water. So as a kid, I picked up on this and asked my dad what the deal was about no black members. His whispered response was pretty lame. "Well you know, Mahl, some Negroes have syphilis, which can be transmitted to others in a swimming pool." Of course, he could have said something much worse like, "You don't wanna go swimming with a bunch of dirty niggers."

At the age of nine, I was sent to the local YMCA for swimming lessons. There were poor city kids, both white and black, who were given scholarships to attend the Y. Hard to believe, but many of those kids didn't have enough money for swimming suits. So for whatever reason, everyone swam in the nude, and no one was ridiculed for not having a suit. As far as I was concerned, there was only one benefit for nude swimming. When diving into the pool, boys quickly learned to avoid the belly flop. Male skinny dippers know what I'm referring to.

On Fridays at the Y, we assembled in a big room to sing hymns. Some old guy banged the hell out of the piano, and another guy led us in "Onward Christian Soldiers," "Lift High the Cross," and other hymnal toe tappers. He always urged us on to sing really loud, no matter how bad it sounded.

Then, after the singing, our names were called, one by one, to get a locker key so we could change into our gym clothes. I cringed when my name was called. In those days, Mahlon Haines Dickinger was not the coolest of names. Honestly, how many Mahlons do you know?

The original Mahlon Haines was a self-made man who developed his fortune selling work boots. He had about forty stores and sold the shoes really cheap. After he made his fortune, he became a philanthropist. He got a big kick out of giving a silver dollar to random people in the street. When my dad was about ten years old, Haines gave him one of those dollars. That impressed my old man, and sure enough, when I was born, he gave me The Shoe Wizard's name.

I would have been happy with a name like Barry or Gary or Greg or Mutt or Jeff or Butch or even Hey You... anything but Mahlon Haines Dickinger. So this guy who gave out the keys always made a big deal of my name. He'd shout out, "Mahlon Haines Dick-ing-er. Come up here and get your key!"

I'd meekly lower my head, grab my key, and beat it the hell out of that room before anyone jumped on the "Dickinger" bandwagon. Actually, this dispenser-of-the-keys was an okay guy. He'd give me a wink and a slap on the back, as though he was saying, "I know that's a weird name, but it's your name and that's something to be proud of. I know you can handle it." Character building shit, right?

After getting the locker key, the kids flew down the steep wooden steps, changed into gym clothes, and had a half hour of wild-ass gym. We'd play battle ball and do tumbling stuff like the acrobats in the circus. Three guys would lie on a mat and one would roll toward one of the others who would jump over him, and on and on. And then we'd play kick ball. For bases, they used wrestling mats folded into five-foot squares. You'd kick the ball and run like hell until someone hit you with the ball.

Like I mentioned before, a lot of the kids were from poor families, both white and black. So some of them played in their bare feet. I guess they didn't have enough money for sneakers. And those kids played the hardest of them all, without shoes. Many of these black and white kids who played so well together at the Y, ended up fighting each other about ten years later in the York race riots.

After the half hour of gym, we'd have what they called a free swim. But before that, we were visually inspected by the phys. ed. guy for any kind of weird rashes or fungi or jungle rot. Then everyone jumped into the pool, naked of course, and splashed like hell for about thirty minutes.

Not being the best of swimmers, I'd find a spot in the corner of the shallow end. I never felt like moving into the liquid frenzy that always took place. Eventually, we were released to the locker room, where we dried off and got dressed for the ride home. That is, if my parents remembered to pick me up. There were times when I walked the three miles home, or if I was lucky, I'd catch a ride on a public bus.

In the winter, my mom told me to wear a hat because when leaving the Y, I'd have wet hair and the hat would stop me from getting a cold. I wore a Humphrey hat like some Englishman might wear. It had red and black corduroy stripes.

I really liked that hat, and no one else seemed to have one like it. One day after the swim class, I couldn't find my hat in the locker room and went home with wet hair. The following week at the Y, I saw some black kid wearing the hat. It was pretty obvious it was my hat. Plus, it had been purchased in my part of town, so I was convinced the kid stole it.

Fortunately or unfortunately, I was really good at avoiding confrontations. So I ignored the kid, went home, and complained to my mom about it. Usually very compassionate, she was the last person to complain to about losing a hat. Her response was, "Well, the boy probably needed it more than you do, so don't get upset about it. We'll get you another one."

And that's what they did. But after that, whenever I went to the Y, I'd hide the damn thing. I figured I was an easy target for hat swipers. So I'd leave the Y with wet hair and never did get a damn cold. I also believed one of those poor white kids could have taken the hat just as easily as that black kid. And Aunt Edna, the words *nigger* or *white trash* never popped into my head.

In my early years, I watched black athletes like Willy Mays, Hank Aaron, Bill Russell, Oscar Robertson, and Jim Brown. They were positive images. But in the early '60s, Muhammed Ali, aka Cassius Clay, popped on the scene. He won an Olympic medal in the light-heavyweight division in 1960.

A couple years later, he became world famous with his defeat of Sonny Liston, who was the most feared fighter at the time. Clay, a big underdog, taunted Liston before and during the fight to the point where Sonny totally underestimated him.

Clay took him out in just a few rounds and went totally crazy with his "I Am the Greatest" stuff. At the time, that kind of boasting rubbed me the wrong way. But when Clay beat Liston a second time, I started to see him in a different light. He backed up his talk with his fists. And I saw Clay/Ali as a true boxing talent. After awhile, I started pulling for him.

Besides black athletes, I listened to many black singers and musicians. When I was in sixth grade, I attended Friday night hops at the Reliance Fire Company. Many of the best records were by black singers: Brook Benton, Sam Cooke, Little Richard, and others. After school, I watched American Bandstand. Dick Clark hosted all kinds of black entertainers, although I don't remember seeing too many black kids dancing on the show. It seemed like mostly kids from parochial schools who were the star dancers. But Clark was definitely responsible for putting tons of black entertainers on his show for white kids to see and hear.

In the early 1960s, my hometown was not exactly in the vanguard of the civil rights movement. However, there was a local merchant named Sol Kessler, who owned an appliance store. He was one of the few local merchants to hire a black person. No big deal, right? But the black guy wasn't just someone who mopped the floor after hours so no one would see him.

I'm talking here about Ritt the Record King. His real name was Torling Ritter, and he had his own department at Kessler's. It was a full-blown record and hi-fi/stereo department. He prided himself in knowing just about every record and recording artist that ever existed. So I'd go in there and try to stump him by asking for some obscure jazz recording. He'd immediately walk over to one of his stacks and pull out what I asked for.

He always came through, except for one time, when I asked for a recording by the Afro-Blues Quintet plus One. The poor guy's eyes bugged out, and he almost swallowed his cigarette butt. In fact, he got a little pissed and insinuated that maybe I shouldn't come in anymore. But then I ordered the record through the mail and showed it to him, which reestablished my cred with him.

When I got to high school, there were only two black kids in the school of 900 students. Their names were Anne and Sam "Snookie" Sanders, both always on their best behavior.

Anne was in my class. Attractive and well dressed, she never walked with her head down or in a subservient posture. At times, she asserted herself about various issues, and I'm sure some of the others thought she was pushy or outspoken. She never dated anyone from school, mainly because the only black boy was her brother. And the idea of a black girl dating a white boy was virtually unheard of.

Ann was not immune to negativity in the classroom. The school's chemistry teacher Jacob "Jakie" Amspacker was a legend. A short, balding man, he had taught at Gettysburg College before coming to West York. He was a respected teacher and member of the community.

For many years, Jakie's classes were comprised of just boys, because back in the day, girls seldom took college prep courses. But as time went on, more girls showed up in chem class, and Jakie didn't always appreciate their presence. And like others in his generation, he held on to verbal expressions that were inappropriate and outdated. So when Anne Sanders was in Jakie's class, she had to deal with a double whammy: being female and black.

One day, she was standing to recite, as we all had to do, and she was having trouble coming up with an answer. Jakie blurted out, with a smirk on his face, "A ha! Looks like there's a nigger in the woodpile," meaning there was something amiss in the situation. Everyone in the class cringed. Anne stood there and just kind of took it. I'm guessing she mentioned this to a guidance counselor or maybe the principal. And I'm sure she told her parents. But as far as I know, nothing ever happened to Jakie. He continued to teach into the next year, when he suffered a heart attack in front of one of his classes.

And speaking of the last year Amspacker taught, Sam Sanders just happened to be in the class that witnessed Jakie's coronary. As I mentioned before, Sam was like Anne in the sense that he never caused any trouble and was well-liked by everyone. He dressed well, played trombone in the band, and was an above average athlete in football, basketball, and track. He was also a member of the cool guys' clique, palling around with these guys, in and out of school. However, he never dated a girl from school, so his social life was also limited, like Anne's.

Up to that point in my life, the Sanders kids were the closest I came to knowing black people. When you think about it, they were pretty much like the other kids in the school, although I don't pretend to know what it was like for a black kid to go to an all-white school in those days. And I don't mean to keep harping on my dad, because he wasn't a mean person, but he had a story about Anne and Sam's father.

He said Mr. Sanders was an employee of the local post office, and on his salary, there was no way he could afford the nice, three-bedroom rancher on Sycamore Road. So Dad inferred the NAACP financed their house to integrate the lily-white neighborhood. I suppose that was a possible explanation. But despite people's fear of integration and lower property values, the Sanders family conducted their lives in a suitable manner and caused no problems.

Anne later became a published author. Sam, a National Merit Scholar, went to Antioch College in Ohio and later became a physician. Somewhere along the line, he must have gotten the royal shits of towing the line and doing the white thing, because he entered the Nation of Islam and became one of Louis Farrakhan's righthand men.

So by the time I got to Rio Grande College, I thought I knew everything about the racial situation in America. I was the typical "colorblind" free-thinking liberal. However, when a black person approached, something clicked in the brain—*that's a black person*, and by that I don't mean I was threatened or intimidated. But the mere identification of blackness indicated instinctive racism. Let's be honest. When any person comes toward us, we all intuitively make value judgments: rich, poor, well-dressed, shabbily dressed, or ethnic background. Most people don't admit to that, but we all do it. And by adding the black factor pushes the issue toward racism. So although I considered myself to be racially aware, I knew I would always be in some way a racist. ***[Motherfuckle!]***

John Coltrane, tenor and soprano saxes, jazz giant; great albums like
Blue Trane, My Favorite Things, Giant Steps, A Love Supreme.
Best solo on an album with singer Johnny Hartman, "My One and Only Love."

MLK's Death

Riots after King's assassination: 100 cities, 39 dead,
2600 injured, 21,000 arrested

As mentioned before, Ron Hansen had been a popular speech prof at Rio for three years but then left to pursue his doctorate. The day after Martin Luther King, Jr., was assassinated, Hansen was back at Rio, visiting some of the profs and former students. In the morning, he came into the cafeteria for coffee. A bunch of guys saw him and called him over to say hello. He seemed genuinely happy to see them.

One of the guys, Jake Hoover, said, "Hey Hansen, how 'bout that murder of King?" He said it with a sarcastic smile, thinking the former prof would agree with him in the sense that, *Yeah, they finally shut up that nigger*.

Without saying a word, Hansen cold-cocked the son of a bitch in the mouth and left the cafeteria. Apparently, Hoover got the message. No complaint was filed.

Dizzy Gillespie, trumpet, composer, leader.
High energy ambassador of bebop.

Dick Gregory

"If it wasn't for Abe Lincoln, I'd still be on the open market." –Dick Gregory

As part of the Artist and Lecture Series, the college scheduled comedian/activist Dick Gregory to speak. Having seen him on a few TV shows, I found his comedy to be crisp, inventive, and a little irreverent. He ended his shows by putting a white glove on one hand and then clasping his other hand, encouraging whites and blacks to live harmoniously.

Getting his first break at the Chicago Playboy Club, Gregory could have had a lucrative career as a comedian. But after publishing his book *nigger* (sic), he became a frequent participant at civil rights events, especially in the segregated South.

To show his desire for political change, he declared his candidacy for president on the Peace and Freedom Party ticket. His campaign included speaking on campuses, thus his trip to Rio Grande.

I'm not sure how he got invited to ultra-conservative Rio. It was probably Student Senate President Mike Taylor or maybe Prof. Bill Wyndham who initiated it. The administration was easily agitated by the slightest possibility of controversy, so I'm guessing they didn't know shit about Dick Gregory and his leftist leanings.

By the time he got to Rio, Gregory was in full agitator mode. When word got out that some crazy, loud-mouthed Negro was coming to campus, the whole student body showed up, including some local yokels who, I'm sure, had a bunch of lynching ropes and twelve-gauges in the back of their pickups.

The speech was held in the cafeteria, the usual place for guest speakers. Actually, it was a decent venue since it was a relatively new structure, with a carpeted floor and good acoustics. The large room was filled to the brim, the whole way up to the milk-dispensing machines. The only problem was that the east and west walls were totally glass, which meant that any wacko sniper could take a bead on the speaker from 100 yards without anyone knowing they were there.

The assembled crowd was amped up in anticipation of this controversial black guy. The small group of radical commie pinkos and the black student union were enthusiastically shaking in their seats, hoping Gregory would stir things up with incendiary remarks that would totally piss off the administration, most of the faculty, and a large part of the student body. The larger redneck sector was sitting there, allowing themselves to prejudge Gregory as an uppity, outspoken nigger who should never have been allowed to get within twenty miles of this racially pristine campus.

I, of course, being the mature man-of-the-world, sat there with open mind, hoping no stupid asshole would stand up in the middle of the speech and shoot the guy. To add to my tension, I was pissed because Jane Barakos was sitting in the first row beside Eugene Giddens, my Sociology prof. I didn't like the fact that he was screwing around with her. After all, she was supposed to be my babe by this time, but I, of course, had screwed that up a long time ago.

The tense atmosphere was allowed to ferment, because Gregory was ten minutes late. When he finally arrived, he was wearing a light-blue jump suit and a tan jacket. When he started talking, it was immediately evident that he spoke with intelligence, confidence, and preparation. He had given this talk many times, often in trying circumstances, so he was ready to deal with this place. His humor was sharp and cutting, but he spoke in a low-class vernacular, which didn't endear him to the doubters in the audience. But it did a lot for the black kids, who were grooving as though they were listening to a black Baptist minister.

Gregory started going over his concerns about the American public and government. He got into the generational thing, calling politicians like Chicago's Mayor Daley and Lyndon Johnson old men who were stuck in the past and were out of touch with the general public. He predicted the two-party system would disappear in the near future and that big business and capitalism were stomping on the U.S. Constitution, controlling politicians with their money.

Gregory mentioned the usual stereotypes of blacks: they're all ignorant, stupid, and lazy. According to him, the only way blacks and minorities could make the American public aware of their problems was to become violent or to threaten violence. This quickly perked up the ears of everyone present, but in different ways. The blacks and left-wingers were thinking *Burn, baby, burn*, and the right-wingers were thinking *It's time to stomp on those ungrateful minorities and show them who's boss.*

He thought the U.S. intervention in foreign countries was immoral, especially in Vietnam, which was a contrived war, destroying the spirit of the country. When he became president, he would immediately bring home the troops.

He proposed a creative way to end the war. If a majority of American men stopped shaving, stopped buying razor blades, this would have a profound effect on the steel industry. It's not an expensive item, but think about how many people shave every day, both men and women. When a popularly used product stops making money, drastic measures have to be taken.

The steel industry has a big effect on the American economy. When U.S. Steel goes on strike, then the auto industry panics. Then the rubber industry panics. And so on and so on. And then all the Washington lobbyists start buzzing the ears of the damn congressmen, and that's when things start to change. Like Gregory said, big money runs the country.

So that was a hell of a lot for the audience to chew on. At times, he was crude, but there was a method to his delivery. People had to be shocked to get their attention. Many of the students left the cafeteria with a different perspective about the country, politics, race, foreign affairs, and a whole lot of other crap.

I hated to be a pessimist, but I didn't think there were enough people in the country who wanted to stop the war, the bastards. They only thought about themselves, and they didn't care about those poor guys over there who were being shot up and getting all screwed up in the head. And they didn't care about how this war was tearing up the country and how it was going to affect things for years to come.

We could have had all the Dick Gregorys speaking out and all the campus protesters doing their marching, but until the politicians got out of the WWII mindset and realized the war couldn't be won, then things would continue to be fucked up and people would continue to die.

So Gregory traveled to another campus. His ideas would be enhanced by another speaker at Rio in a few months. This was little Rio Grande College, but it directly or indirectly created a healthy diversity of thought in many minds.

Isley Brothers, "This Old Heart of Mine," "Shout," "It's Your Thing."
A young Jimi Hendrix played with them.

Mock Election

"There are no dirty words, only dirty minds." –Lenny Bruce

Just after Gregory's visit, the *Columbus Evening Dispatch* brought an electronic voting machine to campus for the purpose of a presidential mock election. The unsurprising results were as follows:

- Richard Nixon, 173
- George Wallace, 109
- Hubert Humphrey, 49

Write-Ins:

- Dick Gregory, 47
- Eugene McCarthy, 10
- Pete Rose, 8
- Nelson Rockefeller, 2
- Paul 'Bear' Bryant, 1
- Woody Hayes, 1

Two additional questions:

Should the U.S. stop all bombing of North Vietnam in hopes it will help peace negotiations?

- YES, 110
- NO, 211

Should women return to below-the-knee skirt lengths?

- YES, 32
- NO, 293

Buddy Rich, great big-band drummer, but also played in small combos.

Athletic Prowess, or Lack Thereof

"True terror is to wake up one morning and discover that your high school class is running the country." –Kurt Vonnegut

Just off the east side of campus was Raccoon Elementary School, which had no bearing on the life of the college except the local school district allowed Rio to use the gym for intramural basketball.

Although I played intramurals at the junior college, I didn't play in these games, which were contested on a rather intensive, blood-lust level. Since there was no football team, a lot of the teams were made up of frustrated football types who needed some kind of physical competition in their lives. I always knew basketball included physical contact, but I didn't go for bloody noses or loss of teeth or broken ribs. These games had only one referee, and that guy was usually from Pi Delta or Kappa Omega, so guess who got the good calls.

I loved to play the game, but under the right circumstances: setting picks, passing to the open man, and calling fouls when appropriate. Someone told me one time I played with a smile because like I said, if everyone plays the right way, basketball can be a lot of fun. But when it turns into a show of strength and intimidation, call me a wimp, that's not for me. Besides all that, if I played enough games, my glasses inevitably got broken by an elbow or a wayward pass, and I didn't feel like walking around campus with tape wrapped around one of the temple-arms or the nose bridge of my frames.

Another reason I didn't play was that I had a weird arthritis called Brittle Spine Syndrome which caused my vertebrae, hip, and pelvic bones to slowly fuse. This had a direct effect on the surrounding muscles, so anytime I did strenuous exercise, I was sure to be stiff for a week afterwards. I could barely get out of bed in the morning.

When I was in eighth grade, I went out for the track team. I did all the exercises but never got into decent shape. I was in one track meet, ran in one event, and came in last. So that was a big hint I wasn't making the Olympic sprint team. Another aspect of this condition was that it gave me one of the more distinctive walks on campus. I could be identified from anywhere, simply by my crazy walk.

Despite this physical deficiency, I still loved to play basketball. After the intramural games, everyone went back to the dorm or out to Tycoon Lake for some beer, but no one locked the gym or turned off the lights. So I'd go in there and have the gym to myself.

It wasn't like shooting on an outside court, where there were cracks in the macadam or the rim was crooked or the ball sailed into some damn mud behind the basket. In the gym, you'd kick the ball against a wall so it came back to you without stooping to pick it up. It was therapeutic, away from everything, just shooting hoops. To me, shooting a basketball was just as relaxing as playing catch with someone, no pressure to perform, score, compete, or impress. But also, the act of shooting was a miracle of physics.

I modeled my jump shot after Oscar Robertson's. He was always so smooth, anywhere on the court. The more I shot, the better I got. And when I broke down the shot, I found it amazing how all the elements come together to produce the beautiful sound the ball makes when it hits only net.

Things like going up on the toes, the springing of the knees, hands and ball over the head, left hand on the side of the ball and right hand on the back, the right hand imparting back spin at the correct release point, and the flex of the right wrist toward the basket. The eyes and the brain working together so that distance and angle from the basket and arc of the ball and speed of the ball are all factored into the shot.

At times, I'd get in a zone when just about everything went in. No thought about mechanics, just feel. I'd experienced that in some pickup games, where I'd run down the court, get to the right spot, and just fire up the ball. It was all physical, just involuntary brain activity.

That didn't happened often, but it was like hitting the sweet spot on a golf club or a tennis racket or a baseball bat. You couldn't explain how it happened. It just fuckin' happened. But it was a really good feeling, almost as good as sex, of which I knew very little at the time.

But anyway, I'd shoot hoops at 10:00 P.M. some nights, and my brain would wander in all directions.

-Jump shot from the left side of key... thinking about how neat Jane Barakos was.

-Layup on left side off backboard... thinking about her semi-raspy Philadelphia accent and her big brown eyes.

-Scoop shot directly in front of basket... thinking I might have a chance if she wasn't so hung up on that damn fraternity/sorority thing.

-Jump shot from right corner... hearing the opening of Herbie Mann's "Coming Home, Baby."

-Fade away ten footer... reviewing yesterday's discussion in Poetry Class.

When I was in the zone, I could hit the back of the rim without popping up the ball. Instead, it would just nick the heel, shoot straight down through the hoop, and hit the floor so it would return directly to me and I could fire up another one without a dribble. It was like achieving perfection in the most limited but satisfying way. Shooting hoops was like going to a damn shrink and temporarily unloading a bunch of cerebral garbage. I loved shooting hoops in that little old gym.

Herbie Mann, flute and tenor sax; Jewish guy from Brooklyn playing funk.

Bobbie Jo Pulling the Train

"The truth will set you free, but first it will piss you off." –Gloria Steinem

A few weeks after I got to Rio Grande, I noticed a few students had part-time jobs. Things like picking up litter, sweeping sidewalks, and scrubbing dishes in the cafeteria. I figured they needed the money. But then I found out they weren't doing this because of financial need. They were working off a disciplinary punishment from the previous year.

One time after Christmas break, not much was happening on campus as usual. Everyone was kind of getting on each other's nerves, so a spontaneous food fight exploded in the cafeteria. It started with a few guys tossing bits of food back and forth. Soon, other people were getting hit, and things quickly escalated.

Yeah, that's right. This was a four-year college, not junior high school. Tables were turned on their side for protection from flying mashed potatoes, meat loaf, and other available food, thrown in the masterful style of The Three Stooges. Everyone had a great old time. But somehow, various people were singled out, probably with the help of some damn administration brown nosers. Punishments were levied in the form of public service.

One of the convicted perpetrators was Denny "Banana Nose" Pettit, some skinny guy from Columbus who tended to do just about anything to fit in with the cool crowd. He and a few other guys worked the evening shift in the kitchen. Actually, it was a pretty good job, because they got all kinds of leftovers like cookies and desserts that were going to be tossed at the end of the day. Occasionally, these guys would grab a Salisbury steak or two from the kitchen refrigerator and heat it up in a popcorn popper in their dorm room.

So while they were working off their sentences, there was a non-student girl in the kitchen with them. Her name was Roberta, but she preferred to be called Bobbie Jo. She came from a poor family who lived in a shack out toward Tycoon Lake. About sixteen or seventeen, she dropped out of school to help with the family's expenses. Bobbie Jo soon became the center of attention, since most of the kitchen women were a lot older. The student workers played grab ass with her, and although they got a little out of hand at times, she enjoyed the attention.

She took a shine to the Nose, and because he hadn't been real successful with any campus babes, he strung her along, acting as though he was interested. You could easily see where this was going, basically the back seat of the bastard's car. But like I said before, he would do almost anything to impress his buddies.

He came up with a plan to entice Bobbie Jo into his room in the Mole Hole. After he had his way with her, he'd persuade her to service a few of his buddies. In other words, she was going to pull the train. Pettit had been bragging about how easy it was to persuade Bobbie Jo to do the dirty deed, and he told his buddies he could probably get her to do this crappy thing. And this, of course, was met with great enthusiasm by most of Pettit's pals.

One Saturday night, Pettit sneaked Bobbie Jo into the room he shared with Doug Gross. I'd been drinking in Hack Wack's room. When word got out what Pettit was doing, everyone flooded into the hallway.

Pettit was in the room with her for about a half hour. He came out, totally naked and sat down on Jack's bed in his room. He said she told him she might be pregnant, but she didn't seem too upset about it. And no one seemed too concerned about that either. After all, who wants to think about her being pregnant when there's a chance you could get in there and get an easy piece?

So since Jack had called seconds, he quickly went in to Bobbie Jo. As this whole thing transpired, I guess Pettit started thinking about the implications of her being pregnant and what was going down at the time. He was getting upset about all the guys being in on this thing, making noise and shit. What an ass! Like what the hell did he expect when he brought a girl on the floor?

Jack took about forty-five minutes. He came out and said he got two nuts off. He said he had to talk to her a lot, and she kept asking for Denny. So I started to think it was pretty obvious she didn't want to do this. Then I thought it didn't matter how stupid she was or how poor she was or how needy she was. This whole thing was fuckin' wrong.

But in Jack's mind, she was just a piece of white trash, so it didn't really matter if you forced yourself on her, right? He acted as though he really accomplished something. Like he was a goddamn Don Juan.

Next Ray Stokes went in, rubber in hand. He was out after about ten minutes. Apparently not a lot of romancing went on.

Bear was next. This would be his first time. What a show! He was walking around in just his shorts, big-ass belly hanging out, hair growing from the back of his neck down to the crack in his ass. The guys were giving him a rub down, like how they rub a boxer's shoulders before the fight begins.

Ballsie told him to just get a smell of it and don't expect too much, which was probably the same advice his dad gave him when he took him to a whorehouse in Huntington when he turned sixteen. So in went Bear as all the assholes were hooting and egging him on.

Out he came after about fifteen minutes. He threw down his dirty shorts and grunted, "I couldn't come." He said he went in, put his arm around her, and said, "Are you ready?" Like he was really concerned about her, the asshole. So fuckin' suave!

The next guy was Hank. When he came out, I happened to be walking by the door and saw her sitting on the edge of the bed... a pale, skinny girl, softly crying. All the black guys on the floor except for Al Matson were lined up to go in. When Malcolm went in, I could just imagine Bobbie Jo's state of mind at that point. Malcolm was about 6' 7".

The poor girl was doing this just for Denny, not for all these other guys. I guess she thought it would help cement things between her and him. So although there were more bastards still lined up, Pettit finally called a stop to things. He said he wanted to get her home, especially before her old man got the twelve-gauge out and came looking for her. Really pathetic.

So those guys who didn't get in on the action were pissed at Pettit. Obviously, the bastard did this whole thing because he thought it would make him look cool, but I guess it kind of backfired. As I was watching, it never entered my mind to jump on the train. I mean I was no big-time moralist, and I was probably about the most horny bastard within two miles of the damn campus. But going into that room, under those circumstances, would not have been any kind of turn-on for me. But in a way, I wasn't any better than Banana Nose or any of the other jerk offs. Because I didn't do anything about it. I didn't try to stop it. I didn't intervene. I just hovered around with the rest of them. So what could I have done... really? *[Motherfuckle!]*

Mavis Staples, fantastic earthy voice and big-time soul.

Abbie Comes to Save the Day

"Suffering is what brings us towards happiness."
–Bernard Malamud, The Natural

The English Department had a series of Contemporary Literature courses, one of which was The Existential Imagination taught by Bill Wyndham. Considered to be one of the better Rio profs, he projected a kind of wise-guy persona which most students liked.

He had degrees from Dartmouth and Vanderbilt. With that background, you'd expect him to walk around, smoking a damn pipe, wearing a jacket with elbow patches, and driving an MG TD, a Healey 3000, or a Triumph TR3. Instead, he drove a faded green Ford Fairlane Town Sedan.

Like most English profs, Wyndham would give reading assignments and expect rigorous discussion in the next class. He always did a good job at eliciting responses, but around the middle of the semester, class discussion deteriorated for whatever reason, and Wyndham got a little pissed.

One day, he came into the lecture room, put down his briefcase, and sat on the table in the front of the class. He didn't say a word. He didn't look upset, but this awkward silence went on for about five minutes. It seemed like a damn hour.

Finally, someone asked a question about the reading. Someone else attempted to answer. And for about fifteen or twenty minutes, the class conducted a spontaneous assessment of the assignment. All kinds of insights popped out of some of the most quiet doofusses. One thing led to another, and Wyndham jumped in. It turned out to be one of the best damn classes of the semester.

Another redeeming aspect of this guy was his young wife. She had short blonde hair, a cute little body and lots of short skirts. She was unpretentious and so not-into-how-neat she was. Skipping around campus, she said hello to everyone with a great smile. I remember thinking, *How do you find someone like her?*

People said I looked a lot like Wyndham, which didn't mean shit to me. I was a hell of a lot better looking. But one day, this nice looking freshmen girl came up to me and timidly asked, "Mr. Wyndham, I wasn't sure about the assignment you gave us this morning."

She caught me off guard, so I mumbled, "Sorry, but I'm not Wyndham."

She apologized and shrank away. But if I had been really cool, I should have said, "Well, my dear, walk with me to that bench and tell me what you don't understand. I'm sure I can straighten things out for you." Or I could have said, "Sorry, I'm not Wyndham, but I'm an English major, and I'd be glad to help you with your assignment." And then, of course, she'd fall head over heels in love with me, we'd have a couple kids, and we'd travel all over the damn world. We'd die when we were about 125 fuckin' years old.

But as usual, I couldn't think fast enough, so I missed an opportunity.

Anyway, I signed up for this existentialism course which included the study of several obscure, weird authors. To be honest, not many of them offered a very uplifting view of life. But at the time, I was impressionable, and it fed my appetite for going against the norm and fighting the damn system. You know, *putting it to the man.*

Wyndham started off by providing some of the basic elements of the philosophy. Things like "Man is alienated from an absurd and meaningless world," "Man must be alone, for in his very aloneness is his salvation," "Man's position in the world is unbearable," "His every act is meaningless in an absurd universe."

Cool stuff, eh?

We read Sartre's "The Room," which, among other things, defines liberty as total responsibility in total solitude. We read some Shakespeare, where King Lear finds it is the natural condition of man to be a fool. In Dostoyevsky's *Notes from Underground,* some guy is totally alienated from society. He says that a person cannot love because love is a manipulation of others and self which results in self-hate.

Speaking of weird, we read Kafka's short stories such as "Metamorphosis," where a man turns into a giant bug; and "The Penal Colony," where a torture device elaborately carves the name of the crime into the prisoner's back which results in a painful death; and

"The Hunger Artist," where a starving man displays himself in a caged wagon as a sideshow performer.

Then there was Hesse's *Steppenwolf*, where a man hovers around the outskirts of towns, observing people, kind of like an ofay watcher in Eldridge Cleaver's *Soul on Ice*. And there was Lagerkvist's *The Dwarf*, about a mean midget who symbolizes the evil nature in everyone. There was Kōbō Abe's *Woman in the Dunes* where a man and woman are thrown together in a deep pit of sand. And more selections from Camus, Conrad, Dumas, and Robbe-Grillet. It was pretty heavy shit, but Wyndham made it interesting.

I also had Wyndham for a Black Literature class, which included readings such as Cleaver's *Soul on Ice*, Ellison's *Invisible Man*, Wright's *Native Son*, Baldwin's *The Fire Next Time*, *The Autobiography of Malcolm X* with Alex Hailey, and poetry by Nikki Giovanni and LeRoi Jones, aka Amiri Baraka. These were all substantial works, and they provided a firm understanding, not only of black literature, but also of African-Americans. So for many reasons, I had much respect for Wyndham, both as a person and professor.

He took part in campus protests against military recruiters. I never participated. I didn't think it was a big deal. I figured if you wanted to sign up for the Army or Marines, that was your choice. No one was holding a gun to your head, except, of course, for the damn selective service. It didn't matter how many times you protested the draft, you weren't going to change that.

Another reason I didn't participate was I didn't care much for the type of students who protested. Not that they were bad people, but I felt they tended to be narcissistic. That's really judgmental, but many did the hippie thing with the hair and clothes. And again, they were free to do all that stuff, but consciously or unconsciously I think they did it for attention, and I never enjoyed being around people like that.

But then again, there were lots of non-hippie types who were pretty damn narcissistic. And I suppose some might have put me in that category, with how I didn't tie the laces on my Jack Purcells, and how I sewed an Alligator patch on my fake Baracuta jacket, and how I wore beat up Clarks desert boots without socks. But then, of course, I was a lot cooler than those damn long-hairs.

Anyway, Wyndham was part of that scene, and the administration didn't like his participation. They didn't like it when he wrote a letter to the college newspaper *Smoke Signals* about local cultural apathy and how the college should offer a course on Appalachian Studies. And apparently, some of the faculty resented him because of the things he taught—which was bullshit, because his curriculum had to be OK'd by the administration.

Maybe they didn't like him because he was too popular. Or because he had a hot wife. Or because he ate cupcakes at faculty meetings. In any case, he was eligible for tenure around this time, and the damn administration wasn't going to grant it, for whatever reason they could cook up.

The whole campus knew the administration was meeting on March 18 to determine Wyndham's status. Things were heating up. People were pissed. Everyone knew he was a good prof, and if there was one thing Rio needed, it was more good profs.

Then it was announced that Abbie Hoffman was coming to campus. That's right, Abbie fuckin' Hoffman, the leader of the Yippies—the Youth International Party—one of the leaders of the protests at the Democratic convention, and one of the Chicago Seven... or Eight or Nine, depending on how you were counting.

Some Rio students knew Hoffman would be at Antioch College around the same time Wyndham's hearing was scheduled to take place. Antioch, the ideal place to be if you leaned toward the liberal side. Hell, they had sanctioned mixed-gender nude swims in the college pool.

Somehow, these guys arranged to bring Hoffman to sleepy Rio the night before Wyndham's hearing. Word got out, so this was big-time shit for all concerned: blacks, whites, jocks, freaks, commuters, faculty... the whole shebang. And to add to the tension, there were rumors the FBI would be hiding in the bushes and doing all kinds of surveillance shit, because Abbie was considered so damn subversive and radical.

On the evening of March 17, Community Hall was packed to the gills. Someone hung up a big white banner with a peace symbol over the stage. There was more energy in this place than when Bevo was firing up seventy or eighty points a game back in the early '50s, and more energy than when that crazy Negro Dick Gregory showed up last Fall.

Clark, Zittle, and I sat toward the front. Jane Barakos and Prof. Giddens were in front of us, but that didn't bother me, because the whole damn place was shaking. Soon, in came the Young Democrats Club—all three of them—followed by Hoffman. Someone started an introduction, but Abbie interrupted and perched on the edge of the stage.

He looked like the typical wacked out anti-everything protester, strung out and tired, with frizzed out hair, t-shirt, jean-corduroys, and boots. But he fed off our energy and started with, "Here's a little movie about Pigs and Yippies. If you look closely, you can see people fucking in the weeds." So with that said, the lights dimmed, and everyone went crazy with anticipation as the grainy, black and white movie flickered on the small projection screen.

The film started with Mayor Richard Daley welcoming delegates to the Democratic Convention. Crowd scenes from silent films were interspersed with cops clubbing protesters as Phil Ochs sang, "I Ain't Marching No More." Next, Daley was telling cops to shoot to kill arsonists and looters. "Policemen aren't there to create disorder," he said. "They're there to preserve disorder."

Then some guy dressed like a TV ad man did a sales pitch for the Yippie Helmet, worn to protect your head during a police confrontation. Standing behind a table strewn with various vegetables and fruits, this guy took a police truncheon and hit an egg yolk, then a raw egg, then a tomato, a squash, an eggplant, and a pumpkin. Next, some crazy dude's head was sticking up through a hole in the table. As the truncheon came down, the next frame showed the bloodied head of an actual protester.

This was followed by more scenes of the carnage with police rioting at the Dems' Convention. Abbie was shown going crazy in front of a crowd of supporters, which led to a bunch of Yippies carrying a live pig down the street, the pig representing their presidential candidate. And finally, a gang of Yippies was dancing like the Rockettes to the tune of "You're a Grand Old Flag," except 'Flag' was changed to 'Pig.' It was pretty strong shit, and the progression of the film created a real frenzy in the audience.

When the lights came back on, the first thing Abbie said was that he liked Community Hall. He had been speaking on campuses over the last few months, and most of them had highly polished, fancy-schmancy assembly areas. He found them to be sterile. But this place, he said, had personality, despite it basically being just four walls with an old stage and a concrete floor. He was tired of debating all kinds of pseudo-metaphysical, theoretical shit, but here at Rio, we were dealing with a pragmatic confrontation of what was ethically correct for the student body, faculty, and the college.

In other words, he posed the question: *was one of the best profs on campus going to be retained and given tenure or was he going to be given the boot?* He read from the faculty handbook, "Nothing controversial that is irrelevant to the course material should be discussed in class." He added, "Students have the right to protest college policy as long as it does not impede the normal operation of the campus."

He went off on a tangent about freedom of expression and how the college was doing what General Motors does and what the government does in terms of suppressing expression and shit like that; in other words, administrative tyranny.

Then Ron Hansen, the former speech prof, got up on stage. He explained why he left Rio and how the place was always afraid of controversy and how their tight-assed mentality constricted the free flow of ideas and inhibited academic integrity.

One of the more intellectual students, Steve Ormanoski, spoke eloquently and emotionally about what Rio meant to him. He was thankful for his academic scholarship, but the place could be so much better if the administration opened their minds and recruited more professors like Hansen and Wyndham.

Then Abbie jumped off the stage and walked up the center aisle. "Okay, that's enough talking. So what are you going to do now? What are you going to do?" He was met with uncomfortable silence. So he said, "Why doesn't someone else get up there and tell how they feel?"

So Mike Taylor went to the front and said, "Tomorrow, while the Administrative Council is meeting, I'm going to take out a few books from the library and sit on the library steps and wait for the decision on Professor Wyndham."

Then good old Ballsie went up front and said in his usual folksy way that he thought something should be done about this whole thing and how he was going to take out some library books also. So he really got everyone, especially the jocks, thinking about things because although Larry was an open-minded guy, he was also respected by the hardheaded rednecks.

Next, Bill "Ripple" Davis jumped on stage. "I'm one of those drunken niggers you see around here. You gotta be drunk to go to this school." More shouting and laughing.

And finally, Big Bill Green, one of the most respected students and the college's best athlete, got up and said, "I'm gonna take out some books from the library tomorrow. I got a full-ride scholarship at stake here, but they can shove it if I can't have my dignity."

And that brought down the damn house. Big Bill rarely said anything controversial, but when he did, it was hard not to jump on the bandwagon.

The whole thing came to a close, and everyone streamed out of Community Hall with something to talk about and think about. Those who had come with the preconceived idea that Abbie Hoffman and his ilk were all pinko commies, left even more convinced that he should be locked up. But others left with a slightly changed view. Abbie had a likable side, which won over many of the doubters.

He was a little over the top, but I was swept up in his enthusiasm and his seemingly sincere belief to keep Bill Wyndham at Rio and to improve this place. He didn't have any irons in the fire here. He didn't have to come down here. And he wasn't condescending like some celebrities might have been.

So Clark, Zittle, and I stormed back to the dorm, knowing exactly what we were going to do the next day. I had always done things in a safe way. I never took risks. I never wanted to stir up things. But after that evening, there was no doubt I'd be on those damn library steps with Ballsie, Mike Taylor, and the rest of them.

The next day, just before band practice, I went over to the music room and told Old Man Krone I wouldn't be in band because I was going to the library to wait for the outcome of the Wyndham thing. I don't know why I bothered to tell him, but that's what the hell I did. He smiled condescendingly and basically said he didn't think that was a good idea, but it was my choice. So off I went across campus to the library and met up with Clark and Zittle.

There was a ton of people on the steps, inside the library, and on the pavement and street in front of the library. I didn't exactly like what I saw. There was too much organization going on. In my eyes, they were too flippant about the whole thing. People were singing, chanting, clapping, and mocking the administration. But despite the mixed feelings, I still wanted to be on those steps in support for Wyndham.

As I looked over the crowd, I saw Janie Barakos standing over there, smoking a cigarette. She looked like a damn angel. And seeing her there encouraged me to stay on those steps and take a stand.

Someone had set up a small P.A. speaker system. Osmolinski picked up the mic. Speaking from the heart, he talked about his grandfather who died from black lung the previous year. He promised to get an education and make his grandfather proud. He was grateful to Rio for his scholarship but had to support Wyndham because he was a good prof and didn't deserve to be dismissed.

Next, Hansen took the microphone and put a more intense spin on the situation. He added an urgency to those assembled. Everyone was waiting for a decision to come down from the paneled conference room on the second floor of the library. But it seemed like they were taking forever and intentionally stalling. That just added to the energy of the crowd as they grew louder and more raucous.

Around 12:45, the administration sent out Yale Gary, who was a student representative on the Administrative Counsel. Always cool and in control, he passed on the message that they wanted us to disperse. It wasn't like he winked his eye when he said it, but everyone felt he didn't have his heart in what he just said.

So we continued to hang around. At 1:15 Yale came out again, but this time with Dean Latuca. He told us the Counsel felt we were intimidating them and hindering the normal operation of the campus. They determined this was an illegal demonstration. We were supposed to disperse and get off the damn library steps.

But by that time, everyone was so wired up and pissed that no one was going to move. Sure, bastards like Nuxall had moved inside the library door and were observing from there, and probably a few others had shrunk away. But the majority of people—blacks, whites, jocks, or whatever—kept their asses on that same spot. About thirty minutes later, Dean Herman came down and said if we didn't leave, he would collect our IDs, and we would be expelled from campus by 12:00 noon the next day.

So Herman and a few administrative toadies started circulating through the crowd, collecting our cards. When he came to me, he hesitated, like he was hoping I'd leave. He knew I wasn't one of the rabble rousers, never caused any trouble.

But I didn't move, so he took my card. At that moment, even though I was pissed big time, I felt really good because I wasn't backing away and playing it safe. I didn't want Wyndham to get the royal shaft from this crappy administration just because they couldn't care less about education, integrity and truth.

So Clark and I gave up our cards. Zittle wimped out, which surprised me. I guessed he was maybe thinking he had to protect his ass in terms of keeping his parental support because of all the other screw-ups he'd been involved in over the last few years.

We later found out that none of the black students were suspended, even though their IDs had been collected. That didn't bother me at all. We all knew the administration didn't have the balls to deal with the NAACP, the Black Panthers, SNCC or the state and federal governments who had provided funding for several of the blacks. And of course the big thing was that the college was trying for accreditation and without the black kids, the school could kiss their chances goodbye.

After the IDs were collected, Hansen was accosted by the Gallipolis sheriff and Rio Grande's mayor/barber and was accused of trespassing. He refused to leave, so they threw him in the cop car. This got Osmolinski really agitated, saying Hansen was his guest and was allowed on campus, so he stood in front of the cruiser, arms folded. The sheriff gunned his engine, but Steve didn't move. Finally, the cop just grabbed him and threw him in the car with Hansen. Then, Kenny Clarke, one of the black students, jumped in front of the car, and the damn cop drove right into him, popping him up on the hood. By now, the crowd was screaming and banging on the cruiser, so the damn cop patched out as Kenny slid off the hood onto the pavement. *[Motherfuckle!]*

Chicago (Transit Authority), "Does Anybody Really Know What Time It Is?" Good horns.

Aftermath

"I Can't See Myself Leaving You," Aretha Now *album.*
Not only her passionate vocal but also her strong piano.

Osmolinski and Hansen were transported to the Gallipolis hoosegow for processing, or whatever the hell they do to commie pinko protesters. Back on campus, everyone just stood around in front of the library. But Clark and I walked back to the dorm. On the way, we passed Barakos, who smiled at me, patted me on the shoulder, and said, "Hey Mahl," which ordinarily would have been a boost. But at that point I was too much in the moment and kept walking.

Everything that had taken place over the last couple days started to sink in. Reality emerged like a bad headache, especially in terms of telling the parents and the big-ass chance of being expelled. Clark would lose his scholarship. And unless I could get into another damn school, I'd lose my 2-S deferment, and I'd find myself doing a hundred push-ups in a mud puddle in a damn boot camp down South.

I called home and did my best to sugarcoat the whole thing, but I also had to be honest because eventually the college would contact the parents. On the phone, Dad surprisingly seemed to accept my explanation, but I'm sure after we hung up, he sorted through what I had said.

Understandably, he would think about how I might've just trashed my college career. Then I had a flashback to when they had first dropped me off on campus. I thought about how Dad never went to college and how he had a lot more ability than I did, and how I'd let him down by doing all this noble-but-stupid protest stuff.

So after the elation of taking a stand and trusting my gut for a change, I started feeling down about myself and how I might have put my career in jeopardy. Clark called his parents and said they didn't take the news very well. His dad and brother Carl would be coming to campus to pick him up.

Since I had to get my butt off campus by noon the next day, I started packing. I had to find a place to stay since Spring break wouldn't start until Friday, when I would bum a ride back east with Zittle.

He came into the room and was all upset about flaking out at the demonstration. He said I could stay at the apartment above the Last Chance Carryout. But then I found out the Gallipolis newspaper was calling us rioters, vandals, and anarchists, so I quickly assumed it wasn't a good idea to be seen in town with those crazed rednecks cruising around looking for college students to beat up. Word got around that those who needed housing for the next few days could come over to Bill Wyndham's apartment and things would be discussed about who was going to stay where.

That evening, I walked over to the faculty housing and found Wyndham's place. When I got inside, I found a damn party going on. The Beatles' *White Album* was playing and people were eating chips and pizza. All kinds of sissy, hackneyed phrases were being thrown around like "power to the people" and "peace out, brother" and "put it to the man." They were all wound up about how we showed up the administration and how they mishandled things.

And yes, that might have all been true, but I didn't feel like sharing in the revolutionary spirit. Apparently, I must have looked like I was in pretty bad shape, because Prof. Giddens asked if I wanted him to call my dad and explain things. "Sure," I said, but in the back of my mind I thought, *Please don't make the situation any worse than it already is.*

I called Dad and explained that my sociology professor was going to talk to him. Giddens presented the case to Dad in his usually cool and measured manner. When I took back the phone, it seemed like things made sense to him. But I felt bad for Dad because Giddens had smoothed things over. So I pictured Dad telling Mom, and I could see the two of them going over all the possibilities at the kitchen table.

After the phone call, Wyndham said Hansen and Osmolinski had been fined and released after they had been roughed by the local gendarme. A lawyer from the American Civil Liberties Union had been contacted, and this guy was going to investigate the actions of the administration.

Then Wyndham said that even though the lawyer was with the ACLU, he still had to be paid, so there was a need to accumulate a defense fund, meaning a plea was going out to solicit money. So that was another thing to worry about... asking Dad for money because of my screw-up. Anyway, after awhile I started to get the craps of all these organizational details and just wanted to find out where I could stay until Friday.

Miles Parker had volunteered to keep someone for the next couple days. That sounded good to me because I always got along pretty well with him. I forgot he had gotten married recently, so he and his wife and little girl were living in the faculty and married student complex. When I got to their apartment, Miles and his wife said I could drop by any time and they'd be glad to put me up for a couple days.

I walked back to the dorm and wished Clark good luck with his dad. I found Zittle just before he was leaving for a night of drinking and told him to be sure to pick me up at Miles' place on Friday. He said he wouldn't forget. The next morning, I shaved off my mustache and tried to work on the damn education research paper but found it really hard to concentrate.

The next couple days were some of the longest of my life, up to that point. Miles and his wife were real good to me, sharing their meals and apartment. They had a nice place and made me feel comfortable in an awkward situation.

On Thursday, one of my fellow suspendees was driving on Rt. 35 and noticed a grass fire that seemed to be getting out of control on some guy's farm. He relayed this to the rest of my partners-in-crime who thought it might be good public relations for us to offer our help. So we piled into a couple cars and went to this guy's field.

When we got there, it didn't seem like much of a conflagration. I had seen grass fires before where a farmer would intentionally start one to keep weeds under control. That's what this reminded me of, although there was a fairly strong breeze which kicked up some substantial sparks. Anyway, we got out of the cars and asked the farmer if we could help. He looked at us kind of funny, noticing the long hair and our general appearance. He said, "Did you bring any shovels or hoes or rakes with you?"

And of course, we said, "No. We thought you'd have some."

So the old guy said, "My boy and I can take care of this. Now get off my property or I'll call the damn sheriff."

We got back in the cars, pissed off because the old guy was so ungrateful. But maybe someone should have thought about the practicality of extinguishing a fire instead of doing it just so we'd look good in the eyes of the public.

On Friday, I kept waiting for Zittle to pick me up. But of course, that didn't seem to be happening, so I called the phone in the Mole Hole and got someone to track down Dirk. Finally, he came to the phone and said he was on his way. He just had to say goodbye to Elaine. So after what seemed like a damn hour, he showed up in his green, big-finned Plymouth, and we were on our way.

On these rides back to PA, he usually popped some uppers to keep awake which made him talk even more than usual. On a previous trip, he wanted me to drive so he could drink beer. But he couldn't find a bottle opener (this was before twist-top bottle caps), so he tried to open a bottle on the door of the glove compartment. When that didn't work, he opened the car door on the passenger side and started banging the bottle cap on the edge of the door frame. When it finally opened, beer sprayed all over the car's interior while I was driving sixty-five miles an hour through a blinding snow squall.

Dirk and I did the long-ass drive to the Harrisburg exit of the PA turnpike. I jumped out, ran through the toll booth area, and met up with my dad. Dirk made a U-turn and went north to Mount Carbon, which was close to Pottsville where the Molly Maguires were executed and where the country's longest working brewery still operated—good old Yuengling. Dad and I went twenty miles south to old York, home of barbells, Peppermint Patties, and race riots.

As we drove, the inevitable subject came up. Dad and I had about thirty minutes to hash over my predicament. To his credit, he was surprisingly understanding. I guess if I had been protesting the war or if I had tried to burn down a campus building or if I had put LSD in the campus water supply, he would have been more upset.

But he seemed to understand the thing about Wyndham, the stupidity of the administration, and my good intentions to improve the school. So I admitted I could have chosen another way to express myself, and I apologized for all the hassle and consternation I was putting him and Mom through. Then, after a few minutes, I passed out for the remainder of the trip home. *[Motherfuckle!]*

Bob Dylan, "Like a Rolling Stone...How does it feel?"
Electric guitar at Newport Folk Festival.

After Abbie

LBJ won't seek re-election.

Spring Break 1969 saw thousands of college students driving to Daytona Beach for all kinds of frolicsome activities. At least, that's what I read in the papers. Actually, I never really knew anyone who did that. Hell, I never knew anyone who frolicked anywhere. Florida was a long-ass drive, and even if I had friends who wanted to do that, I don't think I could have found the energy. The college had sent a telegram to the parents:

MR AND MRS RUSSELL DICKINGER:

THIS IS TO NOTIFY YOU THAT YOUR SON OR DAUGHTER HAS BEEN SUSPENDED FROM RIO GRANDE COLLEGE AS OF THIS DATE MARCH 18, 1969. YOUR SON OR DAUGHTER WAS PARTICIPATING IN AN ILLEGAL DEMONSTRATION AND BEFORE ACTION WAS TAKEN YOUR SON OR DAUGHTER WAS GIVEN THE OPPORTUNITY TO LEAVE THE DEMONSTRATION. YOUR SON OR DAUGHTER REFUSED TO DO SO AND CONSEQUENTLY YOUR SON OR DAUGHTER HAS BEEN SUSPENDED. THE HEARING FOR THE SUSPENSION OF YOUR SON OR DAUGHTER BEFORE THE EXECUTIVE COMMITTEE OF THE BOARD OF TRUSTEES WILL BE HELD AT 6:30 PM APRIL 10, 1969 AT THE HOLIDAY INN IN CHILLICOTHE OHIO

DR A R Svenson, PRES
RIO GRANDE COLLEGE

A few days later, they sent certified letters, further clarifying the charges and procedures for the hearings. Each suspendee had to scrounge up two witnesses who had observed them during the demonstration. A written statement, not exceeding 300 words, had to be prepared concerning the details of their participation in the demonstration. And on and on, with all kinds of legalese shit.

And guess what? After all this threatening language, most of it was thrown out the damn window. Students and parents had to trundle themselves to the Chillicothe Holiday Inn, fifty miles north of Rio Grande. The damn board of trustees addressed the group and basically said we were all bad boys and girls and if we did this again, our asses would be grass. Or, in the words of the trustees' lawyer:

> "The fact that you have been disciplined as stated does not preclude charges being filed against any one or more of you whose conduct may have been or whose conduct may in the future be considered by the Administration as sufficiently detrimental to the institution and of such nature that they may believe you are not the person or persons that the Rio Grande College Corporation under the laws of the State of Ohio, through its administrative structure, wishes to have on its campus."

Before the hearing was concluded, one of the trustees asked if any student wished to make a statement. Ron Strebig stood up and addressed the old farts.

"Thank you for giving me the opportunity to express myself. First, I want to say that I greatly respect the members of the board of trustees for your efforts to support and develop the institution of Rio Grande College. Before coming to Rio Grande, I served two years in the United States Army, and after I was honorably discharged, I was happy to find that I had been accepted as a student.

"Since being at Rio, I have found the college to be suitable to my academic needs, but I also believe it could be more effective by recruiting even better professors. That was why I participated in the demonstration because I believed Professor William Wyndham was one of the best professors on campus. He has greatly enhanced my ability to interpret serious literary selections, a skill that also enhanced my understanding of myself and the world around me."

After Ron presented in such a lucid and respectful manner, the president of the board of trustees bluntly said, "Well boy, and yes, that's what you are, a boy... you have an awful lot to learn about how the real world works. Be seated."

And that was it. We were reinstated—but had to behave ourselves. The bastards!

[Motherfuckle!]

Cannonball Adderley, alto sax, industrial-strength soul,
"Mercy, Mercy, Mercy," played on the Kind of Blue *album.*

Sherry Cherry and Tom Shelley

"The '60s aren't over; they won't be over until the Fat Lady gets high."
–Ken Kesey

After all the fear and loathing settled down on campus, things eventually got back to normal. However, relationships evolved into an "us or them" basis—those who had been part of the Wyndham thing and those who hadn't. I still got along okay with the Mole Hole crowd, but now I was thrown into the rebel category. A few freshmen like Tom Shelley and John Borsa latched on to me as a cool guy, I guess. I put up with them for various reasons, one of which was that Shelley had a Dodge Dart, which was good for beer runs.

Every Spring there was a May Day celebration, similar to the Homecoming stuff in the Fall. Greeks and Independents had all kinds of frolicsome activities on campus, including a dance in the new gym.

Shelley hooked up with some babe who supposedly liked to put out, and he got me a date with this girl's friend, Sherry Cherry. I'm not shitting you. That was her name. The date was a casual thing. We went to the Kanauga Drive-In just north of Gallipolis on Rt. 7, and we brought along some sure-fire coitus-inducing booze... cherry vodka and screwdriver, all pre-mixed and ready to go.

"Girls like the taste, and they drink it real fast," exclaimed the wide-eyed face of eighteen-year-old Thomas Shelley.

We went to the drive-in, which was showing *The Green Berets*, a movie that Vietnam vets totally trashed and laughed at because it was a John Wayne flick which had no semblance of reality. But Shelley and I were not there to see the movie.

Sounds terrible, I know. These gals were over eighteen, and I assumed they had done the "drinking at the drive-in" thing before. Sure enough, the bottles of cherry vodka and screwdriver emptied in a matter of minutes. So after a bunch of giggling and gabbing, we left the drive-in and started driving back to Rio.

On the way, I started making out with good old Sherry Cherry in the backseat. She had some big-time poofy hair going on, and she was a little chunky. But the cherry vodka had apparently touched her hidden libido because when we started kissing, she really latched on to me.

We kissed until my lips hurt. I figured maybe she wanted some other stimulation, so I started groping. Eventually, I got my hand under her shirt, undid her bra, and got some pretty good feels, if you know what I mean. She seemed to be okay with all that... so my hand went south of the border, and I started rubbing between her legs. But that was as far as I got. I could accept that. But it wasn't for any lack of trying.

Anyway, before we got back to campus, Tom decided we should go out to Filthy Frank's to get some beer. This Frank guy lived in a shack with his wife and four little kids out at Tycoon Lake. He sold live bait, beer, Slim Jims, pork rinds and other nasty stuff. Apparently at one time he attempted to build some kind of structure but ran out of money, because there was an unfinished foundation beside the shack. This served as a sty for Frank's hogs, whose aroma added to the rustic ambiance.

When we arrived, Shelley and his girl went into the shack to get the beer. While they were doing that, I started going after Sherry again. Everything seemed to be progressing well, when something must have snapped. She started sobbing.

That brought things to a quick halt. She didn't offer an explanation. But on the way back to campus, something was said up in the front seat about her having had an abortion. She didn't impress me as the kind of girl who would get pregnant. But then again, who was I to know who might get pregnant?

When we got back to campus, Shelley pulled into the parking lot beside the new gymnasium, presumably with the idea of going into the dance. At that point, I'd had enough of Shelley, his girl, and good old Sherry. I didn't feel like making the scene, so I jumped ship and scampered back to the Mole Hole into the Stokes twins' room to watch some TV.

Pretty damn pathetic. Over the next week or so, I saw Sherry in the cafe or other places on campus, but we didn't make much eye contact. In fact, I'm not even sure she recognized me, since the only other time I had been around her was in the dark. *[Motherfuckle!]*

Cream: Clapton, Baker, and Bruce, lots of music from those three.
"Crossroads," "Badge," "Spoonful"

Clark Gets Married

Bobby Kennedy killed, June 6, 1968.
106 GIs killed on that same day in Nam.

In my little world, things were going okay for a change. I interacted with a female for more than five minutes. My classes were working out, and I was kind of looking forward to student teaching next semester. But just as I was getting back into the routine, Clark dropped a bombshell.

He and Dianna decided to get married. By the end of Spring semester, she would be finished with her two-year business school, so they thought this would be a good time to tie the knot. I guess they had gotten to the point in their intimacy where it just made sense to be together.

Their plan was to find an apartment close to Rio. Dianna would get a job, and Clark would finish his last two years. They set the date for August 16, and Clark asked me to be his best man. I was cool with that, but my main problem, besides losing a good roommate, was that I'd be without a damn record player in the dorm room.

During the summer, I slaved away at the casket factory for a buck-sixty an hour. I did all kinds of jobs, from throwing rough boards into the big planer to polishing the finished caskets at the end of the line.

The factory was located in downtown York, which in 1969 was pretty damn hot, racially speaking. Tensions between the white and black populations had been rising. Local blacks continually asked for a police review board that would maybe create better treatment of the blacks, who were frequently the targets of out-and-out police brutality.

But the various mayors and city councils always rejected such pleas. This stance of the local government directly or indirectly contributed to an increase in white gangs, notably the Newberry Street Boys, the Girarders, The Swampers, and the Yorklyn Boys, all of whom made regular sorties into black neighborhoods, where they were sure to find a West Side Story kind of fight. Understandably, the black kids became more and more strident. Several racist cops added to the tensions by encouraging the white gangs.

Many of these same black and white kids had played together so well at the YMCA ten years earlier. Now they were pitched together in all kinds of ugly conflicts. In an attempted show of strength, the city of York placed an armored vehicle on the streets and drove it through the already agitated black section of town. This only stirred up more resentment.

One night, unknown assailants fired shots at this big-ass vehicle, and a bullet somehow pierced the metal armor, hitting rookie police officer Henry Schaad, who died a few days later. This inflamed local rednecks, who, with the encouragement of several cops, decided some kind of armed response had to take place. They couldn't help themselves. It was just the way they were raised.

So on the evening of July 21, while Neil Armstrong was taking one small step for man on the moon, a large assemblage of white assholes ambushed a carload of black people who were visiting York, resulting in the death of one of the car's passengers. Instead of taking one small step into a bright future, York quickly sank into an abyss of violence, not unlike other insane examples such as the War of the Roses, the Hatfields and McCoys, the Capulets and Montagues, the Crusaders and Muslims, the Molly Maguires and the coal industry, and on and on and on. All hell broke loose. The governor declared a state of emergency and called up the National Guard.

Throughout this whole period, I worked the night shift just a block or two away. While working on the supply end of the big wood planer, my coworkers and I kept thinking we could be firebombed at any minute, since all the doors and windows were wide open because it was so damn hot. Our work station was directly adjacent to a back alley, just the place from where a Molotov cocktail could easily be tossed.

At that time, with all this racial shit going on, I wasn't very proud to be a Yorker. So going to Ohio for a wedding, although not my favorite kind of activity, was a welcome relief. A couple weeks before the big event, I went downtown to Gregory's, my dad's favorite clothing store, and got measured for a tux. I sent the measurements to Clark so he could pick up my rental out there.

So as thousands of rock fans were piling onto the grounds of Max Yasgur's farm for the Woodstock blast, I took off on my first plane ride, Harrisburg to Youngstown, Ohio. I was wearing my spiffy summer olive-green poplin suit, cordovan Bass Weejuns, a Gant button-down tattersall shirt, and a black-with-brown striped rep tie. I'm not sure why I got so dressed up. I guess it was the accustomed thing back then.

As I boarded the plane, I passed one of the stewardesses, who all of a sudden started gushing over me as though I were a long lost friend or something. It was way beyond the usual "Hello, have a nice flight" thing. She looked like she was only about nineteen or twenty years old. So of course, I immediately fell in love.

As she showed me to my seat, I looked back, projecting a casually cool look, when I tripped over my damn Weejuns and fell face-first against the armrest of the seat, pushing my glasses askew on my forehead. So much for the love affair.

When I finally got settled, I noticed my seat was in a semi-reclining position. This was fine throughout the flight, until we entered the landing zone, and we were instructed to put all seats in the upright position. I tried everything, but nothing worked to pull up the damn seat.

So on the approach to the landing strip, I leaned forward so it looked like I was in the right position, which added to my already nervous feeling about flying. By the time the plane landed, I was soaked in sweat, and my back was in a deep muscle spasm. As I limped out the door, my face colorless and streaked with sweat, I passed that damn stewardess, who just kind of smirked at me.

Clark picked me up, and we drove to his hometown of Southington, a few miles west of Youngstown. We got to the Buck homestead, a modest three-bedroom brick two-story, built after the war, and I was introduced to the clan.

Clark's mom and dad were originally from West Virginia. His dad was a veteran of the European theater, where he captured the Nazi flag that Clark had hung in the dorm room. He reminded me of Clark, friendly but low key with an intelligent air about him. His mom was outgoing and loud, but in a nice way. After the war, Clark's dad got a factory job in the area. He and Clark's mom quickly got married and produced Clark's older brother Carl, the veterinary student at OSU. Throughout the whole weekend, I kept thinking Carl should have been the best man instead of me.

There were two more Buck boys. Larry was kind of a wild ass, favoring his mom's personality. And Wayne, the youngest, just kind of melted into a big overstuffed chair in the living room, where he apparently spent most of his time, reading books and eating homemade popcorn out of a large wash basin.

I quickly got acquainted with the family over a meat-and-potatoes dinner. Then it was time for the wedding rehearsal. Off we went to Southington Christian, a typical small town church with the usual altar, pulpit, and pews.

Dianna had selected three maids of honor: Maraleena Heck, Janet Stanszkolski, and her sister Janey. Larry and Carl were going to do the usher thing. Mrs. Winifred Brickman was on the organ, and the majordomo was the Reverend Marian Bonert. She was a real take-charge type and a stickler for detail. As a result, she kept most of the wedding party on edge about doing the right thing at the right time.

This, in addition to the thick humidity in the non-air-conditioned church, caused one of the maids of honor, Maraleena, to pass out. She went down like a rock, and somehow her legs ended up in a spread eagle position above her head. The poor girl was totally exposed: nylon stockings, garter belt, panties, the whole package. Someone helped her to a chair, where they pushed her head between her legs, which brought enough blood to her brain to bring her back to an embarrassed consciousness.

Pastor Bonert was pissed because someone had the nerve to disrupt this important rehearsal, so she jumped right back into instructing how things had to work at the big show. But by this time, most of the participants just wanted to get the hell out of the place and let poor Maraleena recover some semblance of composure and self-respect. So after a few more agonizing minutes of instruction about how to place a ring on a finger and how to say "I Do" and how to lift a veil and kiss the bride, everyone took off.

I assumed a bachelor party was in the offing, hopefully with some sleazy entertainment like a dancing girl or stag flick. But that wasn't in the cards. I guessed Clark's teetotaling parents might've gotten to him about getting drunk the night before. So it was just Clark and I who went out on his last night of freedom. And knowing Clark, that's probably all he wanted to do anyway.

He took me to a local bar where he could get regular beer, despite being under twenty-one. Apparently, the owner did some kind of black market shit, because he had a lot of items like record albums, big candy bars, bottles of cologne, glitzy jewelry, and other "hot" stuff behind the bar. It wasn't like he was hiding it or anything. And it was all really cheap. Clark took a gander at the records and bought a Simon and Garfunkel album, *Parsley, Sage, Rosemary, and Thyme,* which seemed a little tame for him who was into loud stuff like Cream and the Doors. I guess he thought Dianna would like it. Anyway, we had a decent time, drinking and talking.

The next day, I tried on the rental tux. I didn't exactly look like Frank Sinatra, and it wasn't real comfortable, but what the hell. The ceremony started at 1:00 P.M., and everyone arrived all spiffed up, including the Reverend Bonert who was sporting one of those old-lady hats with a few fake flowers bouncing around on top.

Clark, Carl, Larry, and I took our places to the left of the dapper pastor. Winifred struck up the wedding march on the organ, and in came the maids of honor, including Maraleena who seemed to have recovered. Before she passed out, I had seriously considered making some time with her. But after seeing her exposed nether regions, I had trouble making eye contact.

Then came the star of the show, Miss Dianna Eileen Arbogast. She was a natural beauty, with a great complexion and long auburn hair, and she couldn't hold back a big smile as she walked up the aisle on her dad's arm.

Everything went without a hitch, no surprises, no passing out. Mr. and Mrs. Clark Buck strutted up the aisle to the back of the church. Pictures were taken, and then everyone filed downstairs to the basement for the reception.

For me, this was rather excruciating, since I didn't know anyone. I was amused by Clark's brother Larry, who talked continually and played with the wedding favors. I kept thinking of a frosty mug of Stroh's, but that, of course, didn't happen.

I gave a brief, generic toast to Clark, nothing creative or profound. I could have said something about the great fun we had searching for porn in Columbus or getting suspended for being in an illegal demonstration, but I didn't think that would go over real well.

Clark and Dianna went to some place in West Virginia for a honeymoon. The next day Carl and Larry took me to the airport, with Larry still wearing his rented tux. It was Sunday and the tux couldn't be returned until Monday, so he wanted to get as much use out of the uncomfortable suit as possible.

Sergio Mendes and Brazil 66, fresh sound from Brazil.
"Mas Que Nada," good song.

Swimming in the Shower Room

1969, first strain of the AIDS virus migrates to the U.S. via Haiti.

In early May, the temperature was unseasonably hot, like upper-eighties. Apparently, there was some maintenance policy that the air conditioning in the dorms couldn't be turned on until a later, specified date.

Harris, Gross, and I came back from the Willow, and as soon as we got inside the dorm, we just about fell over from the stifling heat. All the windows were open, but there wasn't any air moving. Mike groaned something about how great it would be to jump into a swimming pool. Then Doug said, "We could make our own pool." And sure enough, that's what the hell we did.

The shower room had ten shower heads along three of the walls. The fourth wall had a frosted sliding window. We put wet towels over the two drains. Someone got a piece of three-quarter inch plywood from the construction site behind the dorm and propped it against the opening of the shower room with a chair. More wet towels were put around the plywood to keep the water inside the room. All the showers were turned on, full blast. We went to bed as the water slowly rose.

By the time we got up in the morning, the water had risen to about four feet, and guys were diving over the plywood and off the ledge of the window. Others were just floating around in the cool water, thanks to good old Rio ingenuity.

Jefferson Airplane, Surrealistic Pillow, *great album.*
Jorma Kaukonen, great guitar.

Wildwood, Summer of '69

The Greenwich Village Stonewall Riots
evolved into the Gay Rights Movement.

It took four hours to get to Stone Harbor in South Jersey. The family had been doing this for a long time. Awkward at my age to vacation with the folks, but I needed to get away from the casket factory for a few days. They did their best to stay out of my way. But Stone Harbor was a family town, so there was little chance of bumping into any loose women like back at the Blue Willow.

The evening before we returned home, I told them I was going to Wildwood to see my buddy Zittle. Surprisingly, my older sister let me drive her Mustang. Thinking back, I can't believe she did that. I'd never let a schmuck like me take my car. Anyway, off I went in the dark blue '66 Mustang hardtop.

I took the coastal road south through Cape May and Wildwood Crest to the ultimate shore town of debauchery... Wildwood, New Jersey. I parked on a side street close to where Zittle said his ice cream job was located and started walking the boardwalk, looking for a Twin Kiss stand. I had to fight my way through the noisy crowd, many of whom were probably from South Philly, North Jersey, and surrounding areas. After passing all kinds of t-shirt stands, cheesesteak stands, and saltwater taffy stands, I found the ice cream place. It had two flavors—vanilla and chocolate, served separately or swirled together—thus the name Twin Kiss.

There was Dirk, his hands in the cash register, stuffing his pockets with tens and twenties. He said the boss didn't count the money, so it was easy to get away with the sticky-fingers thing. This was his day off. He'd been making out with the cute little Italian he worked with, screwing around with his boss' wife, and, when things got a little slow, drinking high balls in the back room. I know that sounds like some hefty bullshitting, but knowing Zittle, there was probably more than a little validity to all that.

He was surprised but glad to see me. We took a walk down the boardwalk to meet his younger brother Gregg, who was working a bingo club. This place catered to widows, divorcees, and old maids. With a deep, dramatic voice, he called out the numbers. I guess the old ladies liked this. Anyway, Dirk walked directly up to him, disrupting the bingo game, and introduced me over the microphone for the whole damn place to hear.

"Hey Bud, this is Mahl. We're gonna get fuckin' wasted tonight."

Gregg said, "Cool... under the B, 14."

So the two of us walked out with Dirk carrying a gallon of Seagram's over his shoulder. We headed down the boardwalk to see Griff Brady, Dirk's old buddy back at Rio. Griff had been looking forward to a summer of working at the shore as opposed to cleaning smoke stacks in Nitro, West Virginia. However, he was caught stealing and ended up with a crappy carnival job, putting kids on and off a little Ferris wheel.

He had turned into a real slob, worse than at Rio. But what really hurt was that he flunked out and had been quickly re-classified by the selective service to 1-A. He received his draft notice, passed his physical, and was soon being shipped out to some damn boot camp. In the meantime, he was rapidly destroying himself with pills, booze, bad food, and unsanitary living.

So Dirk and I broke away, jumped in the Mustang, and drove to their motel, which happened to be the third place they'd rented that summer, apparently having been kicked out of the previous two. What a pig sty! Four screw-offs living in a two-and-a-half room unit.

It seemed this shore-thing wasn't anywhere near as great as Zittle had boasted. Soiled clothes on the floor, no sheets on mattresses, food-caked dishes stacked in the sink, and everywhere, all kinds of stains... stains I really didn't want to identify. So Dirk sniffed a couple shirts, found one that was the least objectionable, and we were in business.

Then he woke up Jack Grogan, another guy from Rio, and the three of us and the gallon of whiskey jumped into Dirk's green Plymouth. We were off to some broads' apartment a few blocks away. Back at school, I never knew if Jack was a full time student or just visiting. He wasn't around much. Anyway, when he was there, he was usually with some nice looking gal.

At the girls' apartment, there were three or four babes who looked interesting. They were from Philly and seemed glad to see us. Dirk,

Jack, and I pulled up chairs at the kitchen table, and the Seagram's was cracked. This was a straight-no-chaser night. Dirk filled our glasses as though we were drinking iced tea.

It didn't take long until we were all pretty much in the bag. Jack slid off with one of the nicer looking gals. Dirk said he didn't feel like batting the shit with any broad, so the two of us sat there and talked about things at Rio, like who flunked out, who dropped out, or who got knocked up, stuff like that. I guess he got this info from Elaine through phone calls and letters from Canal Winchester, her hometown.

The evening progressed with the girls coming in and out of the room at various times, but it became obvious that nothing of substance was going to happen. Then, around 2:00 A.M., in came Chessy. Or it might have been Jessy, but I seem to think it was Chessy. Who knows? I was kind of smashed by that time. She was coming back from her waitress job. I guessed she was Italian, but she might have had some Jewish in her. For all I knew, she might have been Outer Mongolian. It really didn't matter, because she carried herself real well, which I always found to be a turn-on.

She wasn't flighty like the others. She was wearing a yellow blouse so tight you could see her chest between the buttons. It was pretty damn obvious she wasn't wearing a bra because her nips were protruding. Very impressive. Things were starting to look up for this horny bastard from the casket factory. She went into the bedroom to change and came out wearing a green t-shirt, and again, no bra. And to top off her ensemble, she was wearing black panties. That was it... t-shirt and panties. Damn! So all of a sudden, Zittle's life at the shore was looking pretty damn good.

She sat down with Dirk and me and batted the breeze a little, all the while effecting a smug but not obnoxious attitude. Compared to the other girls, it was refreshing to talk with someone like her. Of course, since I was pretty much in the bag, I was quickly impressed with any girl who might look at me cross-eyed. Unfortunately, she had just put in twelve straight hours of waiting on tables and wanted to go to bed.

So into the bedroom she went, and I just kind of followed. I sat on the bed as she crawled in. In the background, I thought I heard Dirk and Jack leave, but by this time I was fixated on the female beside me. After all, this kind of situation just didn't happen in my world, so I thought I should take advantage of things. I started to put the make on, but I was in the awkward mode, and my mouth wasn't working real well. Of course, I thought I was being really suave. I started talking, mostly about sociological shit, and despite my condition, she seemed to be somewhat interested.

"So you know... an organization is on the decline when they stop seeking their goals and start worrying about self-preservation," I said with a slight but earnest elitist twang.

She just looked at me with a blank stare.

Then I started dropping some snobbishly academic shit about books I'd been reading. "I think Hesse is spot-on about how *Steppenwolf* reflects today's society. Vonnegut's *Cat's Cradle* defines 'karass' as the crowd of people we fall into in our life, and I'm thinking that you, Chessy, are part of *my* karass and I'm part of *your* karass, and I think that's really important, and we should come to terms about what part we play in *our* karass, and maybe this is a really good time to investigate that. What do you say... huh?"

She matter-of-factly interrupted with, "I'm majoring in art at Temple in Philly."

"Well hell, that's a fuckin' coincidence," I said. "My uncle is the damn president of Temple."

She laughed and punched my shoulder saying, "Yeah, right, you bastard. By the way, what's your name?"

"My name? Buddy Blavat."

"You mean like Blavat as in Jerry Blavat, the Philly DJ?"

"That bastard. He's my first cousin. I taught him how to dance, and he stole all my moves."

"You're such a fuckin bullshitter."

As things progressed, she said she preferred grass to alcohol, which was cool with me. But I was like "fucking this and fucking that," and I'm sure I wasn't being real coherent.

Somehow, I thought she was kind of warming up to me, so I slowly started grabbing for body parts. She didn't seem to mind. And then, somewhere along the line, she lit up some weed and gave me a toke or two. But my babbling led me to say something like, "I'm really fuckin' horny. What do you think about making out a little?"

The next thing I remember is the blonde coming in and saying that Dirk and Jack were leaving. So I put on my sandals and glasses, and took off down the steps, trying to catch them. But the bastards were gone.

What I should have done was jump back in bed with Chessy, but instead I started walking, trying to find Zittle's place where I had parked Sue's Mustang. So my night of possible romantic bliss came to a screeching halt: no phone number, no address, no nooky.

So I was walking and walking and couldn't find the damn place. I saw other bastards seemingly doing what I was doing, staggering around, trying to find their damn cars. I asked this one guy, who was saying good night to his girl, if he could help. I apologized for ruining the mood, but he was real good about it. I told him I thought the motel had "Lake" in the name. He stuck his head in the nearby phone booth to look in the phone book, and there wasn't one damn "Lake" motel in Wildwood.

I thanked the guy and started walking again. By now, my kidneys were telling me I had to piss. So out of necessity, I took a leak on the side of a house. I had been walking for what seemed like a long damn time, thinking it had to be about 6:00 A.M., but it was still dark. I was so tired I sat on a side porch and tried to sleep, but a damn mosquito truck came by, spraying some kind of lethal bug killer all over me, which almost made me throw up.

I got my sorry ass up and started walking, which by now had created blisters from my damn sandals. I decided to get back on the boardwalk to retrace my steps and almost got run over by a bunch of old people and kids riding bikes. So I got off the boardwalk and got some coffee at a corner restaurant, which actually helped. But I was getting desperate, so I flagged down a passing cruiser, told the two cops I was looking for a dark blue Mustang, and they let me in for a ride.

It was a black guy and a white driver. The black dude was cool about things, but the white bastard started lecturing me about drinking and shit. Along the way, they picked up a girl, who was apparently kind of bombed like me and was also looking for her car. She was real cute—nice eyes, short black hair. She said she was from West Virginia, which immediately led me to think of her as a damn hillbilly.

But she attended Kenyon College in Ohio, which was a pretty good private school. Somehow, despite my inebriation, I remembered that John Crowe Ranson, the poet, had gone to Kenyon or maybe he taught there, so I suavely laid that spicy info on her. She just laughed, probably never having heard of the old guy. So I thought, *Damn, this is my kind of girl.* But it wasn't exactly the best atmosphere to get anything going at this point. It's kind of hard to put the moves on a girl in the back of a damn cop car. And, of course, I forgot to get a phone number or address.

Somehow, the cops found Zittle's motel, and there was Sue's Mustang, with all four tires still on and no noticeable scratches or dents. I briefly thought about going in to see Zittle, but I knew I had to get back to Stone Harbor. I drove up the coastal road, and understandably, the folks were really pissed because they wanted to leave a lot sooner. I went home with Sue in the Mustang, but she did the driving and didn't say a whole lot of anything for the next four hours, which was fine with me because I had a hammering headache. ***[Motherfuckle!]***

Archie Bell and the Drells, "Tighten Up." Performed at halftime in Astrodome at UCLA/Houston epic basketball game. Archie Bell was wounded in Vietnam.

Hair and Haight, August '69

Manson and the gang murder eight, including Sharon Tate.

Dad and his boss Dietz Keller went to a casket convention in San Francisco. The National Casket Manufacturers Association sponsored this big event which encompassed every aspect of the industry: wooden caskets, metal caskets, plastic caskets, interiors of caskets, spring mattresses, feather mattresses, embroidered pillows, and on and on and on. Dad liked to joke, "It's a dying business," "We work on the layaway plan," "Har, har."

These conventions were usually a chance for Dad to let his hair down, to let loose. At the perfunctory cocktail parties, he was the one to wear the lamp shade on his head and dance on the bar. Somehow, Mom found out about this disgusting behavior and started to accompany him on later convention trips. But this time, when he came home from San Fran, we all asked, "How was the trip, Dad?"

He said, "San Francisco is a beautiful town. We went to Fisherman's Wharf, rode the cable cars, saw Alcatraz in the Bay, and rode over the Golden Gate Bridge. Good stuff. But then we took a tour bus through some disgusting part of town. It was full of pan handlers, dope addicts, and filthy weirdos. I couldn't believe what I was seeing."

I suppose Dad saw Haight-Ashbury from a different perspective than I would have.

He went on, "So then one evening, we decided to go to a theater to see a show. Someone at the convention gave us free tickets. It was supposed to be a musical. I was thinking it might be something like *My Fair Lady* or *The Sound of Music*. But, instead, it had really loud music, and the actors came off the stage and jumped around in the audience. And at one point, some of them took off their clothes. And after a few minutes of that crap, Dietz and I got the hell out of there. It was terrible."

So Dad had a chance to see *Hair* for free and left before it was over. *[Motherfuckle!]*

John Lee Hooker, bluesman, "Bang, Bang, Bang, Bang,"
"One Bourbon, One Scotch, and One Beer"

Blind Date

The 6000th U.S. plane is shot down in Nam, November 1969.

Jim "Hack Wack" Nuxall and I had a kind of strained relationship, especially after Clark left and got married. I humored him because he had a TV in his room, allowing me to watch ballgames and other shows.

If we needed ice for booze, I was the one to go to the student center and tell the ladies in the grill that my friend had a twisted ankle and needed ice to keep down the swelling. That excuse worked two or three times, but then I had to change it to another injury because I was afraid they might catch on. So basically, we put up with each other as a matter of convenience.

Hacky had a girlfriend back home. They had attended the same parochial school and church camp. He kept talking about how classy and smart she was. He'd call her every week at exactly the same time on Saturday night, and because the pay phone in the Mole Hole was right outside Room 12, I had to listen to the whole shitty conversation.

For some reason, he never went home to see her except on holidays. I found that hard to understand, because he always said how great she was and how much he missed her. It wouldn't have been real hard to find a ride back to Cleveland, but he never took off from school to see her.

However, one time around the beginning of November, the two of them cooked up a scheme for her to come to Rio. Being a good, upstanding Catholic gal, she had to come with a damn chaperone. So they decided she would bring one of her girlfriends, and I would be the designated date for the other girl. When Hack Wack asked me, I had just put down three or four beers, and without giving it much thought, I said I'd go along with the whole thing.

But a few days before the big event, I started thinking about this blind date arrangement. I didn't feel real good about it. First, I'd have to put up with all of Hack Wack's bullshit and how wonderful it would be when the two of them finally got together after all those phone calls and mushy letters they had written without being able to see each other face-to-face for all those weeks, and now they could finally hold hands and have maybe a few hugs and, geez, maybe a kiss or two, but they wouldn't even think about having sex because they were both saving themselves for their wedding night because they were such good Catholics, and they didn't want to let down their parents and their priest, and it would all mean so much more to them and all that fuckin' shit.

But I had committed to this thing, and if I didn't go through with it, I'd have to put up with even more of Hacky's damn bullshit, so at that point I couldn't really back out and maybe run the risk of losing TV privileges.

The second thing was that I didn't like blind dates. I had been on a few, and none had gone well. It was so damn unnatural and awkward. The people who arranged the thing always told me that my girl had a really great personality, which of course meant she was homely as sin and more than a tad overweight.

Needless to say, I wasn't exactly in the right frame of mind. But old Hacky was so damn excited he could hardly contain himself. He reserved a room at the College View Motel up on Rt. 35, and on one Saturday afternoon, the two vestal virgins arrived.

Peggy, Hacky's girl, was nice looking, but she was a little too goody-two-shoes for me. Her short, tightly curled hair was too exact, and her clothes were like something a forty-year-old woman would wear to church. She was one of those sickeningly bubbly broads who thought everything was so wonderful and so damn funny.

When we met them at the motel, it was a big-time reunion for all three. I had to just hang back for a few minutes while they tried to catch up—"How was the trip?" and "Did you have any trouble finding the place?" and "I can't believe you're actually standing in front of me," and all that other mundane crap. Eventually, Hacky got around to introducing me.

Surprisingly, Peggy's friend Fawn was rather nice looking. She had long, light brown hair, a decent face, and a slim figure. She reminded me of a girl who would go to an all-girls college and who prided herself at being a deep thinker and who wrote all kinds of arcane but super-sensitive poetry and whose favorite book was *The Fountainhead*. And guess what? She went to the damn College of Mount St. Joseph, a girls' school which was started by the damn Sisters of Charity. It was the next thing to being a fuckin' convent. And yes, that's right... her favorite author was damn Ayn Rand.

As soon as I saw how nice she looked, I felt kind of bad about not dressing a little better. I was wearing my usual get up that I put on when I went drinking up-river, although I was pretty sure my shirt and sweater didn't stink (too much). Plus, I had dabbed on a few ounces of good old English Leather.

So after all the pleasantries were dispensed with, the two gals put their bags in the room, and it was decided we'd go down the road to the classy but unpretentious Bob Evans Sausage Shop. I actually liked the place, even though their famous sausage didn't measure up to the Pennsylvania Dutch smoked sausage I had been raised on. They had a really good chili, and that was what the four of us ordered.

After all, the other three weren't really concerned about food, as they continued to gab about all the really delightful things going on in their charmed lives back in Shaker Heights, their section of Cleveland. Actually, they didn't live right in Shaker Heights, which was big-time upper class. They lived in South Euclid, but they felt it was close enough. Bunch of bullshit.

I guess in his excitement, Hacky didn't remember that the Bob Evans chili could always be counted on to produce a healthy charge of stupendous farts about an hour after eating all those kidney beans and ground chuck. Anyway, when the chili came to the table, it was steaming hot. So real suavely but discreetly, I started to blow on it to cool it down. As I was doing this, I looked over at the demure Miss Fawn. She was just sitting there, holding a spoonful of chili. So trying to add to the congeniality of the moment, I interjected something insightful like, "This chili is really hot."

And she responded with, "The proper way to eat hot food is to hold it over the dish until the spoonful has cooled." So that indicated to me that I was in for an evening of hoidy toidy bullshit.

Hacky and Peggy kept going on about all their great experiences at Fort Clarke, the Catholic summer camp they had attended as kids and later as camp counselors. The place where the counselors all wore white polo shirts, buttoned at the neck and black Bermuda shorts and black knee-high socks. They talked about how they loved to hang out with the various priests who supervised the place, sitting around the campfire in the evening, singing those catchy camp songs. And of course, they always looked forward to being there next summer but then remembered they would both graduate college in the Spring and they'd be too fuckin' old to do that shit anymore. They literally had to hold back the tears.

Hacky, Peggy, and I eventually finished our damn chili, but Fawn-baby was still sitting there, holding her third spoonful while it cooled. By this time, the two love birds wanted to get back to the motel room so they could spend time in a more intimate setting. So we paid the check, left the Sausage Shop, and headed back up Rt. 35.

But when we got inside the room, Peggy remembered she had left her cardigan back at the restaurant, which she really hadn't, of course, but they used this as a ruse to get back in the car so they could make out a little. But that, of course, left Fawn and me in the motel room, which had a non-functioning TV. I understood why those two would want to be together for a while, but I sure as hell didn't want to be stuck in the room with this babe who cooled her chili by holding each spoonful for five minutes.

But when those two left, I guess the dynamics of the group changed because Fawn all of a sudden became more congenial. It was like she didn't have to put on her hotsy-totsy image in front of the other two, so we actually had a fairly decent conversation. Plus, Hacky had brought along some Southern Comfort, and that helped cut the edge.

Fawn said she made it a practice to never have more than one drink. I said my practice was to have at least five, but she wasn't amused. As she started sipping the hooch, I told her I liked jazz. She had actually heard of Coltrane and Miles and a few others. Then we talked about some of the courses she was taking, like the Lake Poets and Lord Byron and a bunch of classical and romantic writers.

Things were rolling along rather smoothly when I asked, "So Fawn, have you ever done any pot?" She screwed up her nose and didactically stated, "You don't *do* pot… and… you don't *smoke* pot. The proper term is *to blow grass*."

And at that point I thought, *Holy hell! How the fuck would she know anything about smoking or blowing or puffing anything*?

I quickly decided that Hacky owed me big-time for having to go through those few hours of bullshit. And TV or no TV, the next time the bastard wanted ice, he was gonna be hiking his fat ass up to the damn Student Center. *[Motherfuckle!]*

Smokey Robinson and the Miracles, "Tracks of My Tears," "Ooo Baby Baby." Why did he sing so high? But he carried it off.

Rio Without Clark

1969: Appalachia had a poverty rate of 17.8% of the population

Whoever said, "The more things change, the more they stay the same?" was full of shit. I was doing okay in my classes, but without Clark around, my study regimen started to flag. After all, this was my fifth year of college, and I was ready to get out and make some money, as long as I wasn't drafted, of course.

Clark's replacement in Room 12 was Tim McGurt. He was a total opposite of Clark. Up front, I have to say that, in all actuality, he wasn't a bad guy. He was clean and stayed out of my way. It was just that I couldn't stand his phony fuckin' guts.

I usually liked Jersey guys. I liked their accent and their swagger. But McGurt was continually trying to impress everyone for some damn reason. He was president of the Newman Club and also in a damn fraternity, Sigma Theta. For him, externals were always important. I could go into all kinds of psychological analyses, but I never warmed up to the son-of-a-gun. Let's be real here. He wasn't Clark Buck.

I was renting a turntable from some shmuck down the hall for two bucks a week so I could again play my records. The female problem was still painfully evident, but that would change in the second semester. I still palled around at times with Larry "Ballsie" Ball and Howie Utley, but then I kind of fell into the dark side. I started frequenting hillbilly bars, and my partners-in-crime were two members of the Mole Hole elite, Mike Lewis and Donnie Gross.

Mike was a great guy. He was a competent swing man on the basketball team, freaky fast and a good shooter. Although he came across as a country-type of guy, he was continually on the make with the gals. I think basketball players, in general, are the most skilled at trolling for women. I'm sure other athletes would question that. Maybe it had something to do with the skimpy uniforms. But anyway, Mike liked to hit the local bars and play pool, at which he was pretty damn proficient.

The other derelict who usually came along was Donnie Gross, built like a fire hydrant with receding blond hair and a fu manchu. He was loud and obnoxious but had a popular following on campus. The kind of guy who walked into the cafe or the Redman and about half the place would immediately shout in unison, "DONNIEEE!" I didn't really care that much for the bastard. He was on the baseball team, which tended to lean toward the racist side of things. But like Lewis, Donnie had that hillbilly twang, which came in handy when an easterner like me went into a redneck establishment.

I never considered those two as close friends, but somehow I frequently found myself in Lewis' Super Sport, flying up-river to the exotic Blue Willow Lounge and other hillbilly hangouts. Guys like Mike and Donnie had been doing this since their high school days. But I hadn't been part of that, so by tagging along I was making up for lost time.

These sorties were during the week, usually on Monday or Wednesday nights, since Tuesdays and Thursdays were light days for classes. The car ride, with the big-ass engine and blaring country music on the radio was an escape from campus.

I liked the bar scene, rubbing elbows with real people, the common folk, much like the workers in the casket factory. They were upfront about things, but they could also be a little scary, especially with the demon booze in their belly. If you talked with them on their level, if you showed them respect as an equal, you became their friend. But if you patronized them or acted phony, they could sniff you out real quickly as some bogus bastard.

One time at the Willow, one of the locals fell asleep on a chair in the corner, leaning back against the wall, his arms crossed, dead to the world. Everyone started piling empty beer bottles on his crossed arms and on his lap. Inevitably, someone woke him up. He let out a damn yell and all the bottles flew every which way. Everyone laughed like crazy, but the guy who was sleeping got pissed and went and ordered another beer.

Then there was some other guy who was really drunk and upset about his girlfriend, who happened to be in the Willow but who was ignoring him. So he was walking around the place, all pissed off, and after awhile he got so mad that he punched the beer bottle he was holding in the palm of his other hand, which, of course, caused him to break a few knuckles. Blood flew all over the place. Typical night at the Willow.

This will sound condescending, but I pitied some of these people. Many had low-paying jobs, jobs that didn't provide a feeling of pride. Many came from big families, often on the edge of poverty.

Alcoholism tended to pop up, which frequently led to child and spousal abuse. And if there was a divorce, the old man might not keep up with the child support, which might land the bastard in jail. And then, when released, maybe he just got the shits of the family and all that responsibility, and he'd just take off somewhere, which would cause more problems.

And in this area, being part of the Bible Belt, many of the church goers would look down on these good-for-nothing sinners and offer little support, even though the Bible said that good Christians should help the poor and lonely.

But then on the other hand, many of these folks were more happy than their so-called middle class church-going relatives. And many of them found fulfillment despite their limited living conditions. So like a lot of things, I guess it was wrong to classify people by their financial situation or their social milieu. Because at this point in this boy's life, I sure as hell wasn't the happiest bastard in the world. ***[Motherfuckle!]***

James Taylor, first non-British performer to sign with Apple,
Sweet Baby James.

Doug Farley

The day Wall Street stopped, October 16, 1969.
Bankers joined forces with hippies and folk singers
in the streets against the War.

Every semester started with a slight change in personnel. And on a small campus, you didn't have to do much to get noticed. When the term began, a totally out-of-place vehicle could be seen slowly cruising around campus. It was a black Lincoln, like the one crushed in the James Bond flick *Goldfinger*.

The guy driving this tank was Douglas Farley, 6' 3" and somewhere in the neighborhood of 375 pounds, and that wasn't 375 pounds of muscle. He was from Manhattan, and his parents had seats on the New York Stock Exchange. So I immediately thought, *Geez, if he's that rich, what the hell's he doing out here at Reo Rio, when he could get into just about any school with an under-the-table donation?*

I never got the whole story, but like a lot of Rio students, he must have screwed up at another school, like flunking out, drinking on campus, selling drugs, molesting the school mascot, or accosting some poor bovine in the horticulture area.

I knew, for a fact, he was intelligent, congenial, and inoffensive. Despite his natural charm, I'm sure the fat-issue was difficult to live with. It was literally the elephant in the room. I mean when he walked in, you could just see everyone's brain saying, *Holy shit, he's fat*.

But Doug had a presence about him that stopped anyone from ever saying that to his face. To compensate for his large girth, he always wore a necktie, navy blazer, khaki slacks, and clunky black wingtips. He walked slowly with a seemingly painful step, which came from the fact that his weight had caused a few of the bones in his feet to literally snap. It was said that his feet would never heal unless he lost a ton of weight or spent a year in bed, neither of which would ever happen.

Lastly, he was a good looking fat guy: great hair, neat voice, and contagious laugh. He didn't have the usual Jersey/New York twang. I never knew anyone from Manhattan, but I suppose that was the basis for his classy delivery. And just one more thing about his appearance. Doug lived on the third floor of Holzer Hall. He had a personal elevator key to get upstairs. From what I heard, he took late-night showers when no one else was around.

Of course, Doug's trademark was his Lincoln. He took out the back seat and kept a half-keg in there at all times. So Doug, Zittle, and a few other alchies would drive this tank out to the reservoir or some out-of-the-way farm lane, and get boozed up.

But after awhile, they got tired of drinking in the mud-splattered black Lincoln. Or maybe the damn behemoth (the car, not Farley) just broke down and wasn't reliable. Whatever the case, the guys decided they should go together and rent an off-campus apartment so they could hang out there and drink when they wanted. The only stipulation was that the commode in the bathroom had to be situated in the perfect position to accommodate Doug's fat ass. And apparently they found the perfect dumper.

In fact, they found something even better than just having a good bathroom. They rented the upstairs apartment over the Last Chance Carryout, which meant they could go downstairs and buy booze whenever the place was open. I guess the grumpy Italian owner, Frank Pisano, decided to give them a break on the rent because he wanted to keep these booze hounds as clientele.

He put up with them, despite the fact that they continually gave him a hard time every time they were in his store. Whenever the bastards left the place, you could hear the old guy say, "*MOTHERFUCKLE!*" (emphasis on the first and third syllables) as though he was saying, *Just give me your goddamn money and get the fuck out of here!*

So after they got their apartment, Zittle decided it would be a good place to smoke weed. I'm sure on big-time campuses, people were smoking all over the place, but I can honestly say I never saw any of that at Rio, on or off campus. One time, Dirk told a bunch of us that someone from Jersey was bringing grass and asked if we wanted to get in on it. I said I was interested. Only problem was that I always had trouble inhaling when I smoked a cigarette, which I rarely did. So Dirk said I should practice inhaling by smoking cigars.

For about a week before the stuff came, I gave this inhaling thing a good shot. I bought a couple packs of Swisher Sweet Perfectos. After two or three days, I was making some progress despite the fact that my throat, mouth, and tongue became really irritated. Plus, I was thinking it wasn't a good idea to do this weed thing because it was illegal and who knows what shit might be mixed in with the grass and it would lead to hard core drugs and I could end up in jail as some convict's bitch. Hell, I was paranoid before I even took a big old toke.

Anyway, Zittle said when the stuff arrived, we'd meet up at the Last Chance apartment and go into a purple reefer haze. But all my agonizing was for naught because whoever was supposed to bring the Jersey grass never showed up. I'm sure if anyone tried hard enough, they could have gotten some weed from somewhere like Columbus or maybe even old Gallipolis, but that was the last I heard anything about getting any hootch while I was at Reo Rio.

So back to Doug Farley. He easily insinuated himself into the fabric of the campus. Despite his upper-class background and his coat and tie and size, he became one of the more popular persons around the place. He served on the Student Senate and various committees. He could bullshit with the best of them, but especially with the likes of Dirk, Mike Taylor, Joe Scarfo, and just about anyone who wanted to get really drunk, because boy, could he ever drink.

Although he associated with a variety of people, Doug, like Zittle and most of the guys in the drinking crew, was not in a fraternity. And like me, they found the pledging process and other things about Greek life to be sophomoric and stupid. I always thought it was ridiculous to pay dues just to make friends, especially on a small campus.

I mean it just wasn't natural to think that everyone in the frat would like everyone else in the frat. That was a phony assumption. There were no fraternity houses at Rio, so in places like the cafeteria, each fraternity would sit together. When someone told a joke, they'd all laugh, whether it was funny or not. And they all acted like they were sincerely interested in each other's lives, which was all a bunch of phony bullshit.

So anyway, for some damn reason, Farley and Zittle and a few other guys decided they wanted to start their own fraternity. Their bylaws would dispose of all the petty shit like carrying a bowling pin around campus and paddling the pledges and making fools out of them, ad nauseum.

They decided they'd use the Last Chance apartment as an off-campus headquarters. It sounded okay to me, although I still didn't see the need to get organized. Maybe Farley thought it would look good on a resume. I'm sure his old man was a big frat guy at his Ivy League school, probably encouraging Doug to go the same way. But Rio didn't even have a national fraternity.

One Saturday evening, I was in Room 12, contemplating my failure to have a date, when Farley walked in. McGurt was out on some *far out* soiree with his fifteen-year-old girlfriend. So Doug plopped down on Tim's bed, causing a permanent sag to the bed frame, which later added to McGurt's propensity to complain even more about his bad back or sore legs or stiff shoulder or whatever. So being the congenial bastard, I told Doug I liked his necktie. He immediately took it off and gave it to me. Apparently, that was S.O.P. in Upper Manhattan Society, to give your tie to someone who offered a compliment.

So when Doug told me about the plans for the new frat, he included me as an original member. I was flattered, but the more he talked, the more my brain was saying, *This is too much organization. This is too much like the other frats*.

But I didn't express any reservations. And I was surprised when Doug asked me to help draft the bylaws, I guess because I was an English major. I reflexively said, "Hey, a great name for the frat would be I Felta Thi."

The big guy wasn't amused.

I had no feel for technical writing, but I said I'd be glad to help. So Doug slowly rose with a grunt or two off the bent bed and sauntered out the door. I never heard anything about the new fraternity after that. I think Farley and the rest of them probably came to the same conclusion as me, that we weren't fraternity types.

Little Anthony and the Imperials, "Tears on My Pillow," "Going Out of My Head"

The Moratorium/Teach-In

At the 1924 Paris Olympics, Dr. Benjamin Spock won a gold medal in Men's Eight Rowing. "To win in Vietnam, we will have to exterminate a nation."

Wednesday, October 15, 1969, was supposed to be a national stoppage of college classes to assess the war and hopefully bring a halt to things in Southeast Asia. At the time, I knew some people at Millersville State back in Pennsy. When I asked how effective the Moratorium was on their campus, they said there was no Moratorium. No classes were canceled, and there was only a minimal protest by the student body. So after hearing that, I felt kind of proud of Rio Grande. This little college produced more political interest in a really important event than one of those so-called respected PA state schools. But as I reflect on Rio's Moratorium, it also could have been a tad more enthusiastic.

I didn't know what was happening, but I knew I wouldn't be going to four of my classes. That morning in the bathroom, Bill "Ripple" Sanford, one of the black brothers in the Mole Hole, said he didn't sign the list for those who were cutting classes, because he didn't want to get into any trouble, thinking some professors might make some shit out of it. This was the same guy who last Spring jumped on stage with Abbie and called Rio a dinky school, and he didn't care if he lost his scholarship. So much for the old revolutionary spirit.

Then Pigman came in and said something like he didn't sign up either. Like if he participated, he'd get into some kind of trouble or something. And this was coming from the same guy who was perpetually drunk, in and out of class.

Next was bastard Nuxall who said he wouldn't even think about participating. He was going to all his damn classes. He wouldn't want to miss something because he'd get so far behind. Something like this was un-American. He said those who were doing this were "all a bunch of fools. It's stupid."

So after all those intellectual insights, I gave the whole thing a second thought, but only briefly. I reflected on all the shit over in Nam and how damn stupid that whole war-thing was. So I decided to go through with it, even though no one in the Mole Hole was participating. But I had to find out what was going on. Nothing had been announced.

I went to the Student Center and nothing was happening there. I went to the library, nothing there. I ran into Rick Miller, but he didn't know shit either. So we went to Davis Hall, which was apparently where everything was taking place.

The usuals were there, the "free thinkers." Rick settled in with a few of his Pi Delta buddies, so I found a place to squat and waited for something to happen. Over the last year or so, after going through that whole Wyndham thing, the suspension and dealing with the so-called campus radicals, this kind of uncertainty seemed like standard operating procedure. There were plenty of good intentions but never any concrete organization. So there was a lot of sitting around and waiting.

Prof. Sam Jones was supposed to talk. After a few minutes, he showed up with his class. He was stockily built and looked like he would be a hard-ass right winger, but he displayed a healthy view of both world and domestic affairs.

He began with a retrospective about what got us to this point. He thought it was time for an immediate withdrawal. In his eyes, the war was a big mistake, and it was right to express public outrage.

He saw how the war was adversely affecting not only the soldiers but the entire nation. It was pulling the society in two directions. And although he was for open dissent, he also offered a strong warning about the eventual growth of repression, similar to what happened during the McCarthy era, just a few years ago in the '50s.

He said society goes around in cycles. The late '60s might be a time of liberal courts and liberal expressions, but eventually there would be a repression against all of that sort of thing which could be just as dangerous if not worse than all the unrest of the '60s.

So I just sat there when he asked for questions. I didn't ask if the fear of repression was a justifiable factor for staying in Vietnam, to keep bombing and to keep killing over there. I thought that would have been a valid question. But I sat there and didn't say anything.

Not that I was afraid, but time was running out. Everyone seemed to have gotten to their limit of concern about the war. They were getting antsy to get the hell out of there. It was like they all showed up just because it was the thing to do. And now they had done that and that was enough.

It was time to go back to BS'ing with the frat brothers. Dick Garrett kept looking around, making it look like he wasn't too concerned. Actually, that was the way the whole show was, the whole campus, and the whole damn country. Not unless everyone was fully committed would anything ever get accomplished. But I wasn't any better than anyone else, because I wasn't ready or willing to become fully committed either.

So I came to a personal rationalization. I wasn't part of the hipsters or free thinkers or for that matter most of the other kiddos who showed up. And it would have taken a supreme effort to get anything of consequence accomplished about the war, and I didn't have a supreme effort in me. In fact that was the way things were... everywhere.

If you sincerely tried to get something going, it immediately became contaminated by egos, personal agendas, and bureaucracy. Just like Prof. Crabbe saying how the downfall of an organization occurs when it's only concerned about its survival and forgets about its original purpose.

You had to be a real steppenwolf if anything was to be accomplished. You had to keep a disconnected objectivity about you and your actions. That was one hell of a job. You couldn't have any of these big all-encompassing organization type things because that was the end of everything.

Phew! After expending all that introspective energy, I felt the need for a big fucking beer. That evening, I went to supper in the cafe, and the freckled redhead was looking at me, eye to eye. And when she and the brunette left, the redhead looked back at me. Hmmm... So yeah, I sure as hell wasn't any better than those others at the Moratorium. I fell right back to my little world, forgot about the war, LBJ, and all the killing, maiming, and raping.

That was the extent of my Moratorium, a personal boycott of four classes. *[Motherfuckle!]*

The Tymes, "So Much in Love," 1963.

The Willow, Sorority Babes, and Beyond

"I sent the country club a note saying, 'Please accept my resignation. I don't want to belong to any club that will accept me as a member'."
–Groucho Marx

I was screwing around in Hacky's room, watching the Jets-Oilers game (Jets won, 26-17). I had two tests on Wednesday and two papers for Friday. So when Mike Lewis came into Nuxall's room with his face lathered up and asked if I wanted to go to the Willow, I quickly acknowledged his invitation and was on my way.

I put on the $8.80 Devonrite slacks with the worn seat and baggy legs, scuffed up Clarks desert boots, no socks, and beige v-neck sweater over a grey Rio t-shirt. Of course I put on the fake Baracuta jacket with the Alligator patch.

My hair was good in the front and not sticking up too much in the back, just a little frizzy all over. All this as the war was continuing in Nam, and those poor bastards fighting in the jungle didn't give a shit how their hair looked because they were trying to save their asses and their buddies.

Recently, my rapport with Gross and Lewis had been pretty good. But on the way up-river, I was shaking, feeling apprehensive for no real reason. I only had four bucks, which should have been enough, but I seemed to be going through a lot of money lately. Anyway, after stopping at the gas station and Burger Chef, we pulled into the Willow.

Some Pi Deltas were there, along with some of the Chi Delta Chi's: Pam Graten, Phyl Graybill, and not-too-bad-but-not-cool Elaine May (not real cool because of her recent breakup with my buddy Zittle). Also the crippled girl who had been getting around pretty good recently. My buddy Ballsie was also there, so I knew the night wouldn't be totally wasted. The local hillbillies were dancing and whooping it up to the rockabilly sounds of Charley Lilly and the Earthquakes.

So old Pam Graten and her sisters of Chi Delta were pigging it. Graten was on the ugly side—her hairstyle looked like she was wearing a football helmet. I guess she over-compensated by having an even uglier personality. She seemed to enjoy looking down her long-ass nose at guys like me. And for some reason, most of her damn sisters followed along.

Zittle had filled me in on some of the seamier aspects of Chi Delta Chi that few people knew. Apparently, Elaine had spilled the beans to him one night as they were parked in some farmer's lane while they were drinking a couple quarts and doing the dirty deed.

Even though the sorority had only been in existence for about three years, this newness contributed to their strict decorum and adherence to the bylaws. They had monthly meetings in a secret room next to the boiler, down in the bowels of Moulton Hall. When it was time to assemble, a doorkeeper was assigned to let in the members. Only the president and vice-president had keys to the room.

The interior was decorated in sharp contrast to the dusty basement. The walls were covered in dark blue and gold wallpaper, with brass sconces and candles at intervals. On the carpeted floor were a few rows of chairs and some over-stuffed furniture. Further back was an altar which was draped with a white silk cloth, embossed with *Chi Delta Chi* in gold. Candelabras had been placed at both ends.

Entering the room was a ritual in itself. The members lined up outside in single file, seniors first followed by the underclass-women. Each member performed the secret knock, and the doorkeeper greeted them with the ritual handshake. The member whispered into the doorkeeper's ear some obscure Greek phrase, and she was admitted. After everyone was inside, the meeting followed the prescribed protocol.

Zittle said the sorority was started by Mrs. Genevieve Brulay, an old Rio alumna, class of '37. She had lunch in the cafeteria every Sunday after attending the local Methodist church service. As the campus population grew in the early '60s, Genevieve was somewhat offended by the decorum of the coeds as they ate their Sunday repasts.

She yearned for the days when the cafeteria had a prescribed dress code for special occasions and Sunday meals—men in coats and ties, women in dresses. So sometime in 1964, this old biddy approached a member of Rio's board of directors with a plan to start a sorority which would uphold the ideals of proper ladyhood.

Surprisingly, the board member recognized that times were changing, and it would be an embarrassment if such a draconian approach were attempted. So it was decided the sorority would be a semi-secretive endeavor. On the outside, it would appear to be a typical

Greek social group, but there would also be the secret society which encouraged the ideals of proper female decorum.

One Sunday afternoon, the college served a tea in the lobby of Davis Hall, hosted by Mrs. Brulay, an elegant woman who came from one of the oldest families in Gallipolis. She had a real presence about her and apparently impressed the girls because fifteen signed up as charter members of Chi Delta Chi.

They started meeting in the basement of Moulton where Genevieve provided all kinds of charm school instructions: the proper way to walk, sit, eat, shake hands, and carry oneself. Then she got into how to handle men, which of course got the girls' attention. She said a lady should present an image of someone special, to the point of being aloof. That was what men wanted in the ideal woman. It made them respect you.

So the girls subscribed to this concept, hook-line-and-sinker. They took on this attitude, not only when they attended the secret meetings, but also whenever they were together on campus. This was a real bonding thing for them, bolstering them against any personal insecurities.

Needless to say, I didn't want anything to do with Pam Graten and her ilk, either on campus or at the swanky Blue Willow Lounge (except for Jane Barakas, of course). So when I saw them, I walked back to the pool table.

Angel, the waitress, was back there, and she was looking semi-cool in a silk blouse and black, skin-tight slacks. She seemed kind of simple, but she was throwing her eyes at me, like I really caught her limited vision, and like she really dug me looking back at her. At that instant in time, she was the most beautiful woman in the world. But Angel's attention span was about the length of a fart, and she was soon off on some other insignificant but significant encounter of her life.

By this time, I was on my second Stroh's. I watched the pool, as I leaned against the back wall. This older guy, maybe fifty or fifty-five, stepped up beside me. He looked like he was about half in the bag.

As we were standing there, I noticed his deformed hand. All of a sudden, the bottle he was holding slipped out of the bad hand. There was this big *POP*. What was a bottle just a second ago, was now just a mixture of white foam, broken brown glass, and a Budweiser label on the cement floor. I felt sorry for the old guy because this screwed up the cool he was trying to project.

Good old Angel soon came with bucket and mop and made swift work of the little mishap. Apparently, this frequently happened at the Willow, drunks spilling drinks or drunks dropping their beer. I always thought a real, true-blue drunk would take real good care of what the hell he was drinking. What was that excerpt from Robinson's "Mr. Flood's Party?"

Then, as a mother lays her sleeping child
Down tenderly, fearing it may awake,
He sat the jug down slowly at his feet
With trembling care, knowing that most things break

As Angel went about her duties, I stepped back and got a better view of the bottle dropper. It was like he was projecting an image of an older Clark Gable. He had slit-like eyes, a closely trimmed mustache, and greasy slicked-back hair that ended in the back in a DA (Duck's Ass). His face was tanned, like maybe he worked outside. I was thinking he'd had a full but rough life. How many fights? How many jobs? How many women?

He asked me about Lewis. Like was he a local boy? I told him he played basketball for Rio. He said, "He plays pool, too," meaning he was damn good.

Looking for a partner, he got no takers. The games continued to go single. Finally, Lewis won his game, and the old guy got his quarter in. He was off and running. At one time he was probably in good shape, but now he had a noticeable beer gut. His black, pleated slacks broke severely over his shoes, dragging on the floor.

He took off his jacket, chalked up a cue, and assumed the position for a break. With a non-filtered Lucky Strike sticking to his lips, he inhaled unconsciously, exhaling with a slight wheeze as the smoke went into his eyes as he bent over. His body tensed, feet apart, ass taut.

With a confident grip of the cue, he played old style, firing hard, crisp shots. He was running the table. But as he moved after the cue ball, you could tell the booze was taking effect, shambling in an off-balance gait. He missed an easy, straight-on shot. Mike took over, and that was all she wrote. So the old guy had a serious but gentlemanly game with Lewis, and although it was close, Mike beat his ass.

I noticed the old guy wasn't wearing a wedding ring, so maybe he lived alone. Or maybe he took his ring off when he went out drinking. Or maybe he didn't wear the ring because of the kind of work he did.

Or maybe when his old lady left him, he took the ring off and threw it into the river, never wanting to see the damn thing again. Who the fuck knows?

Maybe every once in awhile, he'd put on his suit and come to places like the Willow, with his cuffs dragging on the ground, soaking up beer, soaking up piss in the pisser room, and he would shoot some pool, get a little drunk, and then go home. Kind of sad, but who was I to say he wasn't enjoying life? And if he wasn't enjoying life, it was none of my fuckin' business anyway, right?

Gypsy and Bonnie, two locals who worked at the Willow, were beginning to recognize me. I'd get a smiling hello once in awhile. I got the feeling they'd be fun to hang with. There probably wouldn't be any of that pretentious shit like the Chi Deltas were always strutting around.

But then, on the other hand, Gypsy and Bonnie were about thirty years old which meant they might have three or four kids already. They probably had redneck boyfriends or husbands who would get really jealous at the drop of a hat, and there was a good possibility those guys were somewhere in the Willow at that exact time. So it wasn't a good idea to get too involved with those two. Although, with enough beer in me, I was still prone to slapping them on the butt or giving them a squeeze once in awhile.

The Willow closed down around 2:00 A.M. I jumped in the back of Lewis' Chevy and found myself crammed next to Elaine along with two other guys on the other side of her. We were so close I didn't even have room to fart. The blood had almost stopped on my left side, but I could still feel her every move. It had been some time since I was this close to a girl.

Elaine knew who I was because she had seen me hanging with Zittle, and she was in one of my classes. Probably because she was drunk like me, she put on a semi-move. Or maybe she was just being nice because I was a good buddy of Zittle's. Or maybe she was just a nice person. All I knew was that she wasn't exhibiting any of that Chi Delta shit at that particular moment.

Out of the blue, she said, "So Mahl, where ya from?"

I mumbled, "Pennsy."

"Oh yeah, that's right. I knew that. Dirk told me you used to ride home with him."

"Yeah, that's right. How's Dirk doing, anyway? I miss seeing him."

She ignored that. Instead she said, "I was surprised to see you at the Willow. I thought you stayed in and studied all the time."

"I get out once in awhile."

"So how'd you do on that Denison test?" she asked.

"Well, I didn't read the one book, and I didn't bother to buy the other one."

She laughed at that. And just then Mike hit a hard curve in the road, and she slid even tighter against me, causing her to let out a little grunt.

"Oh sorry, Mahl." And then, "So why do you laugh at Pigman and Donnie all the time? They're both real idiots."

I shrugged my shoulders. "Don't know."

She kept up this banter, as though she was sincerely interested. I could see why Zittle liked her. And right then and there, I fell in love with Elaine May. But Mike was talking his head off as he drove the Chevy, distracting her enough to cut off our conversation.

I was thinking I could make her if I got her alone and wasn't too drunk. But I'd have to keep her away from her damn sorority sisters.

It was a good night, all around.

Yusef Lateef, jazz reed-man: tenor sax, flute, oboe, bassoon, and other non-Western instruments.

Black Panther

"If they had not murdered Malcolm X, there probably never would have been a Black Panther Party." –Bobby Seale

Somehow, an authentic, true-blue, dyed-in-the-wool Black Panther wormed his way into the cozy environs of the RGC campus. Chill Walls was supposedly the assistant minister of information of the Black Panther Party. I'm not really sure why he'd come the whole way to this dinky little college town. I'm guessing he was invited by Mike Taylor and maybe even Bill Wyndham with the idea that he could bring some diversity of thought to the bourgeoisie.

On my way over to Community Hall, I saw Dean Bob Herman running back and forth, sweating his ass off. If anything bad happened, Herman would have to face the board of directors, and they would have his skinny ass tied up in a damn tree somewhere. I imagined he had the local fuzz and vigilantes situated all over the place.

Some guy was pissing behind a bush as I approached the building. This place had so much class. I went inside, the same venue where Bevo scored all those points back in the early '50s. The hall was surprisingly full. I didn't see anybody to sit with so I took a seat behind Steve Davis and his old man, who showed up because I'm sure he wanted to see this damn nigger and continue to instill in his boy all the racial hatred that he got from *his* old man.

The Panther was late by about five minutes, which gave the crowd more time to foment. Anyway, the pseudo-hippie with blond hair and early beard was fooling around with the video machine, and the local newspaper boobs were there with their tape recorders. So in came good guy Mike Taylor and behind him the speaker. Walls looked a little like Mole Hole brother Herky... tall and thin, with a kind of grace about him. He was dressed in black but presented himself in a totally non-threatening way.

In a restrained tone, he delineated the basic beliefs of the Panthers. He said they weren't racists, and they were basically just looking for human dignity and respect. And then he went into the Panthers' ten-point program.

They wanted freedom to determine their destiny in the black community; full employment; an end to white capitalists robbing them; decent housing; the teaching of the true black history; exemption from military service; an end to police brutality and murder; freedom for all imprisoned blacks; black juries for black defendants; and finally, property, food, housing, clothing, justice and peace for all black people.

This all fed right into the members of the black student union in attendance, and they were soon in "amen" mode, seemingly agreeing with everything he was saying. At first, I was going along with them. It felt good to laugh with the brothers. But then I started thinking it was kind of sad that many of these kids were totally taken in by this. I supposed if I had been in their shoes, I would have been doing the same damn thing.

I knew the Panthers started with the intent to protect the community and feed the hungry. But then they got into the class thing. Eldridge Cleaver read all the Marxist stuff when he was in prison, and of course it made sense to him. If you were oppressed and down and had been kicked around, the idea of socialism always made sense. But I always questioned how practical it was and how it would be difficult to implement in our type of society. Of course, we already had that gigantic socialist program, Social Security, which seemed to be working out pretty damn well, especially for the old folks.

Anyway, after awhile, the Panthers started following the cops around to monitor how they treated—or mistreated—black people on the streets. Of course, the cops got pissed about that and started busting the Panthers as often as they could.

So then they enlisted help from the far left. Leonard Bernstein had them over for tea. They started quoting Mao and embraced this socialism thing, like ridding society of class structure, and everyone getting an equal share of things. So it went from being a totally black thing to a class thing. They needed the help of the white, radical left, which provided not only moral support from people like pediatrician Dr. Spock but also financial support from the upper class lefties.

Then the Panthers decided there was a need for revolution, an overthrow. All previous ties to the oppressive culture had to be pushed aside. That meant no Aretha, no John Lee Hooker, no BB King, no Temptations, no Booker T, no soul. *No soul.* That's right. They were going to take that away from the black culture? Everything had to be done for the sake of the revolution?

Like when brother Herky would immediately turn on Memphis Joe and the Blues. You couldn't take that away from people. But old Chill Walls said you had to get rid of the oppressor. I guess in the eyes of the Panthers, the owners of record companies were capitalistic despots. And the more the Panthers talked about getting rid of the oppressors, the more militant they became. But killing cops wouldn't bring back dead black people, and it certainly wouldn't get the sympathy of the whities.

So Chill finished talking and opened up for questions from the audience. Good old Ballsie stood up. He looked a little like Michael J. Pollard in *Bonnie and Clyde*, but not as goofy. I'm sure his girlfriend back home thought he was plenty good looking. He was from Coshocton, which some might say was redneck country. He and his family liked to use smokeless tobacco, including his mom. Every room of their house had a Coke bottle as a spittoon sitting on a windowsill. But Larry was somehow raised to have an open mind. He wasn't afraid to express his ideas. He was always pure in thought when it came to dealing with people, authentic in every sense of the word.

Larry pointed out that, although Chill said the Panthers weren't racists, just about everything, including the ten points of their creed/manifesto, was one-sided. Chill's response fell back into the revolution mumbo jumbo and didn't really say much of anything. Ballsie didn't get an answer. Or maybe indirectly he did.

Originally, I was for these guys to a certain extent. The Panthers started with good intentions and were a necessary thorn in the establishment's side. They needed to shake things up. But violent thinking would only defeat their cause. And then I remembered where I was, in little podunk Rio Grande, Ohio, and we were exposed to lots of stuff that many more prestigious colleges never confronted.

Rufus Harley, jazz bagpipes, Scotch and Soul *album.*

Peter, Paul, and Mary

"It's a very important thing to learn to talk to people you disagree with." –Pete Seeger

Great musicians, but at first, I had trouble liking them just because of their appearance. Here's this nice looking blonde next to two ugly guys. I kept wondering who's bonking her, or were both of them bonking her, or were they queer or what? And I have no idea why that would bother me, but it did. After awhile, I got over that and just accepted them for their music and later their activism.

In my mind, Mary Travers was the epitome of a classy blonde (sexist to say this, I know). She influenced so many girls to wear their hair like that, but she also had soul in her voice.

There is an early black and white video of the group performing at one of the Newport Folk Festivals. They're singing "The Times They Are A Changing" as the camera zooms in for a close-up of Mary. The wind is blowing her hair, totally obscuring her face. She makes no effort to push it back. She just keeps right on singing with the same intensity. No pretense. Pure beauty. Total truth.

The group's rendition of John Denver's "Leaving on a Jet Plane" knocked me out. The lyrics had no relevance to anything I had experienced, but Mary's interpretation greatly moved me.

Mongo Santamaria, Latin jazz percussionist and leader. Good version of Herbie Hancock's "Watermelon Man," Let's Party *album.*

Homecoming Weekend, 1969

"You can't write a good song about a whorehouse unless you've been in one." –Woody Guthrie

It was that time of year again… Homecoming. And everyone basically expected the same as years past. But Reo Rio could be surprisingly unpredictable. And this year, the school came through with a small but welcome change to the festivities… FREE BEER AT THE REDMAN.

So after the b-ball game on Saturday afternoon, everyone scooted out of Gallipolis and hit the Redman for free 3.2 beer. They all acted like poor souls who were just rescued from ninety days in the desert. People who never drank before were right in the middle of the whole bash. Some professors were mingling and drinking, one most notably being Doc Byrd, keeping pace with Big Doug Farley.

Hell, even Milkshake showed up. People took turns bringing him cups of beer, and he did his best to drink without sloshing all over himself and those around him. But what was funny was that the more he drank, the less spasms he had. Eventually, he was sitting there like a normal person, yucking it up and telling all kinds of crazy stories to the entertainment of those around him.

The upstairs crowd at the Redman overflowed to the basement storage area where two more kegs had been set up. People were standing around or sitting on bags of fertilizer and piles of hoses used to take care of the lawn outside. Then some crazy bastard thought it would be funny to start up the lawnmower. He kept revving the damn thing, causing the storage room to fill up with engine exhaust and dried grass clippings. Despite that, everyone kept drinking until all kegs were killed.

So everyone hightailed it back to campus. The Greeks had to change their clothes because they'd be going to some place like Oscar's in Gallipolis for fine dining, and the rest of the campus would eat in the cafeteria, already spiffed up with balloons and crepe paper in preparation for the scheduled concert. The headline group Steam would be preceded by a blue-eyed soul/R&B group called the Magnificent Men.

My buddies and I somehow ended up at Doc Byrd's place, where a keg had been tapped. We worked on the Stroh's until the show was about to start. Ballsie told me that Dirk Zittle might be back on campus. For some unknown reason, he didn't make it back to Rio for the Fall semester. All kinds of rumors had been flying around. Things like he and Elaine had split up, like maybe she had dumped him, like he took it real bad and couldn't handle it... all kinds of shit like that. Maybe he just got the royal craps of Rio Grande. But Elaine was selected for the Homecoming Court, and it was speculated that maybe Dirk would show up to be her escort.

Somehow this motley group from Doc's apartment, including the good doctor, worked our way back across campus to the caf to see the show. But before the bands got going, a little homecoming business had to be taken care of. For some, the crowning of the Homecoming Queen was always exciting, but this year was even more dramatic. It seemed that some guy had put his name on the ballot. Barry Barton was more than a little overweight and rather sloppy in appearance. But the holdovers from the Wyndham protest, namely the Young Democrats, had been handing out leaflets promoting Barry for Queen, just to screw the system. You know, "Put it to the man." To say the least, the tension was building. After all, college president A.R. Svenson had to kiss the Queen and place the crown on her head. And for the old-school Rio traditionalists, to have some disgusting, overweight slob run for Homecoming Queen was unthinkable, un-American, *verboten*.

As the lights dimmed and the smooth sound of Paul Mauriat's "Love is Blue" hummed in the background, Yale Gary stepped to the microphone and began introducing the lovely gals and their escorts. The next to last contestant was Miss Elaine May, escorted by none other than Mr. Dirk fuckin' Zittle. And as soon as the name Zittle came out of Yale's mouth, the members of the Mole Hole and others erupted with loud hoots of "DIRK! DIRK! DIRK!" It was like everyone was so damn glad to see the bastard. But as Dirk and Elaine took their place next to the other couples, Dirk just stared straight ahead, didn't crack a smile or nod his head. He looked great, but wasn't the cool-guy Dirk of old.

So when the crowd settled down a little, Yale cleared his throat. "And finally, our last aspirant for the 1969 Rio Grande College Homecoming Queen is... Mr. Barry A. Barton."

There was a mixed reaction from the assembled. Most people of my ilk burst out laughing and stood up with our fists in the air, exhorting with shouts of, "Go Barry." Several of the Greeks loudly booed. The old alums in attendance scrunched up their noses, some nearly fainting, when Barry came lumbering out wearing a floppy sun hat and what looked like a soiled blanket wrapped around his sloping shoulders. With a drooping fu manchu mustache and sunglasses, Barry made a more than eclectic appearance.

So with all the contestants on the *qui vive*, the excitement reaching a nervous apex, Yale announced that the leading vote-getter was none other than... (drum roll)... the affable Barry Barton. Old A.R. Svenson, pipe tightly clenched in teeth, came up to Barry and stuck out his hand as far as he could reach without getting too close.

Barry faked like he was going to give the old guy a hug, but then backed away when A.R. waved him off. Svenson grabbed the mic and said, "Barry, this has been a lot of fun, so we're going to give you some special prizes: a free pizza at the Redman and a $10.00 gift certificate to Haskins Tanner Clothiers in Gallipolis. Congratulations. And now Yale, who is the real Queen?"

So that was how the Barry-dilemma was handled. The crown was bestowed on the lovely Alexanne Jacobson, escorted by the phlegmatic but sensitive Keith Repulski, son of the great Rip Repulski of the '47-'48 Phillies.

The group Steam did their set, punctuated by their big hit "Na, Na, Hey, Hey, Kiss Him Goodbye," which later became the standard goodbye song sung by the fans of winning teams throughout the country. Other than that, Steam didn't produce much steam.

However, the opening band, the Magnificent Men, were pretty damn good, covering old Motown tunes plus some of their own material, namely "Piece of Mind," a great song. Ballsie and I talked to their two lead singers, Buddy King and Dave Bupp, who said they were working their way back east after signing a record contract in Chicago. Their next stop was a Penn State frat party.

They said they were the first all-white R&B band to play at the venerable and rowdy Apollo Theater in Harlem. They started their set behind the curtain to warm up the crowd. And then, as the curtain opened, the patrons were shocked to see white dudes up there. But the crowd enthusiastically embraced them. I got the feeling they were bullshitting, but I later found out they weren't lying. And they not only performed at the Apollo, but they also backed up none other than James fuckin' Brown, who just happened to show up without his band when they were there.

Eventually, Greeks went their way, independents went back to the dorm or to Filthy Frank's or to the reservoir, or wherever. A few of the Rio intelligentsia flocked over to Doc's place and attacked the keg in the middle of the good professor's living room.

Lee Morgan, dynamic trumpet, The Sidewinder, Cornbread, Delightfulee *albums. Shot and killed by his girlfriend at Slug's Saloon in New York, age 33.*

Homecoming Weekend, Extended

James Davis, first American to die in Vietnam, 1961

On Sunday, I went to lunch in the caf and sat down with Farley and Joe Scarfo. They got around to talking about Doc Byrd's keg, and it took little to persuade me. Without going back to the dorm, I found myself walking over to Doc's with Farley, while Scarfo drove up to the Esso Station to get more ice for the keg.

To say that Professor Boyd J.K. Byrd was a character is an understatement. When you saw him ambling across campus, you had to smile. His bald head usually had a band-aid or two on it, probably from banging into something while on his last drunk. His eyes were kind of bulging under his raised brow, which gave him a rather mischievous look, like a twelve year old who just did something wrong and got away with it.

He probably had one of the best minds on the faculty. Doc took his position seriously and conducted his classes and experiments with the utmost professionalism. He discovered several new species of local insects and plants. He also developed a rigorous investigation into a cure for leukemia with the use of chlorophyll. Supposedly, he helped a young patient go into remission up in Athens, Ohio. The only problem was that the poor kid's skin turned green.

Doc came from old-money in Virginia. He had studied at prestigious universities like Virginia, Harvard, Penn, and the Sorbonne, where he published his thesis in French. He also served in the Navy during WWII. And although he could have made tons of money in the private sector, he dedicated himself to teaching.

Despite limited facilities and resources, he raised the science department to a higher level. Those who studied under Doc, especially good students like Clark, had nothing but good things to say about him. But to students who never took his classes, all they knew was that he drank a lot, was not married, and might be queer.

When Farley and I got to Doc's apartment, we found him in a wrinkled white dress shirt, tail out in the back, probably the same clothes he had worn yesterday, probably the same clothes he had slept in. A blue knit, frazzled Rooster tie hung loosely from his neck. His slacks were held up with a riding belt, dark blue with a red stripe, and a brass buckle.

The keg was sitting in a washtub in the middle of the living room, amid all of Doc's antiques and strange musical instruments. The old guy was glad to see us, although he wasn't his usual, enthusiastic self, probably because he had been drinking for the last two days. The first thing we did was rinse the green goblets from the night before. They were nice glasses which held exactly one can of beer.

Soon Joe showed up, and the keg was iced. So Joe, Doug, and Doc started to talk, and I just kind of sat back and listened. And as this was going on, we started screwing around with Doc's musical instruments.

One was some kind of fretted thing with one string. The sound was projected from a brass horn attached to the bottom. It was supposed to be bowed, but Doc went crazy plucking the one string. Then he dug out a book and pushed it in front of me, pointing out a photo of his family's Virginia estate. He was obviously proud of the old place, which was a sharp contrast to the dump he was currently living in.

So with the keg iced and the beer going down real smoothly, we were all jabbering away. Scarfo said, "I'm going to Europe next year, probably to Italy and then Switzerland."

I said, "Switzerland? That's where my mom's family's from."

With raised eyebrows, Doc said, "Really?"

Then Farley said, "Mahl's from Pennsy."

Doc said, "Pennsy? What town?"

I said, "You probably never heard of it... York."

Doc said, "I've not only heard of it. I've been there. I bought some antiques from Joe Kindig."

That got my attention because Joe Kindig was a local legend back home. I remembered him as an old guy who had long grey hair and a long beard. He walked around town wearing sandals with no socks, even in the winter. Everyone thought he was some kind of eccentric bum. When Doc added that he was related to Joe Kindig, I thought, *Yeah, right! He's related to Joe Kindig from fuckin' York, Pennsylvania.*

But I found out later that Kindig was not just some eccentric. He was a damn millionaire, known worldwide for his collection of Kentucky/Pennsylvania rifles, suits of armor, and early American furniture. He was a world-expert. So I started thinking about the antiques in Doc's apartment, and maybe they were more valuable than they appeared. Maybe it was plausible that Doc did know Kindig and was acquainted with my hometown.

Usually, if anyone knew anything about York, PA, they were thinking about York Barbell or York Peppermint Patties or the damn race riots, or that York surrendered, paying $28,000 to the Confederates, just before the Battle of Gettysburg. But Doc knew about Kindig and his fine collections of rifles and stuff. So maybe he wasn't just BS'ing.

As the afternoon went on, more people dropped by. Professor Rose came over, and the conversations really got going then. Rose was from somewhere in the Deep South, I'm thinking Louisiana, and he was one of the better history profs. His appearance reflected the stereotype of a Southern professor. A sprig of hair was usually hanging down over his forehead, he wore old-style glasses, his clothes were always rumpled, and he had that neat, Southern twang.

On this day, he was complaining about not being recognized by the administration, despite having written two serious historical commentaries and a bunch of academic papers. He said the college and the students didn't appreciate his academic skills and production.

He also had a big hang-up on Huey "Kingfish" Long. He said Long was the most influential politician of the century, which I thought was an overstatement. But when you think about it, most demagogic politicians are just as corrupt if not more. So Rose rambled on about this, but as he drank more beer, he kind of mellowed out and went onto other rants.

Everything was moving along real smoothly. No TV. No football. No school work. No Hack Wack... but unfortunately, no women. Yes sir, a good Sunday afternoon. Farley started singing Irish drinking ditties. Scarfo said 1959 had the best songs, so he and I sang stuff like "I Only Have Eyes for You," "Sixteen Candles," "So Fine," and "Donna." Doc chimed in with some old folk songs from Appalachia. It turned out that one of his hobbies was collecting lyrics of obscure songs from the mountains of Virginia. He was in his glory as he crooned these old, backwoods lyrics.

As the afternoon wore on, people started to get hungry. So around 5:45, we all made our way to the caf for some solid nourishment, with Doc and Rose tagging along. By this time, I was pleasantly grooving, and it probably would have been smart to stop drinking. But we scarfed down some food and beat it back to Doc's. On the way, we stopped at Rose's place for a few minutes. He had a small white clapboard house. Some guys on campus had said something about his wife being so ugly, but I didn't think she looked real bad. I mean, why should anyone care if Rose's wife was ugly, anyway?

Soon after we got back to Doc's, the keg was finished. There was a unanimous decision to go forward to the Redman. We took off in Rose's VW station wagon— the small model, not the VW bus. Rose was driving, Farley of course was in the front, and Doc, Joe, and me in the back. We got to the Redman, and Doc's car was still there from last night.

We went in, and Doc ordered four pitchers. Soon Farley and Joe got into an argument about Vietnam. It was the old thing about an immediate or a measured withdrawal. To me it was all so simple. What was better? The first one, of course. Well anyway, Farley and Scarfo got into it pretty hot, but neither one was making much sense. The pitchers were soon gone, and Doc kept buying more. He was really sauced.

Jack Grogan came in and sat at our table. We talked about last summer in Wildwood. He said Dirk and he were sorry for leaving me at the chick's apartment. They thought I was getting some action, so they split. Then, for some dumb reason, I took Doc's wallet out of his coat pocket which was there on the back of the chair since last night, and I spilled his cards all over the damn floor. Really poor on my part. I guess I got a little out of hand. So I picked up the damn cards and put them back in his coat pocket, but I don't think Doc even noticed what the hell happened.

The Redman was really hopping, even on a Sunday night. There were a bunch of the "socially elite" in attendance. Some really abused Doc. They saw him as just a clown and had no appreciation for his work, but they still drank his beer.

Supposedly his tab was half his next paycheck. After awhile, the place started to slack off, so Jack, Joe, and I headed up-river. By this time, I was pretty well oiled, and Scarfo was too. Hell, we'd been at it since 12:30. We made the scene at the Gables, but there was nothing happening. So we went down to the Willow, and damn it, same thing. We had a couple beers and split.

Returning to Room 12, I got in bed with my clothes on, and everything was spinning. I put one foot on the floor and that seemed to stop the merry-go-round. I didn't sleep real well, but I felt good about myself in terms of holding the booze.

The next morning, I got up at the regular time, really hurting. I went to the bathroom and scared myself when I looked in the mirror. I had this big-ass headache. I didn't feel like taking a shower or shaving, but I did anyway. I got dressed and thought I looked pretty cool—blue pin-striped Hathaway shirt with button down collar, dress flannels, British Walker burnt leather wingtips. Looking cool but hurting. I ate breakfast and almost threw up a couple of times.

That evening, I went to the caf for supper. While standing in line, cool guy Yale Gary started talking to me all of a sudden, like on a "Mahl" basis. Maybe it had something to do with me hanging with Farley, Scarfo, and Doc at the Redman. Or maybe it was just because we were standing in line in front of everyone and he wanted to look like Mr. Congeniality.

Hell if I knew, but we were talking and yucking it up about all kinds of things. I got my food and sat down with Farley, Davis, Singer, and Yale. My new-found popularity was kind of unsettling. It was almost like, *Damn, now I have to be entertaining and witty and all that shit.*

So Davis said something about Wyndham working in a paint shop. He said he was bitter about losing his job and how few people supported him. If I had been in his shoes, I would have felt the same way.

On the other hand, there might have been different ways to deal with the administration. But knowing Wyndham had that Dartmouth background—and knowing most Dartmouth guys are rejects from Harvard—I thought maybe he didn't really have a good grasp of what the common schmoe had to put up with on a daily basis. And I know that was really bourgeois of me to think that, but it was the way life was for most working stiffs.

So overall, this had been quite a weekend, with all the drinking and bar hopping and talking with the high society types. But after hearing that thing about Wyndham, my attitude came crashing down, and I wanted to get out of this place, badly. But of course, there was no place to go, and I didn't see a whole lot of promise for the future. *[Motherfuckle!]*

Arthur Prysock/Count Basie *album. Prysock, a greatly underrated singer. Basie was Basie, the epitome of cool.*

Refrigerator

Vietnam, 1965: 65-70% of U.S. Marine casualties were caused by land mines and booby traps.

The Fall semester brought more changes to the Mole Hole. First, Clark got married and moved into an apartment with Dianna in Gallipolis. Once in awhile I'd go in there to visit, and although I was always welcomed, I felt like an interloper. After all, they were newlyweds, and there wasn't much that Dianna and I had to talk about. Sometimes, Clark would stop by in the Mole Hole, and it was always good to see him. But it wasn't like old times.

I spent a fair amount of time with Hack Wack, down the hall, mainly because I wanted to see games on his TV. But he could be a real pain. He had gone to Catholic school and was an example of someone who never divorced himself from that parochial world. He was always talking about how great the old school was and how great its athletic teams were and how great the Catholic summer camp was that he had attended for the last ten years and how great the school's faculty was and how great the priests were... "Father this" and "Father that" (who talks about their damn priest?), and how great Notre Dame football was and on and on and fuckin' on. But I wanted to see games on his TV, so I put up with his shit. Stupid, I know.

One day in December, before Christmas break, John Borsa, Tom Shelley, and I were sitting around doing nothing. Someone said something about how it would be nice to have a refrigerator to keep things cold, namely beer. At the time, there was a dorm policy prohibiting things like hot plates and assorted other appliances, which would cause fires or excessive electrical usage. Of course, many guys had popcorn poppers, and I had an electric frying pan which could be used for heating up just about any damn thing, but namely pecan rolls or canned peach halves which I frequently ate.

And then there were those heating coils you'd stick into a mug for instant coffee or tea. All these gadgets were considered dangerous. But hell, the no-alcohol policy didn't seem to stop anyone from storing and drinking booze in the rooms, even though being caught with the stuff could cause a possible expulsion. So anyway, despite all these official regulations, the three of us decided we'd pitch in on the cost of a refrigerator.

We piled into Shelley's Dodge piece-of-shit Dart and went off to Gallipolis in search of one of those small, apartment-sized jobs. Someone on the street pointed us toward Switzer's Appliances on Spruce Street.

We were greeted by a sales lady, who was extremely attractive with long dark brown hair, great complexion, great smile, nice, tight bod, and was only about nineteen or twenty years old, maybe seventeen. And hell if she wasn't the daughter of the store's proprietor. We asked her if she had any of those small fridges, but she said she didn't. So we thanked her and started to walk out. But like all good salespeople, she said she'd talk to her dad in the back room to see if he could accommodate us.

The old man came out smoking a smelly cigar and took us to a big-ass service elevator. Up we went, about three floors, standing beside this really nice looking babe and her dad, who was wearing a wide necktie, an ultra-flashy sport coat, and a half a gallon of aftershave. He threw a mean expression at us because we were drooling all over his virginal offspring.

He stopped the elevator and out we stepped onto a warehouse floor with tons of used washing machines, stoves, and refrigerators. He quickly took us to a full-sized, one-owner-only fridge. It was a steal at $19.99, presumably to get us out of the store and away from the daughter as soon as possible. We shelled out the cash, and the old man loaded the big honker of a fridge onto the elevator. Down we went, with the really nice looking babe who kept giving us the old glad eye all along the way.

Somehow the three of us lodged the fridge into the car's trunk. On the way out of town, we stopped at the Last Chance and bought four cases of Gibbons at the special price of four bucks a case. So with the beer in the back seat and the refrigerator sticking out of the trunk, we flew back to campus, taking Rt. 588 with all its hairpin turns and ups and downs.

I could feel the fridge bouncing back there, imagining bolts and pieces being strewn along the road. Shelley parked the car in the lot between Holzer Hall and the new unnamed dorm, which meant we had to carry the fridge up the sloping parking lot which was covered with mud, ice, and snow.

About every five steps, the big thing would slip out of our hands, and the fridge and the three of us would slide down the damn slope. Soon, some bastards on the back side of the dorm stuck their heads out their windows and started yelling. Then more guys heard this, and soon half the damn dorm was yelling at us. So we thought for sure we'd get caught, but somehow we got the thing inside the dorm and into my closet. I pushed my clothes aside, and it fit perfectly. We got an extension cord, plugged the damn thing in, and the fridge immediately started humming and getting cold.

We ran out to Shelley's car to get the four cases of Gibbons and carried them in under blankets. No one would ever suspect what we were doing—carrying rectangular shaped objects the size of beer cases under blankets. We took out all the shelves in the fridge, stacked the four cases in there, and we were in business. Although we tried to keep the whole thing quiet, word got around. We became the envy of the Mole Hole for having this behemoth in the room.

Unfortunately, the first time I closed the closet, the cord got pinched in the door and threw a bunch of sparks, causing the circuit breaker for the whole floor to trip. All the damn lights went out. Luckily, Everett, the maintenance guy, was sweeping the carpet in the hallway. When his vacuum stopped sucking, he calmly walked over to the circuit breaker and flicked the switch back on. No one investigated what tripped the circuit. So from that time on, as long as we could afford it, we had ice cold beer.

Bill Henderson, another underrated singer. Bill Henderson and Oscar Peterson *album. "I've Got a Crush on You," "I Wish You Love"*

Student Teaching

17,725 draftees died in combat in Vietnam.

One hell of a day! Members of the teaching-methods class were farmed out to the various public schools in the area to begin the student teaching experience. Four of us were going up-river to Middleport/ Pomroy High School.

Sandy Krape, a non-traditional student who was about thirty years old, lived in the trailer park on the west side of Rio Grande. She had a twelve-year-old son and was divorced. Plump, with a big-ass mole on the right side of her nose, she was hard to talk to without fixating on the damn blemish. She had kind of a hillbilly personality, but that was fine. Who was I to stereotype her, anyway? Plus, she was driving the car, and I needed transportation.

Ron Stobursky was one of the members of Pi Delta who did the Indian dance at home games. The poor guy had to carry a small inner tube to sit on because he had an abscess on his tail bone—which dramatically detracted from his Jersey swagger.

Mike Wells was a commuter who was related to Elaine. He was a straight shooter, a really decent guy. What else can I say? And then there was me... So Sandy, Ron, and I left campus and picked up Wells, who was waiting for us in the parking lot of the Eat and Bowl Lanes close to Gallipolis. From there, it took about twenty minutes to get to Middleport/Pomroy High School, which looked like it had been built in the 1920s.

At the front door, Stobursky tripped over the first step and dropped his blue inner tube, provoking nervous laughter from the four of us. Inside, we were immediately hit with the musty old-school smell. There was no sign for the principal's office, so we just stood around while Stobursky went to the bathroom, which was labeled "Boys." For some reason, that also made us laugh, forgetting that just a few years ago, we were going into rooms labeled "Boys" or "Girls" instead of "Men" or "Women."

When Ron came back, we found the principal's office. The secretary was rather hot looking, but she was wearing a wedding ring. Not sure why I noticed this. What was I going to do, ask her for a date? She told us to have a seat, because the principal was in the middle of a phone call. So more damn waiting, but eventually, Principal Charles Bishop took us into his office. He batted the breeze about how rewarding a career in education could be. I guess all the nerves had caught up to me, because I almost fell asleep as this guy rambled on.

So after he went over a bunch of mumbo jumbo about what was expected of us, he farmed us out to our supervising teachers. He personally escorted me down the hall. We passed a girl who looked like she might have been in ninth grade. The principal didn't make any attempt to acknowledge her. She had a shy expression as we approached, probably intending to say hello. But the old guy just kept walking. I told myself I'd hopefully never slight a student like that.

When we found the right classroom, he knocked on the door. Out came Mrs. Apple—Mrs. Wilhelmina Apple, that is. She looked like she was about eighty years old, with lots of wrinkles and shriveled skin on her arms.

He introduced me, but she didn't seem real excited. I could see her students through the window of the door, straining their necks to see what the hell was going on. The principal said Mrs. Apple had been teaching for a long time, but she had young ideas. *Yeah, right!*

I found out later she didn't know she was getting a student teacher. After that, I formed a kind of bond with her. I mean, that was just bullshit. First of all, it was wrong to interrupt her when she was in the middle of a class. And secondly, it was wrong to just spring this on her without even asking.

She said it was nice meeting me and hoped that my experience would be a good one. As she shrank back into her classroom, I thought I saw a trace of smoke coming out of her ears. I thanked Principal Bishop for the orientation and caught up with the other three for the ride back to campus.

That was the extent of our first day at the school. As Sandy drove us back, we all exchanged impressions about our supervisors. It sounded like I wasn't the only one who was less than enthused about this new adventure. Although we didn't say it, we were all confronted with the responsibility of performing in front of kids and bringing the goods on a daily basis. And no more weeknight flights to the Blue Willow for awhile. *[Motherfuckle!]*

The Delfonics, "La La Means I Love You." Nookie music.

Classroom Observations

"One can be intelligent without being particularly logical." –Jean Piaget

So here's the deal. Those damn education classes had done nothing to prepare me for student teaching, let alone *real* teaching. Okay, maybe I hadn't taken them seriously, but the methods class offered little insight into how to approach the various situations in an English class.

Actually, there was one bit of advice that helped. Professor Horton, a short pudgy lady with a big caboose on her, showed the correct way to erase a blackboard. She said you should never erase using a side-to-side motion. You should always use an up-and-down motion. And the empirically proven reason was that when you erase with the side-to-side movement, your back is to the class and your butt is shaking in a suggestive manner. And you don't want to move your butt in a suggestive manner in a high school classroom.

That was basically the extent of my preparation for student teaching. But that was water over the dam, and there was no going back. It was up to me to decipher the code on how to teach teenagers with exploding hormones about dangling participles and the subjunctive mood. So here I was at Middleport/Pomroy High, and like Kurt Vonnegut said in *Cat's Cradle*, Mrs. Apple and all these river kids were part of my karass.

For the next two weeks, I observed the master teacher in her two Latin classes and three tenth grade General English classes. I didn't know shit about Latin. In her first class, Mrs. Apple went through a bunch of verb conjugations. Then the kids did some oral readings in Latin about some of Caesar's war maneuvers.

The kids didn't seem real interested, although I'm sure they believed that Latin was valuable to have under their belt. Since it was an elective class, most who took it were pretty good students, the kind who did whatever the teacher wanted.

In terms of pronunciation, I had no idea if Wilhelmina was doing this correctly. The poor lady had a noticeable lisp, and it was funny because the kids repeated the words with the same lisp. Anyway, I wasn't going to teach Latin, so that meant I only had three English classes, which was bad enough.

The passing bell rang, and the Latin class was finished. Some of the kids stayed in the room for their English class. Just imagine, two straight classes with Mrs. Apple. She was a nice lady, but she was straitlaced, very organized. She had a three-ring binder on her desk which spelled out her every move. I knew I would never be that organized if I ever became a teacher. I'm not even sure I wanted to be that organized.

The kids who came in for the next class were more animated. I had forgotten what it was like back in high school to pass from class to class. It was a brief three minutes of freedom, checking out the girls, goosing some unsuspecting loser, knocking some bastard's books out of his hands, cutting a fart.

So it took a few minutes for the new kids to settle down. As they came in, they all noticed this strange guy in the back of the room. When the bell rang, Mrs. Apple looked at her three-ring binder, and apparently it told her to introduce me. "Class, this is Mr. Dickinger in the back of the room. He is a student at Rio Grande College and will be observing for a few days. Then, he will begin his student teaching experience with you and two other classes."

Some of the kids looked like they couldn't care less. But others saw me as being about sixty years younger than Mrs. Apple, and I assume they kind of liked that. I was wearing decent clothes—clothes that didn't make me look like I was from the 1930s like some of the male faculty.

Then a few of the other kids maybe picked up on the Rio Grande thing. They had heard about the Abbie Hoffman visit and subsequent suspension of students last year. I guessed they might have figured that I was one of those radical college students who smoked pot and burned brassieres, draft cards and American flags.

In any event, I was a brief disruption in the Apple routine, and for most, it seemed like that was a good thing. I started to think that maybe this teaching thing wouldn't be quite as difficult, simply because I was a lot closer chronologically to these kids than most of the other faculty.

Mrs. Apple went back to her binder and followed her schedule, to the letter. The kids slid back in their seats and forced themselves to identify parts of speech and to provide plot details about the short story they had been assigned to read. But every once in awhile, I'd see some of them turning their heads to check me out. Over the next few days, I took notes on how these tenth graders responded in class.

They reflected a wide range of personalities. Some were what you might call the perfect student, showing an interest in the class and the subject matter. Others seemed bored and disinterested. One day, a boy wore his Scout uniform, which to me, showed either big-time balls or extreme naivete. Another was an athlete with bushy sideburns. In a way, they were all individuals but also a reflection of the local society. Each had their own story. Two of them were memorable.

Ted Hairston was one hell of a kid. He was outgoing and tried hard on all the assignments. He looked like he was African-American but had straight black hair. He seemed to fit in well with the rest of the kids. He was reading *Mosby's Raiders* which struck me as odd... a black kid reading about a Confederate war hero.

Charles "Tiny" Richards was the quiet fat kid in the back of the one class. Once in awhile he'd sneeze. And it wasn't just an ordinary sneeze or even just a loud sneeze. It was like his own artistic creation. And he was damn good at it.

You'd hear him revving up in the back row. The whole class came to a grinding halt. Everyone turned around, and Mrs. Apple just froze. Then Tiny started with "Ah... ah... ah..." gasping for air, getting louder with each "ah." And all the kids would gasp with him.

Apparently, they had been doing this since elementary school. When his face was in a painful grimace, he finally blasted a loud orgasmic sneeze, and everyone gasped in relief. Tiny sat there with a big, satisfied grin on his chubby face. It seemed to be so cathartic that I actually expected him to pull out a cigarette and light one up. Poor Mrs. Apple had no choice but to let the class go through this spastic, emotive ritual.

During the first week I arrived at the school, the second marking period came to an end. So it was time for report cards. When I was in high school, somehow the teachers put the grades on the cards by passing them around after school. As a student, I never really thought or cared about how the damn grades got on the report cards.

But at this school, apparently someone decided the procedure needed to be streamlined. So they gave a blank report card to each kid in homeroom. Throughout the day, the teacher would call one student at a time to come up to his or her desk and enter the grade for the marking period. Very time-efficient, right? No problem? I suppose that's how an administrator would see it.

So there was the student, standing in front of the class, with the card in his hand. The teacher would enter the grade in the appropriate box. The kid would look at it, and if he didn't agree with the grade, he'd stand there and get into it with the teacher.

Although the kids all knew it wasn't appropriate to argue with the teacher in front of the class, some just couldn't restrain themselves. After all, kids are pretty sensitive about grades. So that was how report cards were handled at Middleport/Pomroy. And if the kid got a grade he didn't agree with, he'd have to sit there, pissed off, through the whole class. As the day progressed, he'd probably get more and more pissed, until the poor teacher in the last class of the day ended up with students on the verge of committing mass murder.

Then there was the day for the National Honor Society induction. The whole student body was crammed into the old auditorium. On the stage, in neat rows of chairs, were the honor students who were already in the NHS. They were all dressed up, the boys in coats and ties, a few with pocket protectors full of pens and slide rules. The girls wore starched, frilly dresses, two or three of them in white gloves. For these kids, it was a special occasion, as evidenced by their giggly demeanor. After all, except for a few smart athletes and one or two cheerleaders, they were not part of the popular cliques. But this was their day to shine.

The ceremony eventually progressed to the lighting of the four candles symbolizing scholarship, leadership, service, and character. By this time, parts of the student body started to get a little restless. When one of the Honor Society students had trouble lighting a match, some kid in the first row, who had probably been smoking since he was about eight years old, loudly offered his Zippo lighter. Because of the disturbance, he was promptly escorted out of the auditorium, as some of his buddies gave him a round of hoots and cheers.

Now the pump was primed for further disturbances, and things were starting to percolate. A large part of the audience knew there was no possibility they would be chosen for NHS. They were either underachievers, not interested in school, or just plain slow. But others had this thing in the back of their mind that they might have an outside chance.

And here's where the cruel part started. The school had this stupid tradition where members of the NHS would descend from the stage into the audience. They would tap a new member on the shoulder, and the kid would follow them up on stage where they'd get their NHS pin and a rolled up certificate which proclaimed them a member. All fine and dandy, right?

The current members would go into the audience. They'd slide into a row of students and pretend they were going to tap someone on the shoulder, but they'd just stand there behind someone. And the poor kid kept waiting to feel the tap, but it never came, because the damn NHS member would then move to someone else and do the same thing to them. Eventually, they would find all of the new members, but along the way, they'd thoroughly piss off all the others they had faked out.

So by the time these students became seniors, they had seen this farce of a ceremony and were totally turned off by the whole thing. The biggest reason was because most knew the NHS members were rarely true to all four of the virtues. And maybe I was critical of the whole thing because I was never selected for the group, to which I never aspired anyway. *[Motherfuckle!]*

Sam and Dave, "Hold on, I'm Comin'," "Soul Man,"
"You Don't Know What I Know"

The Rubber Hits the Road

"Comfortable shoes and the freedom to leave are the two most important things in life." –Shel Silverstein

I observed Mrs. Apple's classes for about two weeks. Eventually, although it wasn't easy for her, she relinquished one of her classes to me. I kept thinking back to the day the damn principal threw her a curve ball and told her I'd be her student teacher—you know, the one she never said she wanted, the one she didn't know was coming down the pike, the one that was, in a way, a slap in the face.

But all along the way, she acted like a professional and never seemed to hold anything against me for being there. Even so, I could just imagine the wheels turning in her brain about how I might screw up her routine. I might throw the kids off the track that she had tried so hard to control. She'd have to whip them back into shape after I left her classes in total disarray.

Eventually, I got all three English classes, and with Mrs. A's help, I threw the five-paragraph essay format at them. Most kids had a real negative feeling about writing, especially when they were staring at a blank piece of paper. So the five-paragraph format turned out to be a handy method of getting the most threatened kid to get ideas on paper in an organized, lucid manner.

They needed a thesis statement that took a position on some issue. I told them to pick something that pissed them off. After they developed a thesis, they needed three reasons that supported that position. But to be effective, they also had to be aware of any opposing points of view. So then they had to select three opposing reasons to show the other side of the argument.

In order to see both sides, we held mini debates. They had to present both sides of a position. This was pretty hard and often caused some out-and-out hostility. When the classes got a little out of hand, I would see Mrs. Apple in the back of the room, her eyes spinning in their sockets, steam coming out of her ears. But the woman never interrupted and continued to give positive support in whatever stupid or impractical methods I implemented.

All these preliminary exercises built up to the time when the kids had to write the five paragraphs using the prescribed format. Unfortunately for me, this meant I had to read all their pre-writing, which took tons of time back in the dorm, staying up to all hours of the night.

I guess at that point, I was too stupid to realize that an English teacher would do this kind of after-hours crap for thirty or forty years. It wasn't like a damn gym teacher who blew a whistle, rolled out the ball, and collected the same amount in their paycheck.

But when the finished product was presented, it was pretty neat to see what the kids were capable of writing. And it was even neater to see the satisfaction when they saw they were capable of creating a lucid and logical presentation of ideas. And it was all because of the damn five-paragraph essay.

Eventually Mrs. A would ingest massive doses of sedatives which calmed her down enough to leave the room, and I'd be in complete control of the class. Well, that's stretching it a little. I don't think I ever had complete control of the situation, but I was the only adult in the room, let's put it that way.

Mrs. A also let me go beyond the three-ring binder. One day I told the class that they were going to do some creative writing. The hell with the five-paragraph thing. Don't worry about opposing points or thesis statements. I told them I was going to play a musical selection on the record player, and they were supposed to write down what they heard.

"Let your brains go and describe images that come to mind when you hear the music. There are no right or wrong answers. Your grade will be based on your description of the music and on images that the music suggests to you."

I played Carlos Santana's "Treat" from the album with the lion's head on the cover. The selection was an instrumental which went through various tempos and dynamics. I assumed this was something these kids had never heard in a structured classroom. Whether they liked the music or not, it was unique to the class, and they seemed to embrace the assignment.

The selection was only about five minutes long. When it was over, I asked them how they did. They all said they'd like to hear it again, so they could add more details to their notes. And they said I should turn up the volume this time. So that's what I did.

They sat back and grooved to the music, but they also added ideas to their previous list. I told them to use the remainder of the period to expand on their ideas and then take their assignment home and organize their thoughts to illustrate the imagery of the song.

The next day, the kids turned in their papers. When I had a chance to read over them, I was pleasantly surprised at their insights and creativity. Several said we should do more of those kind of assignments. I said I'd work on that, but I didn't want to push it too much, because I was pretty sure this kind of thing would be frowned on by various administrators and school board members. But I had something else I thought the kids would be interested in.

Mrs. Apple's next item in the three-ring binder was a poetry unit. Except for a few girls, most of the kids had a negative response to the idea of iambic pentameter, the Italian sonnet, alliteration... The textbook had some decent selections by poets like Robert Lowell, Wallace Stevens, Marianne Moore, e e cummings, Carl Sandburg, Amiri Baraka, James Dickey, and Gwendolyn Brooks. But the stumbling block was just that... it was a damn textbook.

So after spending the prescribed binder time on the rudiments of verse, I brought in some contemporary songs and introduced them as poems. I typed the lyrics on those stinky spirit master sheets with the blue print and made copies for each kid. Between my record collection and that of a few other people back at Rio, I found enough recordings to keep us busy for a good long time "studying poetry."

So with the sedated Mrs. Apple farmed out to the faculty lounge, the class was off and running with songs like "Twentieth Century Fox" by Jim Morrison; "Suzanne" by Leonard Cohen; "All Along the Watchtower" by Bob Dylan sung by Jimi Hendrix; "No Expectations" by the Stones; "Joe Hill" by Phil Ochs; "Waist Deep in the Big Muddy" by Pete Seeger; "White Rabbit" by Grace Slick; "For What It's Worth" by Stephen Stills; "Puff the Magic Dragon" by Peter Yarrow; and a bunch of Beatles songs like "Norwegian Wood," "I Am the Walrus," "A Day in the Life," and "Within You, Without You." Then, just to show contrast between really good poetry/lyrics and really sappy popular stuff, I played the satiric "The Air" from Frank Zappa's *Uncle Meat* album.

In my eyes, things were pretty hunky dory in the three classes for a few days. Kids were taking an active interest in the imagery and style of the lyrics, and they were listening to rock and roll in Mrs. Apple's classroom. From my perspective, real learning was taking place, but there was just one problem.

The kids were talking about the class to other students in the school, and then those kids would ask their English teachers why they couldn't listen to rock and roll. Then some of them told their older siblings about "Norwegian Wood" or "Puff the Magic Dragon," which some people thought were insinuations about smoking weed.

Finally one day, a janitor was walking by the classroom and heard Jimi Hendrix singing "All Along the Watchtower." He looked through the window of the classroom door and saw some kids doing some serious head bobbing to the music. So he said something to the principal who said something to a member of the John Birch Society who said something to the superintendent of schools who said something to a school board member who said something to a local preacher who said something to my supervising professor for student teaching and finally someone told good old Mrs. Apple who just about died on the fuckin' spot. By the time I was finally confronted with the whole thing, my skinny ass was in a damn sling.

I started to prepare myself for when the cops would come and take me to jail for corruption of minors. But before that happened, I was temporarily suspended from teaching and told to monitor Mrs. Apple as she returned to the classroom.

Now I sat in the back of the room again as Mrs. A tried to salvage her time-honored curriculum and get things back to normal. However, the kids didn't want "normal," and they were unfortunately pretty vocal about it. They complained to their parents and anyone else who would listen, saying they were learning things in my class, and it wasn't just because they wanted to hear music. They were now tuned in to looking for imagery, metaphor, symbol, tone, and devices of sound, all of which were utilized in the various song lyrics.

One of the students, Randy Bentley, had a father who was a professor of British Literature at Ohio University, just up the road from Middleport/Pomroy. Professor Bentley was also a respected member of the school district's board of directors.

He stood up at the specially-called emergency school board meeting and said he believed I was doing a fine job, and I should be given a second chance. His only concern was that I should be more faithful to Mrs. Apple's lesson plans because when I finished my student teaching, she would have a difficult time completing the school year if I had not addressed the pre-set objectives of the course.

Then he suggested I supervise a poetry club after school for those students who wanted to continue with what I had started in the regular classroom. The tight-assed school board reluctantly took the professor's advice, and after a few days, I was back in the saddle, riding the damn three-ring binder.

I also initiated the poetry club as a once-a-week, after-school activity, which was open to any student who wanted to participate. However, because of the extra-curricular time frame, many students couldn't make the meeting. Many lived in rural areas and relied on buses to get home. Athletes couldn't attend because of after-school practices. But there were still several kids who showed up and brought enthusiasm to the group. They also brought their records, song lyrics, and favorite poetry.

Lou Rawls, R&B singer, early albums, Soulin' *and* Live, *both 1966.*

I Need a Ride

Woodstock: Most people who said they were there, really weren't there.

For the first couple meetings of the poetry group, my traveling companions agreed to stay for an hour until the meeting was finished. But then Sandy Krape said she couldn't do that any longer, because Dwayne, her twelve-year-old son, was getting into trouble back at the trailer when she wasn't around. So I had to find another way back to campus.

I told the kids in the poetry group that we'd have to stop our meetings unless I could arrange transportation. The next day after English class, Maria Mapes said her sister could give me a ride since she worked somewhere close to Rio Grande. I said that was cool, but after thinking about it, I wasn't sure if it was a good idea. Riding in a car with two young girls would make me vulnerable to possible false accusations. After all, this was redneck country, and certain elements of the community didn't always display a healthy attitude toward college students. But if I was going to continue the poetry club, I didn't really have much of a choice. So I thanked Maria and told her I'd take her up on the ride.

At the end of the next meeting, Maria walked with me to the front of the school, where we saw her sister waiting in some weird foreign car.

I said to Maria, "That's going to be kind of cramped for you in the back seat, isn't it?"

"Oh, I'm not going with you," she said. "My house is just a block away. My sister'll drive you to your campus. See you tomorrow, Mr. Dickinger."

And with that, she was walking down the street, and I was thinking, *Hmm, this feels a little awkward.*

I looked to my left, and there was this young woman waving at me to get into the car. She said, "Come on, get in. I'll have to push it to get you back to campus and still get to work on time. Maybe next time we could leave a little earlier, okay?"

Before I could answer, she was ripping through first and second gears as my head snapped back, trying to snatch some of my papers that almost flew out the window. The engine in this car was behind the seats, so it was pretty noisy, and she had the radio tuned loudly to some hillbilly station.

My normally awkward first response to a new woman was even more awkward as I tried to get everything arranged on my lap and get my skinny ass adjusted to the passenger seat. I tried to wind up the window, but it didn't seem to want to move, so there was a ton of southeastern Ohio air slapping me in the face. Somehow I blurted out, "I'm Mahlon."

She quickly replied, "Yeah, I know. Mahlon Dickinger. You been creating quite a reputation around these parts lately. All kinds of people know about the stuff you been doing in Mrs. Apple's English classes."

So I said, "Hmm, that doesn't sound very good."

But she went on, "The kids think you're doing a really good job. You're making things more interesting. Maria says she hasn't fallen asleep one time in class since you been teaching. But there's a bunch of old farts in the community who wanted to get you the hell out of there. If it wasn't for Randy Bentley's dad, you'd be back on campus, selecting a new course of study. Somehow, he convinced everyone you should stay."

"Yeah, he really came to my rescue."

"I think it's great what you're doing. It's about time someone got in that school and shook up things."

"Well thanks for the endorsement, but I don't think I'm doing anything really spectacular. There's other teachers doing a lot better job than I am. Poor old Mrs. Apple is a really nice person and teacher." I paused and then said, "Are you sure I'm not inconveniencing you too much with this trip back to campus?"

"No, no. This ain't no problem. I think that club you started after school is important and should be continued. Maria is finally taking an interest in some school activity. She was on the verge of dropping out. She means a lot to me, so I'll do just about anything to look out for her."

"But where do you work? There's not much close to campus that employs anyone."

"I tend bar at The Grande Cafe in Gallipolis. This is a little out of the way, but like I said, I'd do anything to keep Maria involved in school."

"That's really nice of you to take care of her like that. I haven't been in The Grande recently. It was always kind of a dump."

"Well, they tried to fix it up a little. Seems like there are a few more people coming in now."

"I hope they haven't taken the dirty songs out of the jukebox, like 'Golf Game' by Jed and Cousin Sneezy."

"No. They still have that stuff, plus Hank Williams, Ferlin Husky, Patsy Cline, Ernest Tubb, Little Jimmy Dickens... you know. It'd be nice if they put some blues or even some rock and roll in there, but that would probably chase out the hard-timers. You know, they wouldn't want to be forced to sit there and listen to some *Negro* music, to put it kindly."

So then I asked, "What kind of car is this?"

"This? It's a Karmann Ghia. You never seen one before? It's kind of like a spiffed up VW Beetle."

"So how the hell did you find this car in this neck of the woods where about all you see are pickup trucks and big-ass gas hogs?"

"I got it from my boyfriend."

Hmm, boyfriend, eh? That kind of opens up a few more questions. But I was hesitant to push the issue. After all, I'd only been in the car a few minutes and had already talked with her for a longer time than I had with another female in the recent past.

She was taking Rt. 588, and I was trying to keep my eyes on the road through all the hard turns. She didn't seem to have total control of things at the wheel, especially when she was lighting another cigarette while downshifting into a hairpin turn. Meanwhile, I was slamming my foot on the imaginary brake but also trying to get a glimpse of what she looked like.

Attractive, but not the classic beauty, which made her more intriguing. She had great coloring in her cheeks, which were a little fuller than normal, but in a comely kind of way. Her eyes were grey or maybe I should say hazel, and they opened wide when she expressed herself. Her dirty-blonde hair was long and parted in the middle, resting on her back as though she had been driving with the top down.

I was trying to decide how old she was. It was hard to tell because she was covered up in jeans and a blue work shirt which had a small embroidered flower on the collar. I guessed she might be twenty-six or twenty-seven, and I got to thinking, *Hmm, an older woman. She knows things... you know... sex stuff.*

Even though the car was kind of banged up and covered with a ton of road dirt, I said, "This is a neat car. That was nice of your boyfriend to give it to you."

And then she dropped a real bomb. "Well, he didn't really give me the car."

So I thought I'd be cute and said, "What? You stole it from him?"

But she didn't laugh. "About a year and a half ago, he killed himself, and in the suicide note, he said the car was mine."

I thought, *Holy shit.* So I stuttered out, "Hey, I'm sorry. I don't really have to know all this. I'll stop asking questions. I don't even know your name."

She hesitated and then said, "Tavi... my name's Tavi. I don't know why I said that about Smitty. I've had a really tough year. I shouldn't burden you with my problems. For some reason, I just felt comfortable talking to you. I went through some therapy when it happened, but I never really told anyone outside my family about it. I'm sorry."

So there was a long silence of about ten seconds. That was a lot for me to digest. I wasn't used to thinking about someone else's problems like that. I finally said, "He must've been very depressed."

She didn't reply. She just looked straight ahead at the road. I could see she was starting to sob. Then she leaned forward, tears on her cheeks, and pulled off the road. She put her forehead on the steering wheel and her body started shaking. I didn't know what the hell to do or say. Then, all of a sudden, she sat back in the seat.

"He came home from Vietnam. I was really glad to have him back. He seemed fine. He got out of there without any wounds. He lost some weight but looked fine. But he was different. He wasn't happy. He had bad dreams. He couldn't relax. He'd take off on his Indian motorcycle and not return for two or three days. And even though he was happy to be home and was very loving to me, we would have little spats. It seemed like there was nothing I could do to ease the tension."

She paused before adding, "Then one day, he hit me."

I winced and said, "Tavi, you don't have to tell me this."

But she continued, "And even though I loved him, I saw that things weren't going to get any better. So I told him I was leaving. I moved my stuff over to my dad's place, and when I came back two days later to get some more things, I... I found him."

She started sobbing again.

After a minute or so, I said, "Listen, I'm not sure I should be hearing all of this. You seem like a really nice person, and I'm really sorry for all the stuff you've been through, but maybe we should just kind of hold off on this, okay?"

She wiped her eyes, "Yeah, I'm sorry for bringing all this up. You just seemed like an understanding person, and things just started coming out of my mouth. It ain't fair of me to expect that of you. I'm sorry."

"Listen, if you don't want to drive me back to campus after this, I totally understand."

She didn't answer. She eased the car back onto the road. Then, after a minute or two, she straightened her back and said, "No, I said I'd help you out with the ride and I think what you're doing is good for the kids, so I'll be glad to give you the ride. And I won't bring up all that crap like before."

So she continued to drive me back to Rio Grande, and nothing more was said until she dropped me off at the dorm. I thanked her for the ride, and as I was fumbling with the damn door handle, she put her hand on my arm and said, "Mahlon, thanks for listening and not judging me. I won't bring up that shit on our next ride."

And with that, she was gone, kicking up a bunch of loose stones with the Karmann Ghia, heading back to Gallipolis to serve more Stroh's at The Grande. And all kinds of stuff was flying through my head, especially the look in her eyes as she leaned forward to say goodbye. The image of her tear-stained face stayed with me through the evening as I read the kids' papers. Things were sure as hell getting complicated. ***[Motherfuckle!]***

Temptations early years, "Just My Imagination," "Since I Lost My Baby," "My Girl," "Ain't Too Proud to Beg"

Next Ride

"You don't have to burn books to destroy a culture. Just get people to stop reading them." –Ray Bradbury

After a few more days of lesson plans from Mrs. A's three-ring binder, I began to feel more comfortable. Then the poetry group met again, and it was time for my ride back to Rio with Tavi. I said goodbye to Maria, crammed myself into the Ghia, and off we went.

I was going through an approach-avoidance thing. I sure as hell didn't want to go any deeper into her boyfriend issue, but I wanted to see her again and check her out a little more closely. That previous ride was kind of a blur. As I got settled in the car, she gave me a sideways smile, and I saw those eyes, like she was a young kid doing the bashful thing.

I said, "So tell me... what kind of name is Tavi?"

"Actually, it's short for Tavia. It's Scottish and means 'twin'. I had a twin sister, but she died at birth." Then she added, "You know, Mahlon, I'm pretty sure I seen you before. I'm thinking I kicked you and your buddies out of The Grande a couple times."

"Well, we used to drop in on our way back from going up-river, and it was usually around closing. I hope we didn't give you too much of a rough time."

She laughed and said, "No. I got a kick out of your crew." Then she threw a manila envelope on my lap and said, "Here, look at these."

I opened it and found a bunch of 8' x 10" photographs of things like flowers, a cow, trees, and one of Maria with her head thrown back in a big smile. Although black and white, the images were well-defined and very professional—way beyond the quality of regular snapshots.

"These are real good. Where'd you get them?"

"I took them. My dad has his own dark room and lets me develop them at his place."

"You should send them to a magazine or newspaper and get them published."

"Oh, I ain't interested in doing that stuff. I just take pictures for the fun of it."

"What else do you do with your time when you're not serving beer at The Grande?"

"Nothing much. Sometimes I make stepping stones."

"You mean like the things people walk on?"

"Right, but they're ornamental. I pour cement into a circular mold. Then I embed things like dried flowers or clam shells or whatever people want."

"Sounds like you're one of those artsy-fartsy types. So you sell the stones?"

"Sometimes, but I usually just make them for friends or acquaintances. Do you want one?"

I laughed and said, "I don't really have a need for a stepping stone right now, but thanks anyway."

She quickly changed the subject and said, "I'm really sorry about dumping all that stuff on you the last time. It's just that I ain't been too lucky with guys in my life."

And I thought, *Oh geez, here she goes again. I must look like a damn shrink or something.*

She said, "When I was eighteen, I got pregnant. It was all consensual. It wasn't rape or anything. At the time, I was partying a lot and sleeping around—rebelling against my dad and a bunch of other things."

Hmm, pregnant, eh?

"I knew I couldn't have the baby. I didn't really know the guy, so marriage was out of the question, and I wouldn't have been much of a mother for the kid. A friend gave me the phone number of a woman who did abortions across the river. Supposedly, she knew what she was doing and wanted to help girls like me. So out of desperation, I scrounged up some money, drove over the Silver Bridge, and found her place."

I thought, *This is getting a little too deep.*

"I was told to knock on the back door, off the alley. A shabbily dressed woman took me into her kitchen. She wanted to be sure I knew what I was doing and how things were going to work. I was shaking like crazy, but she did her best to calm me down. She warned me there would be pain, but it would subside after the procedure. Then she took me into a room with heavy dark curtains that blocked out all outside light. She told me to take off everything below the waist and to lay back on top of a metal table as she put some towels under me. She opened my legs and inserted something sharp."

I really didn't want to know any more, but she kept going.

"I got nothing for the pain, which was terrible. I soon felt all kinds of stuff coming out. My whole body was shaking. She quickly cleaned me up and packed me with gauze. She said I might experience some cramping and bleeding. But that was it. I gave her the money, seventy-eight bucks—all I could come up with. She said everything should be okay in a few days. And with a smile and a pat on the back, she sent me off. I went home in a daze, but things *didn't* improve. They got much worse, and I had no choice but to go to the hospital. I almost died. I found out that because the abortion had been botched, I wouldn't be able to have children, which was a pretty bad blow."

Oh, geez!

"Then of course, Mom and Dad found out, and all kinds of crap started flying. My mom tried to comfort me, but my dad totally flipped. And I made the mistake of saying the guy who knocked me up was a student at Ohio University. So Dad wanted me to tell him who the guy was. I told him it was a one-night stand and didn't know his name. That just added to his already bad feeling about college kids, especially those hippy-type demonstrators."

So I thought, *Even though I'm attracted to this slightly older babe, I sure as hell don't want to tangle with her old man, especially if he ever found out I had been suspended from Rio and supported the world's biggest hippy/wacko/commie of them all, good old Abbie fuckin' Hoffman.*

But what I actually said was, "Sounds like you've had it pretty rough, with the abortion and your dad and all."

"Yeah, my mom told me that when it comes to men, I'm like a home for strays."

I swallowed hard. *Well, there's no chance an older woman like her would ever want to get involved with me.*

Then she said, "I really don't know why I tell you all this. It gets pretty depressing, but for some reason, I just feel like telling you."

She waited, I guess for my response, but I had none.

So she said, "What about you? What do you do when you're not grading papers or studying for tests and stuff? I'm sure you and your girlfriend have enough going on to distract you from all that crappy school work, right?"

She caught me off guard, and I choked out, "I don't really have a girlfriend right now," hoping to imply that I previously had tons of girls and had just broken up with one.

"I find that hard to believe, Mahlon. I just kind of figured a guy like you, in your last year of college, would be involved... probably planning a wedding soon. You must have something else to distract you."

Trying to think of something besides looking at *Playboy* centerfolds and drinking way too much at the Blue Willow, I said, "I'm kind of into music. I play the piano and alto sax, and I collect jazz and blues records," which ended our conversation because she pulled up in front of the dorm.

She leaned over and said, "Thanks for the talk today. Sometime, we'll have to go to the Snake Pie Lounge."

"The what?"

"Some guy has this place, out beyond Tycoon Lake. He gets bands to come out there to play in his barn. He has a show this Sunday night. You wanna come?"

"I don't know. I'm pretty busy... with school work and stuff."

"Oh, the hell with all that. You think about it. Here's my phone number. Give me a call if you wanna go, okay?"

So I gave her a pen and she wrote her number on the back of my hand.

"I don't know. I'll see. Catch you later."

She took off without returning the pen... damn!

But anyway, I was thinking, *Hmm, I might actually have a date this weekend.*

I dropped off my stuff in the room and went to the cafeteria for supper. Later that evening, while grading papers, I noticed a smudge on the back of my hand and quickly remembered it was her phone number. But about all I could see was 858-42... So I was missing two digits.

Maybe that's a sign... that I shouldn't get involved. Also, I mean... how long and how many dimes would it take to come up with the right phone number?

So I pushed that idea to the back of my brain and tried to get some rest. But I couldn't sleep. I kept thinking about her eyes. Whenever a girl looked at me, even accidentally, I thought, *Hmm, maybe she likes me.*

Eventually, I fell asleep, thinking about Miss February with the bulbous tits.

The original Four Tops with Levi Stubbs: good-time soul music.

Haircut

"Everyone will be famous for fifteen minutes." –Andy Warhol

I slept in on Saturday until 9:30, missing breakfast in the cafeteria. I was too damn hungry to wait for lunch, so I went over to Frank Denny's for one or two of their really great cinnamon buns. Sure enough, they had just stopped making them for the day. So my weekend was off to a piss-poor start.

I walked back to the dorm and checked out the laundry situation. This teaching thing was a pain in the ass because you had to wear clean clothes every damn day.

Since I didn't have an iron or ironing board, I had to get my dress shirts cleaned in Gallipolis. When I first got to Rio, I mailed my shirts back home in a shipping crate. My mom would wash and iron them and send them back. But after awhile, that got to be too much of a pain. Then at one point, I took my shirts to Bernie over in Davis Hall. But that didn't work out for a variety of reasons, but mainly because I couldn't stand her guts. So eventually, I just wore t-shirts or sweat shirts or sweaters.

But when student teaching came along, I had to have a dress shirt every day, so I took them to the A-One Cleaners in Gallipolis, next door to the Last Chance Carryout. If I couldn't find a ride into town, I'd thumb it. On this particular Saturday, I put my dirty shirts into my laundry bag and started walking up toward Rt. 35. Before I got up to the main road, I heard a car coming behind me so I stuck out my thumb and Freddie Bing picked me up.

This old guy must have been about ninety years old. He had been affiliated with Rio for most of his life, first as a student and then as a professor. And supposedly when he was in his prime, he was one of the more interesting profs on campus. In the summers he would go out west and pan for gold or climb the Grand Tetons or other adventurous shit like that. He had a big white, bushy mustache like Mark Twain's but unfortunately had drifted into semi-dementia a few years ago. He was sometimes seen driving on the wrong side of Rt. 35 at a high rate of speed in his big ass 1948 Oldsmobile Club Sedan.

The old guy didn't have much to say after we went through the perfunctory "nice day" shit. I felt sorry for him, because it was obvious his brain was stuck in a damn time warp. However, his right foot was apparently wearing a cement shoe because we were flying down the road at breakneck speed.

Bracing myself, I was reminded of Tavi's driving. Then I started to agonize over calling her about that Snake Pie thing on Sunday night. I wanted to see her, but I didn't know anything about the place. Would it be a bunch of hillbillies or moonshiners or rednecks? And what if her car broke down out there in the boonies? And what if the show went really late and I'd have to get to student teaching the next day? And what if her old man saw her chumming around with me, a damn commie pinko college student? So I was doing a good job of talking myself out of the whole thing. I was always good at that.

Freddie got to Gallipolis in record time and dropped me off at the A-One Cleaners. I gave my shirts to the Italian woman behind the counter and decided to take a walk downtown. Gallipolis was known as the City of the Gauls, reflecting its heritage as a French settlement going back to just after the War of 1812.

It wasn't the typical roughneck river town. It had a nice park which went out to the river's edge. And it had a decent shopping district and a respected hospital. It was also home to a celebrity, Emma "Grandma" Gatewood. She never lived in the town, but her house was on the outskirts. She was the first woman to thru-hike the entire Appalachian Trail. And she did it when she was sixty-seven years old, after raising eleven children and being physically and emotionally abused by her asshole of a husband.

When all her kids were out of the house, she took off, not telling anyone where she was going and hiked the damn trail in sneakers, from Mt. Oglethorpe in Georgia to Maine's Mt. Katahdin. And then she hiked the Trail two more times, plus the damn Oregon Trail from Missouri to Washington State, plus tons of other trails, paths, and mountains. She even got on Groucho Marx's TV show, "You Bet Your Life." She was a relative of Ruth Gavin, one of my English profs.

Anyway, back to Gallipolis. There was a Murphy's 5&10 in town, which had a decent record department, decent at least for me. Many of the records were discounted because they were apparently throwaways from some bigger store where they didn't sell. Every once in awhile, I'd find a jazz record that no one within fifteen miles of the place would buy. If I was lucky, I'd find a good Blue Note album.

One time I found the Beatles' *Magical Mystery Tour* wedged between Andre Kostelanetz and the Ray Conniff Singers. And I was in luck on this day because I found an Impulse album for a buck twenty-nine—*McCoy Tyner Plays Ellington*, with Elvin Jones on drums, Jimmy Garrison on bass, and of course Tyner on piano.

When I left Murphy's, I decided to get a haircut. Over the last year or so, I had let my hair grow. I didn't really change the old Ivy League style. It just got a little longer. Back in Rio Grande, the only barber was the town's mayor/sheriff. His shop was just off the campus which made it accessible... but that was the only good thing about it. He was a nice-enough guy, but he thought he had to entertain every schmuck who came in. He even had a pet squirrel who would come into the shop through a special little window whenever the barber threw down some peanuts.

The old guy liked to brag about how he used to cut Bevo's hair and Newt Oliver's hair and all the other damn b-ball players from back in the day. But the bottom line was he couldn't cut hair for shit. So, for awhile, I'd just wait until I went home to get a haircut. And if things got a little too long before then, I'd cut a few strands off with scissors.

Anyway, I thought I'd give this one Gallipolis barber a try. His shop was on the north side of the town common. So I went in, no appointment required, and took a seat. The atmosphere had a cozy feel, with smells of talc and witch-hazel. There were reproductions on the wall of those crazy dogs playing poker. And then there was the rudimentary pile of newspapers, sports magazines, and copies of *Farm Journal* and *True Detective*.

A few other guys were ahead of me, so I picked up a *Sports Illustrated* and did a little reading. The other men in the shop were, on average, about seventy years old. You could tell they were long-time clientele, talking about all the local yokels, manure spreaders, car transmissions, and other mundane shit like that.

While this chit-chat was going on, one of the old dudes fell asleep. Apparently, the barber thought the place needed a little excitement, so he gave everyone the *shh* sign and started tiptoeing slowly toward the poor guy. He put his mouth right up to the sleeper's ear and yelled at the top of his fuckin' lungs, "HEY!" And of course, the old guy just about crapped in his drawers. All the other pranksters laughed like crazy at the old guy's expense.

So by this time, the congenial barber directed his attention my way and said, "I don't remember seeing you around here, son. Are you new to town?"

Clearing my throat I answered, "I go to Rio Grande College. I came in town to drop off some laundry and thought I'd give you a try for a haircut."

"Well, thanks for coming in." Then he gave me a weird look and said, "By the way, where you from, boy?"

So I went through the whole York, PA thing. And as soon as I identified myself as a college student and an outsider, I saw the other old guys' ears perk up. One of them said, "You ain't one of them commie protesters, are ya?"

I nervously laughed, "Oh no. I wouldn't do anything like that."

After all, I still had to get a haircut, so what good would it do to say I had been suspended for participating in an illegal demonstration, and I thought the damn war should be stopped, and that colored people are just as good as white people, and that Welfare is a good social program?

Apparently, I was convincing enough to make them all think I was not some pinko commie faggot. My turn came and I jumped up on the barber chair. He threw the sheet over me, wrapped the paper strip around my neck, and started snipping. I told him I just wanted a light trim all over.

As my clipped hair fell on the sheet, the old men continued their gabbing. One of them started talking about local vigilante-types who apparently got liquored up on Saturday nights and drove around, looking for some poor black guy to beat up or hoping to find a long haired hippie-type to terrorize. And the old dudes thought those kind of activities were pretty damn funny. They told me it was good I kept my nose clean because you didn't want those damn rascals to catch you doing anything weird.

Right around that time, the barber started putting the warm shaving cream on the back of my neck, which was always a soothing part of a haircut. But as I heard these old bastards laughing about the local rednecks doing their shit, I suddenly realized the straight razor was just a few inches from my jugular.

As the barber wiped off the shaving cream, I broke into a heavy sweat. However, despite all the bad vibes flying around, I looked in the mirror and saw that I actually got a pretty good trim. So I paid the guy two bucks and got the hell out of there.

With the McCoy Tyner record and my empty laundry bag under my arm, I started walking back down Second Avenue. I came to The Grande Cafe where Tavi worked. After that harrowing scene in the barber shop, I figured I could use a beer or two.

The place had changed since the last time I was there, maybe a little cleaner and brighter, but basically the same old place. I wanted to be sure I got real beer instead of that 3.2 crap, so I showed my card to the guy behind the bar and asked for a Stroh's draft and a small bag of pretzels. The Stroh's went down real good, so I quickly ordered another. And as often happened when I drank, my tongue started wagging, so I asked, "Is Tavi working today?"

He said, "She comes in later at 5:00. You know her?"

"I don't really know her that well. I'm doing my student teaching at Middleport/Pomroy High School, and she's the sister of one of my students."

"She's a great gal. She's gone through a lot of shit since Smitty offed himself. But everyone who comes in here really likes her."

"Yeah, there's something about her that's really likable. You don't happen to have her phone number, do you?"

"Sure, give me a minute here."

So he looked through a bunch of papers from under the bar and came up with the number. But before he gave it to me, he said, "Listen Bud, if you're thinking about starting up something with her, just be sure you treat her right, ya hear? Don't do nothing to hurt her. She deserves a lot better than what she's had, okay?"

"Sure, but I don't think anything's gonna happen between her and me."

So I finished the beer and walked out into the bright sunlight.

Then I thought, *What the fuck am I gonna do now? The bartender will say something to her about me being in there and asking about her.*

So as I started walking toward the edge of town, I was kicking myself in the butt, thinking, *Come on, asshole. Make a decision for once in your life.* I came to a phone booth, took out the number, and called her.

The phone rang six times, and then I hung up. Maybe she wasn't home or maybe it was the wrong number or who knows what? So I stood there for a minute or two and called again. This time she answered after the first ring. She sounded like she was out of breath.

"Hey Tavi, this is Mahlon. Do you have a minute?"

"Sure. I was mixing cement for a stepping stone, and I had to wipe off my hands. How you doin', Mahl?"

"I'm doin' good. How about you?"

"Good," she said, giving the word two syllables, with an upward inflection on the second. "So what can I do for you, Mahl?" she said in a flirting voice.

"Well, you said something about going to that Snake Pie thing on Sunday. If you're still planning on going, I think I'd like to go along if that's cool with you."

"Yeah, sure, I'd be happy to take you. I was hopin' you'd wanna go."

"So how's this thing work? What's it cost and stuff like that?"

"Well usually they want you to call them about a week ahead of time, to get an idea how many will be there. But I can call today, and I'm pretty sure we can get in. It's five dollars a head. So how about if I pick you up tomorrow around 6:30, okay?"

"Sounds good. I'll see you in front of the dorm, tomorrow."

"Great, thanks for calling, Mahl. Bye," and she hung up.

I leaned back in the phone booth and took a big breath. I thought to myself, *Tomorrow, I'm going to the Snake Pie Lounge, whatever the hell that is, with this older woman. What the hell have I gotten into?*

I laughed at myself as I walked to the Last Chance and bought a quart of Budweiser. I wrapped the bottle in my laundry bag, put the Tyner album under my arm, and stuck out my thumb. And I couldn't help myself, but I had a big shit-eating grin on my face, and I hadn't smiled like that in a long time.

Billy Preston, piano and organ, toured with Little Richard as a teenager, hooked up with the Beatles; had more musical talent in his little finger than all four of them.

Snake Pie

"I don't want to know what the law is. I want to know who the judge is."
–Roy Cohn

On Sunday morning, I washed a load of underwear, socks, and t-shirts in the dorm's laundry room. Then I spent a big part of the day working on lesson plans and grading papers. That's the stuff I *usually* did on a Sunday night, but hell, this Sunday night I was going on a damn date... with a woman—an older woman.

All through the day, I kept trying to adjust to that thought. I got my outfit arranged: dark charcoal Devonrite slacks, grey t-shirt under tan v-neck sweater, beat up Clarks desert boots, and fake Baracuta jacket with the Alligator patch. Somehow I got through the day, and around 6:30 I saw the light blue Karmann Ghia in front of the dorm.

McGurt wasn't in the room. If he knew about this, he would've made a big fuckin' deal about it. Out through the window I went.

Tavi gave me that bashful look with those hazel eyes and said, "Hi, Mahl. Let's get outta here." I jumped in and she gunned it. She was real animated with a big smile. "So how ya doing? I'm really glad you decided to come along. I think you'll like the show," she said as she searched for a new radio station while flicking a cigarette with her fingers.

She was wearing a short khaki skirt, a jean jacket, and leather moccasins. She had some kind of yellow flower in her hair, which had two little braids that went around to the back of her head. Previously, she always wore jeans, so I hadn't seen her legs. It was hard to keep my eyes off her well-defined calves as she worked the clutch and accelerator.

So to distract me from those legs, I said, "Tavi, tell me about this Snake Pie thing."

She said, "There's this guy, Steve Lesh, who used to be a sound man for some bands. About a year ago, he decided he'd had enough of that, so he took his money, which apparently was quite a lot, and bought this farm out in the boonies. He raises sheep, goats and other critters. He built this little theater in his barn for the purpose of producing shows with really good musicians. They aren't famous, but they're just as good, if not better, than most of the ones we hear on the radio. I guess he still has a lot of contacts in the music industry, so that's how he gets the bands to play in his barn."

I couldn't think why any bands would want to come all the way out to this podunk place just to play in a barn.

Apparently Tavi was reading my mind because she said, "They come because they know they'll get a great reception and to try out new material. Steve doesn't make any money, since he only charges enough to pay the band. He gets people to come through word of mouth. You'll see, when we get there. It's pretty cool."

"Sounds a little strange, but I'm looking forward to it. By the way, what's in this bag?"

"Oh, yeah. I forgot. I brought some wine and snacks. Before the show starts, people do some tailgating in the field where we park."

I opened the bag and pulled out this big-ass bottle of wine... might have been a double magnum. We drove for about half an hour, until we turned left onto a dirt road.

"This'll take us back to the farm," she said. "Hold on, it's a little rough."

We went back this lane with big trees and overgrown weeds on the sides and pot holes all along the way. She was shifting gears all over the place, trying to avoid bottoming out and pulling off the damn muffler.

When we finally got there, I saw the parking lot was this guy's yard next to the farmhouse. There were a bunch of people tailgating as though they were at a football game. One couple had brought two folding chairs and were seated at a small table with a white tablecloth and two lit candles. They were drinking wine and dipping bits of bread into a cheese fondue heated over a can of Sterno. Others were standing around or sitting on blankets, imbibing and snacking. And a few were doing some grass.

This was a diverse group, considering the usual segregated make-up of the surrounding area. Some looked like the college professor type. Others looked like professionals, casually dressed. Some appeared to be actual farmers in their bib overalls. And there were even a few black people. Imagine that!

She parked the Ghia, and Tavi grabbed a blanket from behind her seat. She spread it on the ground, and we squatted down for some wine and snacks. As she was kneeling in a very lady-like manner, she momentarily spread her legs. For a second, I thought my eyes were playing tricks on me. But then I thought, *No, that can't be,* and tried to dismiss it from my horny brain.

She opened the bottle with a corkscrew as though she had done it a thousand times. Then she spread some kind of cheese on a few crackers, and we passed the bottle back and forth. No need for glasses. I wasn't a wine drinker, but this stuff did the trick. We sat there, at first, without saying much.

"I like the wine. It's a step above Ripple and Thunderbird," I said jokingly.

She snickered, "Gee thanks, I guess that was a compliment."

Then I took a bold step and said, "I'm glad I came along. This is a nice diversion from all the school stuff. And you're a nice part of the diversion."

After taking a long pull on the wine, she said, "You're very sweet, Mahl. I feel the same way about being with you. When I come out here to this place, I forget my problems, and it's even nicer to be here with someone like you." Then she said, "Damn, Mahl, this conversation's getting a little mushy, don't you think?"

I laughed and said, "Yeah, but it's a 'nice mushy,' right?"

"Right."

We munched on the cheese and crackers for a little bit and tipped the big-ass bottle of vino. Then she said, "Hey, finish that cracker and then we should go pay and find a good seat inside, okay?"

So we put the snacks and blanket back in the car and took the wine with us as we walked up to the barn. Some bearded guy with long hair was seated at a small wooden table next to the door. He was taking money and stamping people's wrists. When we got up to him, Tavi said, "Hi Steve. I'm Tavi Mapes. I called you yesterday about seats. Do you think you could squeeze the two of us in somewhere?"

He said, "Oh yeah... Tavi. You've been here before, right? Yeah, sure. That'll be ten bucks. Enjoy the show."

We entered the door and went up a flight of unpainted wooden steps to what I assume was once a hay loft. But instead of the typical barn interior, I saw a small stage and a few rows of tightly arranged chairs for about sixty or seventy people. The walls were decorated with enlarged pictures of people like Frank Zappa, Bob Dylan and The Band, Grace Slick, Miles Davis, and John Coltrane.

The atmosphere was that of a small nightclub with no remnants of chickens or straw or other barn stuff. We crammed ourselves into the middle of the second row and waited for the place to fill up. Most people came in carrying wine or small coolers of beer. You could feel an anticipatory buzz in the crowd as though they already knew this would be a good show.

Finally, the band took their places. All black dudes, they were called The House of God Sacred Gospel Steel Band. They had drums, a Hammond B-3 organ, an electric guitar, an electric bass, and, get this, two pedal steel guitars, like the ones used in Hawaiian and country music. And here were these two big black guys sitting behind these steel guitars. I was thinking, *This is strange, very strange, because I never connected black musicians with steel guitars. And I never really liked that country guitar shit.*

Steve-with-the-beard came on stage holding his little son with wild, curly blond hair. He acknowledged the crowd, and they returned the favor. With a slight southern accent he said, "We're in for a real treat, folks. Tonight, we have one of the hardest driving, ass-kicking bands you'll ever hear. Give it up for The House of God Band!"

And before the band could hit a note, the crowd was already screaming, whistling, and stomping their feet. And just like that, they kicked into some hard driving gospel thing at full volume. I have no idea what the name of it was, but they were in top gear from the very first note and they didn't let up.

I looked over at Tavi. She was transfixed, wide-eyed... moving to the music. And then she saw me looking at her, and we both threw our heads back in a big laugh. The band went through several verses at high volume in a lively tempo. Then they slowed things down a bit with "A Change Is Gonna Come," a song I remembered the late Sam Cooke singing.

Out came Monetta, and she leaned right into the song. Impulsively, I put my arm around Tavi and she rested her head on my shoulder. We sat there drinking in the crying sound of this black woman. She put her whole self into it, going all the way up and down the scale of feeling that the song deserves.

When the song was over, the crowd went crazy, and Tavi and I took some big pulls on the wine. The place was heating up and so was

I, still thinking about sitting next to a slightly older woman who possibly wasn't wearing underpants.

As the evening went on, the band kept their intensity at a high level with more gospel-tinged songs. But I guess the Holy Spirit couldn't keep them away from their earthly passions, because they branched into some down-and-dirty blues.

And at that point, in my mind, they were the best damn band in the world. Those guys on the steel guitars played with just as much passion and skill as any Clapton, Beck, or Hendrix. They ended the show with an extended rendition of the gospel song "He's Coming."

Everyone was on their feet, clapping and dancing. Monetta got so involved in the whole thing that she appeared to go into a trance. As she moved around with eyes closed and arms raised, someone actually had to catch her before she fell off the damn stage. At the end of the song, both the House of God Band and the crowd were totally spent as they streamed out of the barn.

Tavi and I had polished off that big-ass bottle of wine. We were well-oiled, as they say. Walking back to the car, I told her I had to take a whiz. She said she did too. Big Steve had previously said that if anyone needed a bathroom, they could go into his house and use his. I told Tavi I'd just go behind a tree. To my surprise, that's what the hell *she* did. As I was watering this big tree, trying to shield myself, she squatted beside me and let it fly. Just opened her legs... no freakin' underwear to pull down.

I thought, *Damn, maybe I should pinch myself.*

When we got in the car, I said, "That was a great show." And I added, "Tavi, I don't mean to be too forward, but did you forget to put on your underwear tonight?"

She laughed loudly and said, "I like the free flow of air down there." And with that, she lifted her right leg and exposed her full glory to me.

Of course, my eyes just about popped out of my damn head, and I said, with a big-ass smile on my face, "Damn, Tavi, you're like no one I've ever known."

And with that, she leaned over and planted a big-ass kiss on my lips. And I kissed her back, and all of a sudden we were groping and kissing like crazy. Then, as headlights from the other cars beamed through the windshield, we both fell against the back of our seats, laughing and out of breath.

So I said, "Where the hell did all that come from?"

"Ever since I've been driving you back to campus," she said, "I've wanted to kiss you like that. I'm sorry, but I think that when you feel strongly about something or someone, you should express those feelings. Life's too short to hold it in."

"You have feelings for me?"

"Yes."

"And you don't think that's jumping the gun a little?"

"No."

So I paused and then said, "Well, I've been attracted to you. But I just thought it was because I hadn't been with a girl in a long time and maybe it was just a physical attraction."

"Well, whether it's physical or not, you have to face that there's a feeling there. And I believe that if you don't act on your feelings, then you're wasting your life away. That may sound stupid and simple, but that's how I feel. That might be a reason why I've had bad luck with guys over the years, but at least I've always been honest with myself and haven't held anything back."

I smiled and said, "Well, you're probably right. It's just that I'm not used to that sort of thing."

And then she put her face right in front of mine, looked me in the eyes and said, very matter-of-factly, "Well Mahl Dickinger, maybe it's fuckin' time you change."

The Allman Brothers. Southern Rock that went much further than the South.

The Roommate

"Lying is done with words and also with silence." –Adrienne Rich

Over the next couple days, I was a different person. I walked with the proverbial spring in my step. I found myself saying hello to people I ordinarily couldn't stand. They looked at me like I had two heads. But I really didn't give a damn. I thought about Tavi and how much fun I had Sunday evening. And how easy she was to talk to and how she continually surprised me with her openness and unpretentiousness. There was nothing about her that bothered me.

She didn't wear makeup or perfume; she didn't need to. She dressed in her own unique but appropriate way. And not that it mattered, but she had a great body, not in terms of the big-boobed *Playboy* figure. Everything was perfectly balanced and feminine.

Her best quality was her voice. It was musical. But she could also cuss like a Marine. Ordinarily I didn't like that in a woman, but with her, the profanities came out in a natural way and were never used to shock or offend. I loved her charm as she "fucked" this and "shit" that. And she never blinked an eye as I shot out a few "assholes" and "motherfuckers." I mean what else could a guy want in a woman, right? And oh yeah... she peed outside. Damn!

But I also thought about the problems she'd had with other guys, and I didn't want to fall into that category... those who disappointed her or took her for granted. Was there something about her that caused her to pick the wrong ones? And was I one of those?

So I still had this approach-avoidance thing. I wanted to be with her, but I'd feel really bad if I hurt her in some way. Then there was also that thing about her old man who hated college boys and who sounded like a redneck asshole. But despite those misgivings, I still thought about her all the time.

Waiting for the next meeting of the poetry club seemed interminable, so one afternoon, I gave her a call. I didn't want to use the pay phone in the Mole Hole, because everyone would hear and I'd get all kinds of damn questions like, "Who is she?" or "What's her name?" or "Is she a townie?" or "You're dating a hillbilly?" So I had to hoof it about half a mile to the phone booth up on Rt. 35 at the Esso station.

It was a Tuesday, around 4:30. When she answered, she didn't have the usual lilt in her voice. She sounded kind of hushed. "Hi, Mahl. I'm sorry, but I can't talk right now. Mike'll be home soon."

And I said, "Who the hell's Mike?"

"He lives with me. It's not what you think, but I have to go. Tomorrow's your poetry club. I'll tell you about it when I pick you up. Sorry, but I gotta go. Bye."

I stood in the phone booth with all kinds of tractor trailers and cars flying by, kicking up loose stones and dust. I kept the receiver at my ear, even though she had hung up. It was like what I just heard didn't register.

I thought I heard her say some guy named Mike lived with her, and he would be home soon. As I left the phone booth, all kinds of shit started flying through my brain. I was pissed at her for not telling me about this. I mean, after all, here I was, finally falling for someone who seemed so damn great, and now she's saying some bastard's living with her.

So I was pissed. And the further I walked, the more pissed I got. Like she was just playing with me, with the no-underwear thing and the kissing thing and the expressing-your-feelings thing and all those other damn things. Maybe she wasn't any different from the sorority bitches and goody-two-shoes and phony babes on campus.

When I got back in the dorm room, I put on two of the most depressing records I could find (Mal Waldron/Eric Dolphy's *The Quest* and the soundtrack from *Who's Afraid of Virginia Wolfe?*), and crawled into bed. Of course, McGurt yelled something like, "I can't stand that shit." But I just ignored him and closed my eyes. *[Motherfuckle!]*

Crosby, Stills, Nash, and Young, tons of talent.

An Explanation

"In three words I can sum up everything I've learned about life: it goes on." –Robert Frost

The next day, I somehow got through the three tenth-grade classes and had a decent poetry club after school, which picked me up a little. We were halfway through discussing the *Sgt. Pepper* album by now.

As I was walking with Maria to the front of the school, I asked her, "What's the deal with this Mike guy Tavi's living with?"

"I really don't know. You'll have to ask her. See you in class tomorrow, Mr. Dickinger." And away she walked.

So trying to keep my cool, I slunk into the passenger seat of the Ghia and looked straight ahead. I didn't say anything because I was afraid the wrong thing would come out.

She opened with, "I guess you want to know about Mike."

I kept looking straight ahead and didn't answer.

"He's just a roommate."

Just a roommate?

Then she said, "When Smitty killed himself, I was a basket case. And although I went to some counseling, I was deeply depressed. But after awhile, I had to get back to work because the bills were piling up, since Smitty and I had shared the cost of the trailer and the other stuff. So I went back to tending bar at The Grande. This guy Mike, who was a regular, would let me unload on him when there wasn't many customers. And although he never had much to say, he was kind of a comfort. His woman had kicked him out, so it was like the two of us were alone at the same time."

I looked straight ahead as she talked.

"So, feeling vulnerable, I told him he could move in with me if he shared the expenses. And that's what he did. Initially, we became intimate. I know that sounds stupid when I was so depressed and all, but that's what happened. But it didn't take long to find out Mike and I are total opposites in personalities, politics, and almost everything else. He works on cars, is into hunting, has all kinds of guns, hates

Negroes, and is basically a functional alcoholic. And none of those things work for me, which he quickly picked up on.

"So we came to an agreement that he could stay if we'd go to separate bedrooms and basically live our own lives. And that's where we are right now. Mahl, you just have to believe me, but Mike and I rarely even speak. He works days, and I work nights. If we have to communicate, we leave a note on the kitchen table."

As I heard this, my anger slowly dissipated. I looked over at her and said, "I just wish you had told me a little earlier."

"Yes, but I didn't think me and you would become a thing, you know? You were my sister's teacher. And then, when I found out what a decent person you were, I didn't want to screw it up, so I just kind of forgot about Mike. I'm sorry."

"So Tavi, if you and I are gonna continue as friends or whatever we are to each other, then I think we should get together and talk things out. I mean, these car trips are nice conversation, but you mean a lot to me, so let's arrange some time so we can really get to know each other. What do you think?"

"Mahl, you mean a lot to me. But I'm not sure about when or where we could do that. We can't meet at my trailer because I never know when Mike'll be around. And I'm guessing the campus isn't the most suitable place either, right?"

So I said, "How about this? Do you know where the Evans Homestead is, just east of Rio Grande on Rt. 35? Directly across from that is a lane that goes back to the Evans recreational area. It's rarely used and there's a hiking trail. Why don't we go back there on Saturday afternoon and take a walk? It's nice."

"Okay. But I have to be at The Grande by 5:00."

"That's fine. Why don't you pick me up around 1:00?"

"Deal."

She took me back to the dorm at her usual Grand Prix speed. And as she pulled in front of Holzer Hall, she leaned over, gave me a smooch, and said, "Tomorrow at 1:00."

Jazz Crusaders, "Way Back Home," bag-full of funk.

Bob Evans' Woods

"If you have to ask what jazz is, you'll never know." –Louis Armstrong

On Saturday, we drove back the long lane to the Evans recreational area. Owned by the Bob Evans estate, it was peaceful with a pond, picnic area, and pavilion.

We started walking and found a stand of mature pine trees that had been planted in straight rows. The bottom branches had been trimmed so it was easy to walk under. The ground had a thick cushion of needles, which provided a pleasing pine aroma. The only sounds were that of birds.

Instead of walking any further, I said, "Tavi, do you still have that blanket in your car?"

"I do. Why?"

"Well, why don't we stretch it out under these pines to just relax a little and talk?"

"Okay... and you might want to bring that six-pack I brought along. I had a feeling you might get a little thirsty."

"You're too much, Tav," and I gave her a smooch before I went to the car.

We spread the blanket on the pine needles and stretched out with beer in hand.

"This is nice back here. I haven't been this relaxed in a long time," I said and leaned over to give her a kiss.

"I feel pretty mellow myself." Then she added with a smile, "I have a feeling I know what's going through your head right now, Mahl."

"So... what?...you're some kind of mind reader? Okay... go ahead. Tell me what I'm thinking."

"I'm thinking... that you're thinking... you want to get your horny hand in these jeans of mine, yes?"

"Well, maybe we should just let the hand do the talking," I replied as I leaned over and gently pushed her on her back. We started kissing as my hand caressed her breast.

"Hmm, no bra today?"

"Or panties," she said with a smile.

"Damn you, girl. You're something else." I started unbuttoning her shirt, and as I did that her hand moved to my crotch.

"Hmm, maybe we should do something about that thing down here."

"Damn, I'd really like to, but I don't have a rubber."

"We don't need one, remember? I can't get pregnant because of the abortion."

"Oh yeah. I forgot. And you trust I won't give you anything?"

"Well Mahl, don't take this the wrong way, but I'm guessing you ain't done much of this sort of thing, right?"

"I guess you know me pretty well."

This was uncharted territory for me. I mean a guy can only read so much about achieving coitus, and a guy can only look at so many centerfolds, and a guy can only read so many *Playboy* Advisers. I mean when it comes to the moment of truth—*il momento delle verita*, as good old Hemingway used to say—when the matador is about to plunge the *verdugo* into the heart of the bull... not that I was plunging any *verdugo*... like you're Karl Wallenda going across Niagara Falls on a fuckin' tightrope.

So all kinds of things were flying through my mind. But I wasn't alone, and without saying anything, Tavi took over.

Things happened pretty quickly, and it seemed that we both came at the same time, as difficult as that might be to believe. She held me tight and told me not to move as she had several spasms while I was inside her. Since this was my first time, I was surprised I got through the whole thing as well as I did, thanks to Tav.

So when she "released me," I rolled onto my back and said, "Tav... do you know how happy you just made me?" I pulled her to me and held her real close and whispered, "Thanks for being so understanding."

"Listen Mahl, and listen good," smiling as she said it. "I've never had a simultaneous orgasm. It's usually been something like, 'wham bam, thank you ma'am,' whether I was ready or not. So the fact that this was our first time and things worked out as they did, I think that means something."

She gave me a deep kiss and wrapped her leg over me.

"I love you, Mahl Dickinger. I love you very much."

I held her tight, feeling her heart beating and feeling her breath on my neck.

"Tavi, you know this is all new to me... and yes, I love you too."

So we lay there for a little bit, looking up through the pines. And then I looked at her and we spontaneously laughed, for no real reason, except that maybe we were really happy at this one particular moment in the fuckin' cosmic flow of things.

Then she said, "I know this is new to you, but I've been here before, and I have a couple words for this afterglow thing."

"Okay, what're the words?"

"Fuck-stupid."

"What?"

"Yeah, fuck-stupid. After sex, both people have this kind of goofy look on their faces. It's like a sleepy smile with your eyes half open, and the brain isn't real quick to respond, and you're just in a kind of silly mood. And I like it, the feeling of being 'fuck-stupid'."

"Yeah. I think I know what you're talking about. And yeah, I like it!"

And with that I pulled her to me, and we rocked back and forth in each other's arms.

Then I said, "So thanks to you, I'm no longer a damn virgin, and because of you, I think I've gotten through this without any psychological scarring, not that I thought that would actually happen. But when you wait as long as I had, all kinds of crazy shit goes through your mind."

"Well Mahl, the pleasure was all mine, and by the way, you were wonderful."

We lay there for a little while, and then I said, "Tavi, there's something in the back of my mind that keeps popping up."

"What's that, Mahl?"

"I keep remembering what your mother said about you being a home for strays and how other guys have hurt you. And I keep hoping I won't be like them, that I won't ever hurt you."

"Well, that's nice of you to show your concern. But Mahl, that's an example of how you over-think things. And like I told you before, it's time to get away from calculating your every move and to go with your gut. I guess that can be scary if you ain't done it before, but in the long run, you'll be happier. But that's just my opinion."

"Well, I went with my gut a year ago and got suspended. At the time, I was upset, but now I don't regret it. And although it's hard to admit, I've always shied away from doing things beyond the comfort range. So you're probably right, but it's hard to change."

"Well, Sweet Face, I'm thinking if I'm around, maybe I can push you in the other direction. What do you think?"

Freddie Hubbard, big-time trumpet, played with all the greats of his day.

Easter Break

"In the spring, at the end of the day, you should smell like dirt."
–Margaret Atwood

The college had a week-long Spring break over the Easter holiday. Because I was student teaching and the high school vacation was for only two days, I didn't go home to Pennsylvania. But it turned out that every other bastard in the dorm was going home.

I had to arrange things with Mrs. Rimmel, the dorm mother, so I could stay. Hell, even she was leaving. She told me the whole place would be locked up, but apparently she trusted me with a key to get in and out.

So I had the whole dorm to myself. After the first couple days, I felt kind of uneasy because it was really, really quiet. I didn't mind being by myself, but like I said, it was really fuckin' quiet. No washers or dryers running, no showers spraying, no radios blaring, no BS sessions, no farting, no pooping, no snoring, no fuckin' nothing. I started having paranoid thoughts about a bunch of local redneck bastards coming by and ransacking the place. And then I thought, *Damn! Why don't I call up Tavi and tell her to come over and keep me company?*

So on Saturday afternoon, that's what the hell I did.

"Hello Tavi, how ya doing?"

"Hey, Mahl. This is a nice surprise."

"So listen. I was given permission to stay in the dorm over Easter break because I'm doing the student teaching thing, and everyone else has taken off. And I was just thinking, since I'm the only son of a bitch in the dorm this weekend, maybe you could meet up with me here in Room 12. We could listen to some of my records, if you know what I mean."

With a laugh she said, "Hmm, I think I'm getting your drift, Mahl. But I have to work tonight, and I won't get off until 2:00 A.M., which means I wouldn't get to your dorm until about 2:30. But that's cool with me, because I'd really like to *listen to your records*." And she let out a teasing little laugh.

"I hate the idea of you driving around when all the damn drunks are on the road."

"That's real sweet of you, but I think I can handle things, so let's just say I'll see you around 2:30?"

"Okay. But be careful, ya hear?"

"I'll be careful. See you in a few hours. Bye."

I spent the rest of my Saturday grading papers, planning lessons, and I even added some pages to the damn Educational Research paper. Around 11:30, I guess I fell asleep. I had kept my desk lamp on so Tavi would know what room I was in. Then around 2:15 I heard tapping on the window, and there she was. I jumped up, let her inside, and gave her a big hug and kiss.

"Geez Tav, you must have gone about eighty on your way here."

She laughed and said, "Not really. My boss told me I didn't have to help clean up and he let me go early. So here I is."

But being the always cautious bastard, I said, "Ya know, I'm thinking it might be a good idea to park your Ghia around the back of the dorm. If your dad or some of his buddies see your car, that might cause those redneck types to start up some trouble."

"Yeah, I suppose you're right about that."

So she hopped out the window and drove around to the back of the dorm. I let her in through the rear entrance, and we went back to my room. "So this is where my honey lives, eh? Interesting wall decorations, Mahl."

"Yeah, real interesting. Look at them all you want, but let's get down to business, okay?"

I grabbed her in my arms and started planting a bunch of kisses on her. But I sensed something was wrong, so I let her go and said, "You alright?"

"Yes Mahl, I'm fine. But I'm really tired."

"That's cool. Why don't we just lay down and get some sleep?"

"That would be nice. Sorry."

"Hey, I'm just happy you're here. We can fool around later."

"Yes, I want to, real bad, but I'm really tired right now."

"Sure, I understand. How 'bout if I get a towel and washcloth and take you down to the bathroom and then we'll catch some Zs?"

"That'd be great."

So we went down the hall, and she freshened up. Then we came back to the room, took off our clothes, flicked off the light, and crawled into my narrow bed.

"Damn Tav, it is so good to have you here, to feel you against me. I love you very much."

"Yes, Mahl. I love you too, and yes I love being here with you. And I will make it up to you in the morning."

She kissed me as we both relaxed and drifted off. Let me change that. She drifted off. I lay there and looked at her. The moon shone through the window, so I could still see her. And I lay there, smiling. And I was probably the most contented I had ever been.

We both slept like we were dead to the world and didn't wake up until about 8:00. Well, that wasn't quite true. My love muscle woke up at 6:00. I was ready to go, but Tavi was sleeping so good, I didn't want to disturb her. So around 8:00 I nudged against her, and she slowly came back to the world with a sleepy smile. She gave me a kiss, which tasted like her last smoke.

She put her leg over me as she became quickly aroused. We started kissing... kissing all over, like we were trying to consume each other, and our hands were caressing, squeezing, clutching. She got on top of me, guiding me into her, and she moved quickly, back and forth, with an urgency I hadn't felt before. She leaned forward on top of me as she wrapped her arms around my shoulders, and we were as tight together as two people could possibly be.

Then she said, "Roll over, quick. I want you on top."

She was looking straight into my eyes and almost crying as we both came at the same time. I collapsed on her as she put her arms around me and held on real tight.

She said, "Don't you dare move," as she had several spasms.

So we just lay there like that for two or three minutes, feeling each other's heart beating, feeling each other's breathing, not saying anything.

So I said, "Are you sure I'm not too heavy for you?"

"Don't fuckin' move, okay? Don't move."

Eventually, I felt a little tap on the shoulder, so I rolled off and looked at her watery eyes and kissed her softly.

"Why are you crying?"

"I'm not. I'm just so happy being here with you. I know this is all so sappy and mushy, but Mahl, I love you so much."

"I love you too Tav, very much."

So we both held each other as I stroked her arm and hair. Everything seemed to be right with the world.

Then she said, with a bit of urgency, "I gotta pee."

So I said, "Let's go down to the bathroom, and we'll take a shower, okay?"

"Okay, but hurry, I gotta pee."

So I got some toiletries, and we ran to the bathroom. I turned on all the showers as hot as they'd go. As the steam started to rise, we both peed right there in the damn shower. And I know this sounds quirky, but watching her pee was a turn-on. And she said the same about watching me.

So as the temperature started rising and we started rubbing soap over each other, we both got into that aroused state again. And although it was a little soon for me, we still gave it a try. We were laughing and clutching at each other and having a great fuckin' time.

As we rinsed off, I kept the showers running on hot to keep the bathroom warm. I put my terrycloth robe on her shoulders, and we went out of the shower room to the sinks to brush our teeth. I shared my toothbrush, which didn't seem to bother her. Then we made our way back to Room 12.

As I started grabbing a few things to wear, Tavi plopped herself on her back on my bed, still with my robe on but the front wide open. And when I looked at her, with those great eyes and that fuck-stupid smile on her face, I thought she was the most beautiful woman I had ever seen.

"What're you doing, Mahl? Don't put nothing on. Let's spend Easter Sunday in bed, bare nekkid. What d'ya think, huh?"

"Well hell yeah, hon!"

So I crawled in beside her. After awhile I said, "Hey, I almost forgot. You came here to listen to records, right?"

"Oh yeah. Why don't you put something on the turntable?"

I stacked some Chet Baker, Miles Davis, and that great Coltrane album with Johnny Hartman. And although Tavi didn't ordinarily listen to this stuff, she said she liked it, so we re-snuggled.

McCoy Tyner, piano, Blue Note albums, one of my all-time favorites, part of Trane's classic group, great side-man and soloist.

Her Old Man

"We're in very bad trouble if we don't understand the planet we're trying to save." –Carl Sagan

Any time I was around Tavi, she'd eventually start talking about her past. I figured it was good for her to unload. So as we pressed flesh under the gaze of centerfolds and beer signs in Room 12, she started talking about her dad.

"He has all kinds of folksy and crude sayings for every occasion. He's also a talented singer and guitar player with his own country and western group called The Oldtimers. Even believes he's the reincarnation of Hank Williams."

I sensed a long dissertation coming on.

"And even though he has a good job at the Kyger Creek power plant, spending evenings singing in bars takes him away from my mom and Maria. This adds to his problems because he drinks too much and flirts too much. In fact, my mom thinks he has a woman on the side. Of course, when she confronts him, that causes all kinds of verbal and sometimes physical fights. When I was still living at home, I would try to intervene, but then he'd turn his anger on me. One time, I was afraid he was going to hit her, so I jumped on his back. He threw me off, and I landed against the refrigerator, causing a gash on my forehead. That's how I got this scar."

She pulled her hair back so I could see.

"When I turned seventeen, I decided I couldn't take his shit no more, so I got a part-time job at a car wash and another at the movie theater in Gallipolis. That gave me enough money to rent the trailer I'm living in now. Somehow I finished high school. A few people, both guys and gals, moved in with me, and we had a kind of commune thing going there. We shared the rent and food and just about everything else—a lot of fun, but it wasn't the healthiest environment. I felt bad leaving my mom and Maria to deal with the old man. Then he disowned me. But I still had a guilty kind of love for him."

I couldn't stop thinking about the "sharing everything."

"And then, one of Dad's buddies told him if he didn't change his drinking and carousing ways, he'd end up going to hell. But if he brought the Lord Jesus Christ into his heart, his life would dramatically improve. So I guess my dad was feeling pretty down and out and remorseful, and he started going to this guy's church, across the river in some little hollow over there. It turned out to be one of those crazy-ass snake-handling churches."

Snakes in church?

"After attending one or two services, he decided he had actually accepted the Lord Jesus into his heart of hearts. He told Mom, Maria and me he was sorry for all the grief he had caused, and he wanted to share his new-found faith by taking us all to one of these church services. He thought he was really changed. So one hot, steamy Wednesday evening, we all piled into the station wagon and drove over the Silver Bridge into Point Pleasant and beyond. It took us about thirty minutes to find the place, back off some lonely, two-lane blacktop. From the outside, it didn't look like a church. It was just a four-sided cinder block building with a few small windows, which were all open because there wasn't no air conditioning. We walked inside and took a seat on one of the green painted benches. The only things that looked like a church was a crude pulpit and an altar with a cross. On the front wall was painted 'Mark 16: 17-18'."

Didn't remember that one from Sunday School.

"As we sat there, waiting for the service to start, we heard hissing sounds coming from three boxes in front of the pulpit. And the contents of those boxes were, of course, the snakes... copperheads, timber rattlers, water moccasins, and any other kind they could round up."

Tavi scrunched up her shoulders.

"Then the music started. There were two drums sets, two electric guitars, and an old upright piano. There were a few men in the front just kind of hanging around, some with tambourines and others with small cymbals. So these guys started whipping things up. The guitars sounded like the typical, twangy country stuff but a lot louder, and the drummers were banging the hell out of the drum sets with no particular rhythm. As the men began dancing around, the music got louder. And then, as things started heating up, they got the snakes out of the boxes. At first, they handled them kind of gingerly, but after a whole lot more whooping and hollering, they got out more snakes, and rubbed them over their necks and their heads, and they weren't holding just one but rather clumps of snakes."

I wondered how that would go over in the Lutheran Book of Worship.

"By this time, the rest of the congregation started moving toward the front, dancing with their hands in the air, some with their heads back and eyes closed. They seemed to go into a trance, shaking and speaking nonsense words."

These people are nuts.

"And as if this snake thing wasn't crazy enough, the minister got out a Mason jar from the back of the pulpit. He held it up for all to see the skull and crossbones label, and then, unbelievably, he took a few gulps of that shit. The bottle was filled with strychnine. Yes, Mahl, fucking poison."

Hmm, maybe the Lutherans should try that.

"Then someone else got a Coke bottle from the pulpit and lit a fuse that was saturated in kerosene. This guy put his hand in the flame. And Mahl, at this point, I just couldn't take it any longer, so I got up with Maria, and we ran out the damn door. My dad didn't even know we left because he was so caught up in the crazy show. So Maria and I jumped in the Chevy and waited for it to end. I pitied Mom, stuck in there trying to give Dad the benefit of the doubt."

Agitated, Tavi got up and started pacing back and forth.

"With the obvious weirdness of the snakes and all that, I just didn't want to be in there. And although the whole thing was so stupid, I actually pitied those people. Most of them seemed to be very poor. They wore old, frayed clothes. Many were missing teeth. And I ain't judging them, but I couldn't help thinking their poverty and ignorance pushed them into believing this terrible thing."

I was listening but also distracted by her lack of clothes as she gestured and paced.

"And yes, there is a passage about this snake-thing in the Bible—that verse painted on the front wall of the church—something about picking up snakes and drinking deadly poison and if you're a believer, you ain't gonna get hurt. I ain't knocking them for believing this stuff. But on the other hand, there are people from other congregations who have been bitten by snakes and died. Or the venom caused them to lose feeling in their fingers."

She pulled up a chair and looked right at me, her voice raised.

"Hell Mahl, this one pastor was bitten, and after three hours, his kidneys shut down, but he refused anti-venom treatment, and then he died a gruesome death. Another man was bitten and he couldn't breathe. A hundred people prayed their brains out, and somehow he survived. He can't talk real clearly no more, but he continues to handle snakes and believes if he is anointed by God, he won't die. But to me, that all seemed really stupid, whether you're religious or not, intelligent or not. It's just really fuckin' wrong! But my dad always came out of these services as a changed man. And for a few days, he wouldn't drink or carouse as much, and he would treat Mom and Maria and even me in a better way. But of course, he'd backslide. So Mahl, that's my dad."

I hesitated and then said, "Geez Tav, that's quite a story. I feel really bad about all the crap you've gone through. Whether it's because of your dad or not, I know for sure you're a good person, and I'm really glad you came into my life."

"Well, I'm sorry for dumping all this on you but thanks for listening." And then, she leaned over and gave me a kiss. "Let's change the mood a little, what do you think?"

"Good thinking."

I jumped up and put on the *Song for My Father* album by Horace Silver, not because she had just talked about her dad, but because I love the record. I turned it down a little and we jumped back in the sack. We held each other, and one thing led to another, if you know what I mean.

We spent the rest of the day in bed, bare-ass naked. Because all the local food places were closed, I had to scrounge around for something to eat. So I went through all of McGurt's shit and found nothing, of course. But then I dug up some packets of saltines I had squirreled away in the back of one of my dresser drawers.

I opened a can of peach halves and plopped them on the electric skillet. I only had one fork, so after the peaches got hot, I stuck the fork in the middle of one, and the two of us ate around it, which led to some sloppy, peach-flavored smooches.

Then we ate the saltines, which made our mouths really dry, so I dug out some bottles of Gibbons from the frig in my closet, and we got a little looped. We poured the juice from the canned peaches over our bodies and licked it off, which was one hell of a turn-on. Then we had to run down to the bathroom and wash it off so we wouldn't get all sticky. Well, that was another damn turn-on, and we got all hot and bothered down there and took one in the damn shower room. So it turned out to be the best Easter Sunday in my whole damn life, and I decided right then and there that I wanted to marry Tavi and live with her, happily ever after.

Jimmy Smith, Hammond B-3 organ, big-time funk.

Tavi's Letters

"Follow your inner moonlight; don't hide the madness." –Allen Ginsberg

Because Tavi was living with Mike and because I lived in the dorm and because her Ghia didn't have much of a back seat and because we couldn't go to motels all the time and because I didn't feel comfortable talking on the phone in the Mole Hole and because the poetry club only met once a week and because of a bunch of other reasons, we didn't really have a lot of opportunities to communicate in an intimate way. So we started sending letters, even though we were only a few miles apart. And in the same way she talked, Tavi's letters were lucid, creative, heartfelt, almost poetic, and I looked forward to every one of them.

Sweetest Face,

As I was driving to The Grande after dropping you off, the sky appeared eerie, dark... and very low. The clouds were heavy... and huge rain droplets started to pound on my windshield. Ahh yes... a small approaching spring storm. Did I ever tell you I love thunderstorms? I love the smell of them, and the way the rain showers hit the trees. It's like they are reaching upward and sucking it up... then the droplets land and bounce all over the place. The buds on the trees are appearing so fast you can almost see them open if you look close. The pussywillow outside my door has buds opening all over it. One day during a storm, I was snuggled on the couch, and I just drifted in silence with the sound of rumbling thunder. Something cozy about it, and I of course thought of you. My longing feeling to be with you, and how great it would be to lay my head on your chest, arms around you, close, kissing you softly, and taking in the moment... Yes honey, that's it... I just want to reach out to you, take you in... and absorb you... just like the trees in a summer shower... I love you, Mahl...until summer showers are no more... Soft kisses...

Tav

Good Morning Honey,

It was so nice to talk with you yesterday afternoon on our drive. I've become so comfortable with our chats. It's almost as if it's an addiction. I thought about what it would be like without these conversations, and it gave me a sinking kind of feeling. I can speak to you so freely, about anything, and I do. What I am trying to say here is I totally enjoy that part of our "thing." The fact that anything can roll off my lips, at any given moment... and you receive these sometimes very explicit comments, as though they are nothing out of the ordinary. Not just our talks in the car... but our conversations when we finally get a chance to be intimate and up close and personal. Like how great it feels to share your body with mine in the closest and most frenzied way and how I can say all these things to you and how I don't feel inhibited or cheap and how much I love being with you and how I could go on and on. That's where we both are so comfortable. Being with you gives me a feeling of freedom I ain't felt with anyone else before. So... that, my dear, is something ordinary people just don't do! I love you, Mahl... Kisses under the full moon.

Tav

Joni Mitchell, non-compromising artist who influenced contemporary music.

Tavi and Mahl, a Couple

"The most wasted of all days is one without laughter." –e e cummings

With this older, free-spirited woman in my life, I started to feel pretty damn good about myself. Although I wasn't aware of it, my ego started ballooning way out of proportion. After all, Tavi said all the right things to me.

She liked my smile and she liked my butt and she said my love muscle was the best she ever had. But besides all that physical stuff, she made me feel good just by being there, having someone to hug and kiss and laugh with. That might seem mundane and normal to most people, but to someone like me, Tav was an elixir, and I wanted to be with her as much as possible.

She continued to drive me back to campus after the poetry group. We always had good talks, which covered all kinds of topics. Even though she only had a high school education, it was obvious she was pretty damn smart... a lot smarter than me.

Coming from big-time hillbilly country, she had some of that twang in her voice. She used double negatives and dangling participles, but she was always lucid and logical. I never got tired of hearing her talk and laugh. She didn't read fiction or poetry, but she was very much aware of the big issues of the day, like the war and nuclear proliferation and civil rights and poverty, which was evidenced especially in her neck of the woods.

Tav was into music and knew the lyrics to just about every damn song from the last ten years, including country and western, rock and roll, R&B and all the popular shit. And unlike many people, she was open to learning about jazz. Of course, there was the artsy-fartsy side of her with her stepping stones that she crafted, but her real talent was her photography.

One time we decided to splurge and got a room at the College View Motel. Like I said, we didn't have many opportunities to be intimate. She went into the office and paid for the room. In those days, there was still the stigma about non-marrieds shacking up, and this part of the Ohio Bible Belt was no exception.

Once we got in the room and got accustomed to the musty smell and checked for bed bugs and other living or dead things, it didn't take us long to get down to business. It was a great release to do that without going to some secluded spot in the woods or going through all kinds of contortions in the damn Karmann Ghia in search of the ultimate coitus.

But as we fell into the fuck-stupid afterglow, Tavi said, "I think that motel manager might've recognized me. He might be a buddy of my old man. He didn't say nothing, probably because he wanted my damn money, but I just got the feeling he knows who I am." That drew a pall over the situation, because this guy might tell Tavi's old man about her being there.

But then she said, "Oh fuck it, Mahl. Let's forget about that shit and have some fun."

So she pulled out one of the cameras she always had with her and took the shade off the lamp on the dresser so there was plenty of light. She started taking pictures of me, some flattering and some not so flattering, in my birthday suit.

Then she placed the camera on the night stand and set the timer so she could get in the shot with me. We had a lot of fun posing in all kinds of crazy positions. And by rolling around on the bed with no damn clothes on, we got excited again and had to take care of things. Somehow, using the timer on the camera, she even got some shots of us doing the dirty deed.

After awhile, we got really hungry. We dressed and drove to the Bob Evans sausage shop about a half mile down the road. I had some of that fantastic fart-inducing chili, and Tavi had a damn tossed salad since she had recently decided she didn't want to eat meat. Something about a time she was following a truck filled with chickens in cages on the way to slaughter and she thought most of them were already dead or half dead.

But she didn't cast any aspersions because I still loved ground chuck, rib-eyes, smoked sausage, and all that other really great red meat crap. Our day together quickly came to a close because Tav had to get to work at The Grande.

Some of the guys in the Mole Hole noticed I was being picked up and dropped off in a light blue Karmann Ghia, which meant I had to come clean about Tavi. Although I usually wasn't the boastful type, I started bragging about how I was seeing this older woman and how really great she was.

I also mentioned the show at the Snake Pie, which none of the guys had ever heard of. I said some things about how there were blacks and hippies and dopers hanging out there. I probably shouldn't have said that because some of those assholes didn't necessarily like blacks or hippies or dopers. You never knew what the hell those guys might pass on to the redneck types in the surrounding area.

Eventually, my student teaching stint was finished. When I walked out of the high school for the last time, I hadn't realized how much I had bonded with some of the kids, especially those who were regulars in the after-school poetry club.

I said goodbye to all of them and profusely thanked Mrs. Apple for putting up with me. But then I had to get back to my studies to be sure I had enough credits to graduate. That meant I wouldn't be seeing as much of Tavi.

We kept writing letters and talking on the phone, and we still saw each other whenever possible. But apparently I didn't have a good grasp on how Tavi felt about things.

She said it hurt, physically, to be away from me. I was touched but also alarmed that maybe she was too hung up on me, if that makes any sense. One time, when she dropped me off at the dorm, she told me to do a little dance to make her laugh, because sometimes she cried as she drove away.

Keith Jarrett, piano genius, played with Art Blakey, Charles Lloyd, Miles Davis. His Koln Concert *is a classic.*

Kent State and Tricky Dick

"Peace on earth would mean the end of civilization as we know it." –Joseph Heller, author of Catch-22

Tavi and I spent as much time together as possible, but our meet-ups were infrequent. So I'd hang around with some of the Mole Hole guys. Monday, May 4, I was sitting at a table at the Redman, drinking some 3.2 with Tom Shelley and John Borsa. Across the room, a TV was turned on above the bar. When the news report came on, we immediately ran up to the TV and instinctively shouted, "*No!*" We didn't want to believe it, but I knew something like this was going to happen.

For several weeks, there was a bad feeling, even all the way down at Reo Rio, that things were spiraling out of control, not only in Nam but also on campuses throughout the country. Nixon ordered the Cambodian invasion, saying this would bring a quicker end to the war. You know... like how effective was all that other bombing? (End of war stat: 4000 B-52 bombing runs, 110,000 pounds of ordinance.)

So Tricky Dick wanted to kill more gooks—Cambodian this time—tipping the scales even more for the anti-war protests. Kent State was boiling. On the previous Friday night, students spilled out of bars into the streets, throwing beer bottles at cops, who responded with tear gas. So tensions were sky high. The mayor of Kent called a state of emergency and closed all the bars.

The next day, Saturday, things got ratcheted up even higher when the mayor said he had received threats that the protesters were planning to destroy the town and campus. I found that hard to believe, but by announcing this, in his own stupid way, he encouraged what was to follow. The National Guard showed up at 10:00 P.M., which fueled the 1000 protesters in the streets, resulting in the ROTC building being set ablaze.

On Sunday, Governor Rhodes went off big-time by making all kinds of incendiary statements. He said the protesters were the most militant revolutionaries that ever assembled in America. "I've taken enough crap from these bums and I'm going to eradicate the problem, using whatever means possible."

Around 8:00 P.M., a large group of students staged a sit-in. Of course, the good old National Guard responded with tear gas and bayonets, causing various injuries. In the eyes of the protesters, those acts basically told them war had been declared.

On Monday, the previously scheduled protest took place on the Commons. With the use of pamphlets and bull horns, the University declared the protest to be illegal, and those who ignored the warnings would be arrested. Around noon about 2000 protesters showed up. When the National Guard told them to disperse, the students started throwing rocks.

The Guard fixed their bayonets and advanced. A lot of the crowd left the scene, but the Guard kept moving in a straight line, not really knowing where they were going. They ended up on an athletic practice field, boxed in on three sides by chain-linked fencing.

The students picked up on this, and the noise and commotion rose. The members of the Guard were shitting themselves, even though they had rifles, pistols, and tear gas. Some witnesses said they saw them forming like a huddle, trying to decide their next move.

After a few minutes, several of the Guard knelt on one knee with rifles aimed at the students. Sure enough the bastards started firing away indiscriminately, sixty-seven rounds. Four students killed, nine wounded. Two of the dead were not part of the demonstration.

Those shootings were not justified. The Guard was not in danger. They were armed, and the students were not. But this extreme example was emblematic of how ill-equipped the government was in handling the protest. It never had to get to that point.

A few days after the Kent State disaster, a similar event occurred at Jackson State, only this time there were two black students killed and twelve others wounded. And guess what? This didn't receive nearly the attention that Kent State did, almost certainly because these were black students.

And to show how out of touch Tricky Dick Nixon was with things, on May 9th around 4:00 A.M. in D.C., he went over to the Lincoln Memorial where tons of protesters were assembled. That's right. 4:00 in the morning. Here comes the world's biggest asshole to talk about war and peace. And he said some of the dumbest crap that ever came out of a politician's mouth.

He talked about college football. Like these kids, who were trying to stop the damn war, wanted to talk about football. Then he talked about his Quaker mother and how hard it was for him to participate in WWII because she was a pacifist and he was by nature a peaceful person. Yeah, right! The bastard spent most of his time in the Navy playing five-card stud. A few days after Kent State, he was quoted as saying all college protesters were bums. *[Motherfuckle!]*

Leon Russell, piano, composer, producer. "A Song for You," great song. Worked with Beach Boys, Clapton, Ringo, George Harrison, Elton John, Dylan, Sinatra, the Stones, Ike and Tina Turner.

Draft Physical and the Lottery

1863: forty-one regulations for not being drafted into the Union Army. Top of the list: manifest imbecility.

Things were going real well with Tavi and me, when just before graduation, I got a letter from the Selective Service, ordering me to get my physical. Apparently, colleges were instructed to notify the Selective Service when seniors were about to graduate. I hitched into Gallipolis, got on a government bus with a bunch of other bastards, and off we went on a fifty-mile ride to the god-forsaken town of Ashland, Kentucky.

I'm sure my physical was just as daunting as everyone else's, but that was no consolation. For most of the time, we sat in our underpants. Some of those guys looked like they had just crawled out from under a rock and hadn't washed in months. Others had gone to great lengths to beat the system. Some tried the emaciated look, while others must have insanely stuffed themselves to go for the obesity deferment.

When the hearing and sight tests were given, some bastards tried to fake being deaf or blind. There were more elaborate attempts, of course, but I was so depressed at that point that I really didn't give a rat's ass what others were scheming. I wasn't that motivated or ingenious. Plus, at this time, they were taking just about anyone who had a pulse.

The physical exam itself didn't bother me as much as this Navy bastard who looked like he was fifteen years old. He read the instructions, word-for-fuckin'-word. I kept thinking this would be just the start of many others like him who would order me around, and that was a pretty sobering thought.

I passed with flying colors thanks to my good health. If I had known at the time that I had Brittle Spine Disease, that might have made a difference. But like I said before, in the Spring of 1970, they were taking just about everyone. Tavi was pretty broken up about it, probably more than me.

All of this draft crap illustrated how unfair the system was. Those poor guys who didn't have the money or inclination for college were prime bait. Honestly, college guys were no better than the non-college guys, in terms of being fodder for a Viet Cong machine gun. So the whole SS program and the damn war sucked the big one, big-time. *[Motherfuckle!]*

Maynard Ferguson, trumpet. Could hit the high notes like no one else. The Blues Roar, *great album. Led big bands with great personnel.*

Graduation

"Courage is being scared to death... and saddling up anyway."
–John Wayne, who never served in the military

Up to this point, I hadn't mentioned anything about Tavi to my parents. It was just something that never came up in my calls home, which were infrequent. And to their credit, the parents never bugged me about the dearth of women in my life. I suppose it just didn't cross their minds. But as graduation day approached, Mom and Dad started planning for their trip to Ohio. Because of the long drive, they were going to stay over in Chillicothe, where they had gone the previous year for my suspension hearing.

They were bringing two of my mom's aunts, Ida and Edna, who always enjoyed tagging along for a good ride. Actually, Aunt Ida would be driving separately in her white '57 Chevy Bel Air Sport Coupe. When I called about commencement details, I casually mentioned that a friend of mine might attend. That got them pretty excited, and they wanted to know everything about her. I just said she was a good friend and I'd fill them in later.

The big day came, and I was glad to see the family. Just before the shindig got started, Tavi showed up and met the clan. She was wearing what I guess you would call a peasant dress, all white, free-flowing, no waistline, a little low in the front.

I was pretty sure she wasn't wearing anything underneath, as usual. She had on white sandals and a thin white band around her head, with a daisy tucked behind her ear. She looked so damn hot I could have eaten her right on the spot—projecting a kind of chic-hippie look. I guessed Mom and Dad weren't expecting her unconventionality... or her age. But Tavi immediately put on her natural charm and won them over with her bubbly voice and expressive eyes.

"Hello, Mr. and Mrs. Dickinger," she gushed. "So nice to finally meet you. Mahl talks about you all the time." (I rarely did).

She instinctively gave each of them a big hug, which was something that didn't happen very often in this family. We weren't really into the hugging and kissing thing, especially when meeting someone for the first time.

But this was another talent of Tavi's. She could talk to anyone, never nervous or intimidated. It was all natural, never a put-on, and everyone always seemed to take to her real quickly. Even the two old aunts fell for the charms of Tavia Lyn Mapes.

Of course, they were happy and *relieved* that someone of the female gender showed up and witnessed to the fact that I was part of the true-blue heterosexual persuasion. Tavi had one of her cameras hanging on her shoulder, and she immediately orchestrated all kinds of poses for us to assume for her creative shots.

The ceremony was held outside on the college green, under big old elms. It was in front of old Community Hall where years ago, Bevo threw up all those jump shots and more recently where crazy Abbie Hoffman riled the troops and got a few of us suspended. When the Wind Ensemble kicked into the rudimentary "Pomp and Circumstance," we all marched out to take our places.

Some old guy from the governor's office gave the usual commencement speech about how our faculty and parents had given so much of themselves and how this was just the beginning of our lives and how things would be rough out there but if we were all true to ourselves and our country, we'd all have wonderful, fulfilling lives.

I know for a fact that ninety percent of the graduating class was just so damn glad to be finished that they really didn't give a royal rip. When he eventually ended, he was given some kind of honorary degree, and they slung a stole of gratitude over his bald head onto his stooped shoulders.

Then we all traipsed across the stage, one by one, to get our diplomas. Of course that meant we had to shake hands with President A.R. "the bastard" Svenson. But we weren't finished, because we had to form a damn circle on the commons and hold hands to sing the Alma Mater.

After that, it was time to say goodbye to friends and acquaintances, but to be honest, I really didn't have any. Zittle was back in coal country, serving Yuenglings at Kelly's Bar and Lounge. Clark was summering in Warren, Ohio, with his bride Dianna, and the rest of my drinking buddies were long gone. I guessed I'd never see them again.

The campus cleared out pretty fast. All those old townies shuffled out to their rocking chairs to watch the same cars leave that had come into Rio in the Fall. Only this time, the townies were smiling because things would get back to normal, at least for the next few months.

I didn't want to—but I had to—say goodbye to someone. I felt awkward in front of the family, so I told them Tavi and I were going to take a little walk.

She said, "I know I'll see you again, Mahl, but it hurts so much to be away from you."

"Yes, I know. I don't like this either. But I have to find out if I'm going to be drafted. And if I'm not, then I have to find a full-time job. Plus, my dad got me back in the factory for the summer. We just have to get through this crappy period. Here's the home phone number. I'll try to call as often as I can. And here's the street address so you can write. You know how much I love your letters."

She gave me a big old hug and held on real long. She started to sob, her whole body shaking. I had to kind of pry her loose. "I have to get back to the folks. Listen Tav, you always told me things will work out, right? I love you very much and I'm so glad you're in my life."

"I love you too, Mahl. You're my whole life."

I gave her my handkerchief for her tears, and we walked back to the two cars where the four of them were waiting. I slid behind the steering wheel, looking forward to driving a car but also dreading the long-ass ride back to Pennsylvania, not knowing when I'd see Tav again. As I was leaving the sleepy village, I looked in the rearview mirror and there she was, standing in her tears and white dress which was billowing in the warm breeze as she waved goodbye until we were out of sight. ***[Motherfuckle!]***

Art Blakey, the epitome of the dynamic drummer, formed The Jazz Messengers with Horace Silver. Started careers of Freddie Hubbard, Wayne Shorter, Lee Morgan, Benny Golson, Wynton Marsalis, and many others.

Post Rio Grande

"Contentment is work so engrossing that you do not know that you are working." –Donald Hall

Off we went, taking the familiar Rt. 35 east, past Gallipolis, up Rt. 7 past the new Silver Memorial Bridge, past the Blue Willow Lounge, past the spewing smokestacks of Kyger Creek Power Plant where Tavi's old man worked, and on and on. The same drive that Zittle and I used to take, through Wheeling, through the PA Turnpike tunnels, and eventually to the Harrisburg interchange, driving south to the soulfully racist town of York, PA—*home*.

I was back in the casket factory, working the night shift. Being a seasoned veteran of summer employment, I was thrown into just about any working station where Henry Ruby, my supervisor, needed me. I graded the raw lumber, loaded boards into the large kilns, fed the rough boards into the planer, sanded moulding, ad infinitum, ad nauseum. I had bad dreams of getting my arm caught in the mole-sander machine or slicing off the palms of my hands on the joiner.

But despite the inhaling of sawdust, the loss of hearing from the high-decibel whirl of machines, and the spaced-out feeling from inhaling the various lacquers and glues, I actually embraced the mundanity. Few high-level thinking skills were required.

Over past summers, I had developed relationships with many of the factory workers. My dad worked in the sales department and was well-liked, so the guys in the shop knew me as "Russ's boy." And even though there was disdain for college kids, I didn't have trouble blending in.

One day, as I was beginning my shift, Dietz Keller, the president of the company and my dad's boss, approached me. "Hello Mahl, good to see you back in the shop. I understand you got your degree and I wanted to give you a little something."

He gave me a small box which I opened and found a Cross pen and pencil set in it.

"Well Mr. Keller, that is very kind of you, but you didn't have to do that."

"Listen Mahl, I've known you since you were this high. Your dad has been an important part of the organization for a long time. I just wanted to give you something for your accomplishment. And one more thing. When I hire a salesman, part of his training is to work in the various parts of the shop, so he knows everything about the production of the caskets. Since you already know so much about our operation, I was thinking you would make a good addition to our sales staff. What do you think?"

This all came as a complete surprise. I knew the salesmen made good money and that this was a generous offer. But at that time, the last thing I wanted to do was sell caskets to funeral directors. So my immediate response was, "Mr. Keller, that's very kind of you to give me the opportunity, but I was hoping to start my teaching career. But thank you anyway. That was very nice of you."

"Well Mahl, why don't you think it over? If you reconsider, the offer is always open."

So I had that to chew on, but I quickly forgot about it. When I told my dad, he looked a little pained, since he had always wanted to sell, but without a degree, that had been out of the question.

It was an unsettling summer. I heard nothing from Unc Sam. But things could have been worse, like getting jungle rot from sloshing through damn rice paddies. I wanted to apply for teaching jobs, but school districts wouldn't give me an interview because I was 1-A.

If I got my draft notice, I hoped to enlist in one of the branches other than the Army and then audition for a military band. I never practiced the sax and piano so much as I did that summer. I did finger exercises on both instruments in all keys, rhythms, and syncopations. I practiced sight reading, playing clumsy things like church hymns and marches. I was never big on practicing before, but it became an obsession.

The distance between Ohio and Pennsylvania wasn't real far, but in terms of my relationship with Tavi, it felt like she was living on the damn moon. Both of us worked nights and slept late into the mornings. Finding a good time to talk on the phone was tough, especially at home. I'd have to pull the phone cord around the corner to the cellar steps to keep the folks from dipping in. And then, after the call, I'd get a barrage of questions like, "How's she doing?" "What'd she say?" "Is she planning to visit?"

And those questions always led to things like, "What church does she belong to?" "Was she ever married?" "Does she have any children?" "Why isn't she married now?" "How much money does she make at the bar?"

Because the phone calls were a task, Tavi and I continued to write letters. And as usual, they got pretty damn mushy. We'd ramble on about how much we missed each other and how being apart just intensified this thing we had. And Tav would always inquire about my job and if I had any luck at getting an interview and how my folks were and Aunt Ida and Aunt Edna. And then I'd ask about her job at The Grande and how Maria was doing on summer break and how her old man was treating her mom.

But Tavi was a woman with great concern for the world beyond little old Gallia County. Even before I left Ohio, she had been dabbling at being an outside agitator in the anti-war protests at Ohio U and Ohio State, both of which were so intense that the two campuses had to be closed for the duration of the Spring term.

She painted a big-ass red peace sign on both sides of her Karmann Ghia... superimposing the semaphore signals for "N" and "D" for nuclear disarmament. Some of her protest buddies from Columbus gave her a bunch of bumper stickers proclaiming things like "no nukes," "make love not war," "ban the bomb," and "flower power," all of which she plastered on the back bumper. She said she felt it was the duty of concerned citizens to express their sentiments for peace to hopefully push the general public into a repudiation of the government's war effort.

I told her that was a noble idea but tried to remind her that the local redneck fringe could easily take notice of her peace-nik car and do something nasty. But she took an "I don't give a shit" attitude, which bothered the hell out of me. Tavi was a personification of passion, and without me around to help release that friendly fire, she naturally directed it into the anti-war melee that was taking place in Columbus and Athens, Ohio. ***[Motherfuckle!]***

The Crests, "Sixteen Candles." Great slow-dance song.

The Job

"We are here on Earth to fart around, and don't let anyone tell you different." –Kurt Vonnegut

I missed Tav an awful lot, but as usual I fell into my own narrow world of complaining about work, living at home, worrying about the draft, and searching for a job. Around the third week of August, I noticed her letters stopped showing up in the mailbox. Then her routine phone calls stopped. So I figured she was preoccupied with some damn peace march or maybe she was mass-producing those stepping stones of hers. I kept writing letters, but my phone calls weren't picked up. I was sure she had her reasons, but I was getting worried... and a little pissed.

Then something unexpected and remarkable occurred. Some damn governmental investigation into the draft lottery found that things were not totally random in terms of how the numbers had been selected. At least that's the explanation I heard, and luckily for me, the magic number dropped from 215 to 195, which meant that my 203 would not be called for induction. I immediately started contacting local school districts about my change in status, and around the end of August, I was granted an interview.

I put on a coat and tie and met up with a superintendent and high school principal. The first question was if I had participated in any campus demonstrations. Immediately, the image of Abbie popped into my mind. I knew I should be honest, but I also needed a job, and I didn't want to jeopardize my chances. I hesitated, took a deep breath, and then said, "Yes, I did. I was part of a sit-down protest for getting a bar on campus."

To my surprise the superintendent laughed and said, "So you like beer, eh?"

The next day, I found out I was hired. And to make things even better, the superintendent said he'd write a letter to my draft board about how the district needed teachers and the administration would appreciate any gesture to grant a deferment for me (just in case there were any draft board shenanigans going on about the lottery and other shit).

So I had a job. But after talking to my department chairman about what I'd be teaching, I felt overwhelmed. After all, it was one week before school started. I'd be teaching five sections of eleventh-grade English, which included three tract levels of grammar, composition, and American literature.

The curriculum included four novels, but there were only enough copies of each for one section at a time. So I'd have four different novels going, all of which I had never read, in addition to the grammar and composition shit, which included one writing sample per week from each kid. So the work load was ridiculous. Plus, I was appointed to be assistant junior class adviser, which meant I had to attend all the after-school construction of the class's homecoming float. So yeah, I was fuckin' overwhelmed. *[Motherfuckle!]*

Sonny Stitt, alto and tenor saxes. Better than Bird.

The Phone Call

The first week of school began on a Tuesday. Two days later, at around 9:00 P.M. as I was slaving over all the preps for the next day, I got a phone call.

"Hello, Mr. Dickinger. This is Maria Mapes, Tavi's sister. Oh Mr. Dickinger, you have to come to Holzer Hospital real quick."

"Maria, slow down. What's the problem?"

"Mr. Dickinger, Tavi was in a terrible car accident about a week ago. You have to come as soon as possible. She was asking for you, but she's been in and out of a coma. I finally found your phone number in her trailer or I would have called earlier. Please come."

Before she hung up, Maria gave a few more details, and none of them were good. It sounded like a bunch of asshole rednecks had been terrorizing the local area, going after anybody and anything that pissed them off.

Somehow, they found out about the Snake Pie Lounge out there in the boonies and burned down Big Steve's barn. And they started accosting anyone on the street who didn't fit their All-American image, like long hairs and blacks. Then I remembered Tavi's Karmann Ghia with the red peace signs splattered on the sides, and I got a really bad feeling.

I told Maria I'd get out there as soon as I could. And even though this was the first week of school, with all the damn prep work and shit, I didn't have a choice. I had to get out there to see Tav. I quickly filled in the parents, and they told me to take the Ford because they knew the '50 Chevy wouldn't make the seven-hour trip.

Driving through the night, I kept thinking I should have gone out to see her when she'd stopped the phone calls and letters. But I'd gotten hung up on the teaching job and pushed her to the back burner.

Seven hours is a long time to imagine what could have happened. *She was in a car accident. She'd been in and out of a coma. She could be near death.* Then I started thinking about those local vigilante types, and how they destroyed the Snake Pie and what they might have done to Tav as she was driving on those back-country roads. It was too much to think about, but I couldn't stop.

I got to the hospital around eight in the morning. As I was running inside, I was met by Maria who had just come down from her sister's room to get some air. "Mr. Dickinger, I'm so glad to see you, but you can't go up to Tavi's room. My dad's up there, and he has a gun. He found some of the negatives Tavi left in his dark room and he knows what you look like. He keeps saying he'll kill you if he ever sees you. For some dumb reason, he blames you for what happened to Tavi. Please don't go up there, Mr. Dickinger," and she started walking down the street.

I couldn't believe it. I went to the information desk and asked for Tavi's room number. The lady said visiting hours for non-family members didn't start until later in the day, but she gave me the number. So I started for the exit but doubled back around and found my way to the floor where Tavi's room was. I thought maybe the old man had left, or if he was there, maybe he wouldn't recognize me. I had to try to see her.

Somehow, I avoided any nurses who might usher me out. Tavi's door was open. Her old man was slouched in a chair beside the bed, his head back, snoring loudly. Tavi was hooked up to all kinds of tubes and her head was wrapped in white gauze. My view from the hallway made her unrecognizable. But just then, some orderly dropped a metal tray which woke up the old man. I took off without thinking.

I got the hell out of the hospital and started driving. And the more I drove, the more pissed I got at myself. I had often wondered what kind of soldier I would have made in Vietnam, thinking I'd be a damn turncoat, running from battle, running from my buddies. And here I was, running from some crazed old man who might or might not have shot my head off. And I was not only running from him, but even worse, running from poor Tavi, who had been so good to me and who had shown me her unconditional love.

Driving through Gallipolis, I intentionally avoided Rt. 588. I thought about all the times I was in a car and the driver was drunk. All the times when one curve could have been misjudged or an on-coming car could have turned into a head-on crash. My buddies and I had cheated death many times. But Tavi had been driving this back road, and she wasn't drunk, and she was helping someone get back to campus. I didn't want to see where the Ghia left the road, crashed through trees, and went down into a ravine. The image of her in the hospital bed was bad enough.

The Ford seemed to drive itself, leaving Gallipolis, past The Grande, the Last Chance, up to Rt. 35, sights I had seen many times before, past The Redman, Bob Evans Sausage Shop, the College View Motel, past the road back to the campus, out by Tycoon Lake and Filthy Frank's, and eventually back that pockmarked lane to the Snake Pie, where Tavi and I had had so many good times. Sure enough, just as Maria had said, Big Steve's barn was now just a pile of charred timbers and ashes, blowing toward the farmhouse. As I drove closer, I saw someone sitting on the ground, next to the now-cold embers.

I parked and sat down with Big Steve.

"Hey, sorry about what happened out here."

"Yeah, thanks. At least no one got hurt. This can be rebuilt, but those bastards went way too far when they ran that gal off the road on 588. Isn't she the one you used to come out here with?"

"Yeah, Tavi. She's in the hospital. She's in pretty bad shape. Have you heard anything about who did all this shit?"

"I heard something about some bastard named Hocking or something like that. Seems he and a bunch of his toadies went all nuclear on a bunch of war protesters on the commons in Gallipolis. I guess Tavi was taking some black kid back to the college, and those bastards followed her car and ran it off the road.

"From what I've heard, it sounds like nothing's gonna happen to this Hocking guy because there were no witnesses... besides the guys in the car, but they ain't gonna do no talking. The black kid was killed and Tavi hasn't been able to communicate anything about what happened. And whoever burned down the barn did it when me and the family wasn't here."

"What're you going to do now? Are you going to rebuild? It'd be a shame to stop all those great shows."

"Well, I've thought about that. I always had a great time arranging things and having all those good people come out. But I'm thinking things would never be the same, and there'd always be the possibility those damn bastards would come out and cause more trouble, now that the public knows what we were doing out here."

"So if you're not going to rebuild, what's next for you?"

"This is going to sound crazy, but I'm thinking about growing a crop of sunflowers. I been reading, and there's a trend for them. Wouldn't it be neat to see all these fields full of damn sunflowers?"

"Yeah, I guess that'd be cool."

"Sorry, what's your name again?"

"Mahl... Mahl Dickinger."

"So Mahl, what're you gonna do? Are you draft-eligible or do you have a job or what?"

"Luckily, I beat the draft, and before all this stuff happened with Tavi, I had just gotten a teaching job back in Pennsy. But by coming out here to see about her, I might have lost that job. Anyway, I had to come. If Tavi doesn't make it, I don't really know what I'm going to do."

"Well Mahl, let's hope she pulls through."

"Yeah, thanks. Hey, I don't want to hold you up here. Guess I better get going."

"You ain't been holding me up. I got plenty of time on my hands now."

I got back in the Ford and pulled away. As I was going out of the lane, I looked in the rearview mirror and saw a little whirlwind playing with some of the ashes. Then I saw Steve's little towheaded boy climbing onto his back. After thinking about it, I thought Steve was right about the damn sunflowers. This place would look pretty neat with acres of those things growing, turning their heads with the sun as it moved from east to west.

I drove back to Holzer Hospital and asked the lady at the front desk if it was time for visitors. She asked who I wanted to see, and when I told her, she said that Tavi had passed.

I just stood there. I couldn't move. Even though I knew she had been severely injured and death was possible, it still didn't sink in. "*Passed.*" The word meant nothing. The Tavi I knew was still alive, full of energy, laughing, singing.

But then, as I left the hospital, reality started to settle in. Her death wasn't a complete surprise. It was something I had been dreading ever since she jumped into the protest movement, with all those trips up to Ohio State and Ohio U. Professor Jones, back during the Moratorium, had said that repression was inevitable, and when it raised its ugly head, it could bring a quick end to free thought and expression. And sure enough, Tavi was a victim of all that.

I knew I would never love anyone like I had loved Tavi. And something told me no one would ever love me like she had.

I took off for Pennsylvania, hollow inside. I couldn't go to the funeral. That would have caused all kinds of problems with the old man, and I didn't want to hurt Maria and her mom any more in their grief.

So I had seven hours of driving to mull over all the things that happened in this small part of the world, and all the great times, although brief, I had with Tavi. As I drove through Pennsy, I thought I saw blue Karmann Ghias all over the place, when actually I didn't see one. And if I passed a car with a young woman in it, she looked more than vaguely like Tavi, in my eyes.

As the radio stations faded in and out, every song reminded me of her. She would have known all the lyrics and she'd be singing along with her head thrown back, projecting her voice. I stopped for gas on the turnpike, and hearing a woman's laugh, I broke down, knowing I'd never hear Tavi's laugh again.

I didn't want the '60s to end. There was always the possibility that things would improve, that things would work out for the better, that the good guys would win, that if enough people got together, any injustice could be overcome. It was easy to get sucked into that kind of thinking. But at the time, the draft calls were topping 400,000 a year, and the war's death toll was well over 30,000. And Dick-head Nixon was in the White House.

I lost the teaching job. I understood that. Even though I looked at teaching as a noble profession, as a way to make the world better, I didn't think I would have been much of a teacher.

My dad said the company had a good chance of getting a government contract to build military coffins. Just another way people were profiting from the War.

A month after getting home, I was out on the road, selling highly polished hardwood and metal caskets with down-filled pillows, soft inner-spring mattresses, and silk interiors. Back in Ohio, Big Steve was planning for next Spring's sunflower crop.

And the War continued... ***MOTHERFUCKLE***

Acknowledgment

Thank you to wife Ruth and daughter Kate for always being there.

To Demi Stevens, editor, writing coach, muse. Thanks for everything.

About the Author

Harv Loucks is a native of South-Central Pennsylvania. In addition to graduate work at Penn State, he has degrees from the University of Rio Grande (BS) and McDaniel College (MLA). He taught in public schools for 33 years and later worked eight years for an energy company.

In 2002 he was one of fifteen Pennsylvania teachers chosen to create a high tech website based on the historical markers in the state. For Harv, this included intensive research on musicians John Coltrane, Mary Lou Williams, Joe Venuti, and Eddie Lang. His research also included the early history of the anthracite coal industry. These efforts led to the creation of ExplorePAHistory.com.

Harv's been married for 41 years, and has a daughter and one-year-old grandson. Over the years, he's hiked parts of the Appalachian Trail, including all of Maryland, Pennsylvania, and segments of Virginia, Vermont, and New Hampshire (Mt. Washington). He enjoys gardening, specializing in raising hellebores and angel's trumpet plants.

Harv spends time researching local history and expanding his collection of jazz albums. Another passion is hitting a small white ball into a cup. He's played in a golf league for over 45 years and is still pursuing the elusive hole-in-one.

Made in the
USA
Middletown, DE